Wild Life of the World

ILLUSTRATED

AN INDIAN TIGRESS SEEKS HER PREY

With stealthy tread the tigress follows a familiar, well-worn path through the night
—and as she strides along, confident yet wary, she is "snapped" by flashlight.

Wild Life
of the World

ILLUSTRATED

ADVISORY EDITOR

DR. MAURICE BURTON

ODHAMS PRESS LIMITED

LONG ACRE, LONDON

MADE AND PRINTED IN GREAT BRITAIN BY
ODHAMS (WATFORD) LIMITED

Contents

CONTENTS (*continued*) PAGE

Foreword

THERE is already a vast literature on natural history, and a large accumulated knowledge. In the following pages an effort is made to summarize this and to set down the observations and experiences of those who have had first-hand contact in the field with the larger of the wild animals, or have ready access to recent information, and to stress more particularly the rarer forms or the rare and unusual traits of those that are already familiar to us and are, perhaps, on the way to being lost to us for ever.

Of recent years a great amount of research has been carried out on animal behaviour. Many new and unsuspected facts have been brought to light, some of which have completely shattered beliefs that have been held alike by naturalists and the interested public for generations past. It is one of the aims of this book to bring before the reading public the latest known facts about animal habits and behaviour and to correct where necessary some mistaken ideas. Many of these ideas will die hard; to be told, for example, that bears do not hug their prey or wolves do not hunt in packs may be somewhat disconcerting. Nevertheless, in the interests of accuracy, such erroneous ideas should be corrected.

In dealing with such a vast subject as Wild Life, it would clearly be impossible in a single volume to cover every branch in a meaningful way. It has been thought best, therefore, to limit the scope of this volume by dealing only with those creatures found in the upper limits of the animal kingdom. The reader will find, therefore, no reference to the worlds of fishes or insects, each of which could fill a volume to itself. An exception, however, has been made in the case of birds, for it is felt that of all wild creatures birds are, perhaps, the most fascinating to the amateur naturalist.

Such, then, is the basis on which this volume was planned, and it is to be hoped that the general scheme will meet with the reader's approval. Each of the authors has been chosen because of his wide knowledge of, or first-hand contact with, the animals concerned; the volume should, therefore, be a valuable addition to the library of every naturalist.

M. BURTON

FIERCEST OF THE BIG CATS

Fully as strong as a lion and fiercer in temper, the tiger is the most dreaded of all hunting animals. Its dark-striped, tawny coat is inconspicuous among scrub and jungle, while in its silent approach it is the very embodiment of sinister stealth.

Weasels, Civets
and Cats

A SHORT while ago a writer described in one of the daily papers how he and a friend had seen a family party of ten stoats, the parents and eight young ones. On being sighted the stoats ran under a log to hide. The writer remarked that from the direction they were travelling they were obviously going after some young pheasants. His friend went to fetch a gamekeeper, while he kept watch. And to cut a long story short, three men, with a gun and some dogs, succeeded in destroying all but one of the stoats. It was an interesting story—of crass ignorance, stupidity and injustice!

If every human being travelling in the direction of a bank were assumed to be "obviously going" to rob the bank and arrested, our courts would be busy. No. The evidence on which these stoats were condemned would be inadmissible in any court of law. This is not to deny that a stoat may occasionally take a young pheasant, just as a man will sometimes hold up a bank.

Let us look at the other side of the picture. Stoats are the arch-killers of rats and mice—carriers of disease—that do millions of pounds' worth of damage annually in raids upon crops, stored foods, poultry-runs, pheasants, and property. In addition they prey on rabbits, a pest second only to rats.

In the heyday of game preserves the "keepers' gibbet," the rows of "vermin" hung up in the woods, was a common feature of the countryside and helped, there can be little doubt, to implant in people's minds the idea that stoats, weasels, rats and a few other things were very much of a kind. They were "vermin," and the logic was as follows: all rodents are vermin, therefore all vermin are rodents. Therefore stoats are rodents. In fact, stoats, weasels, martens and their relatives are as markedly carnivorous as any animals, as shown by their teeth, which include well-developed carnassials.

Our attitude to predators has undergone a marked change in recent years, with the growing knowledge of their value in curbing pests of one form or another. Examples of the predator's role can be drawn from various parts of the world, and will be dealt with at appropriate points in the following pages. Several can be found in Britain.

The small, reddish-brown animal with the black tip to its tail is to be seen in the countryside throughout Europe and northern Asia. The stoat (*Mustela erminea*) is, however, not a common sight, for it is a wary, speedy and alert animal, which hunts mainly in the undergrowth. An animal less wary would have suffered a greater diminu-

9

PREDATORY STOAT

Contrary to a common belief, the stoat is a carnivore and highly predacious. Its white winter coat is the highly prized ermine that adorns royal robes.

tion in its numbers, for not only has it been persecuted for its alleged depredations among game preserves, but its coat, which turns white in winter, provides the ermine symbolic of noble rank. The secret of this change is little understood. It occurs regularly in the northern parts of the stoat's range, but an ermine can sometimes be seen in winter in the milder southern counties of England. Apparently temperature and light are the deciding factors, but further than this we know little of seasonal colour-change.

The male stoat is 1 ft. long, with a 4-in. tail, the female being much smaller. A closely related species is found in North America (where it is called a weasel) and in North Africa, north of the Atlas Mountains; there is also a distinct species in Ireland, the Irish stoat (*M. hibernica*).

Stoats usually hunt alone, except when the young are old enough to follow their mother, when a family party of up to twelve may be seen. It is these family parties that have given rise to stories of their hunting in packs. They follow their prey by scent, tirelessly and persistently. In self-defence, against cats and foxes, they will discharge a thick, yellow, evil-smelling liquid from their anal glands. It is debatable whether the paralysis induced in a rabbit by the approach of a stoat is due to sight or smell of its enemy. At all events, whatever it is, the rabbit offers little resistance, the stoat killing it by a bite at the base of the skull, after which the brain is usually eaten first.

Weasels (*M. nivalis*), two-thirds the size of stoats, are the smallest of all the Carnivora. Again, the females are markedly smaller than the males, and in some parts of England are known as " cane weasels," because of the mistaken impression that they belong to another species. So far as is known, there is only one species in Britain, though a second, the Least weasel (*M. rixosa*), still smaller than the Common weasel, is found from western Europe to eastern Asia, and even North America. This is a strange thing, yet the fact remains that, in spite of extensive trapping by gamekeepers as well as zoologists, no Least weasel has ever been caught in Britain.

The polecat (*Putorius putorius*), half as big again as the stoat, its fur a creamy-buff with long black guard hairs, is also found in Europe and northern Asia. It is believed to be the nearest relative of the domestic ferret.

In Britain it has been driven to a few strongholds in some of the Welsh valleys, where it feeds on rabbits, voles and frogs and, like all of its kind, occasionally on poultry. Still, there are a few bank-robbers among men! At all events, the Forestry Commissioners favour the polecat because it keeps down the destructive rabbits. Its fur is valuable, that of the Asiatic polecat, known as fitch, being largely used. Its cousin, the mink (*Lutreola vison*), of Europe, northern Asia and North America, has a lustrous fur of much higher value, and, although mink is now largely farmed in North America and Scandinavia, nearly a million wild skins reach the market annually.

The history of the various species of martens is very similar to that of their close relatives the stoats and weasels, which they resemble in general appearance though they are more squirrel-like and have long bushy tails. In Britain the Pine marten (*Martes martes*) must at one time have been common, for "hunting the mart" was, in medieval times, a national pastime. In addition to the sport it provided, its dark rich brown fur was valuable. It is normally a tree-dweller, though with the loss of the ancient forests it has had to take to the fells and mountainsides, feeding on rabbits and mice in out-of-the-way places. Secretive, alert, quick in action and blessed with a high degree of native intelligence, the marten is not easy to see; its natural habit is to watch a human intruder from the cover of a rock or the trunk of a tree, moving round as the intruder moves so as always to keep hidden.

Today, we should like to see the Pine marten back in something like its old numbers to combat the grey squirrel, for squirrels are its normal food in the forests that are its natural home.

The American marten (*M. americana*) is similar to the Pine marten but has a richer fur. Even more valuable for its fur is the North American fisher or pekan (*M. pennanti*), which is larger than the Pine marten, and darker, sometimes almost black. Like all the martens, it is steadily retreating before the advance of civilization. It is one of the most powerful of the smaller carnivores. In addition to killing rabbits, squirrels and other martens, it will kill porcupines, rolling them over and tearing at the soft underside, and will even put up a good show against the dogs used to hunt it.

The rich, dark fur of the sable (*M. zibellina*), found from European Russia

SMALLEST CARNIVORE
The weasel is smaller than the stoat, but of similar habits, and is one of the fiercest of animals. So far as is known, only one species is found in Great Britain.

to Japan, has for a long time been the object of a valuable trade. Its fur was formerly in great demand for the court of Imperial Russia, and the search for sables had much to do with the opening up of Siberia. Now it is present in small numbers only, and efforts are being made to farm the animal and to re-introduce it to its former haunts.

The wolverine (*Gulo luscus*), also known as the glutton, is the largest of all Mustelidae. It is confined to the northern half of North America and to the arctic and sub-arctic regions of Europe and Asia. Badger-like in build, it is 4 ft. long, and dark brown, with a pale brown stripe along the sides. It appears to be fearless and its prey includes almost any mammal, even deer. This, and its habit of robbing traps as well as the food caches laid down by hunters, may account for its alternative name, although it is probably no more gluttonous than any other active carnivore.

The weasel-like Mustelidae are typically found in the northern hemisphere, although there is the Himalayan marten (*Martes flavigula*) of India, Burma, southern China and Malaya. There are, however, two members of the family in Africa, the black-and-white-striped zorille (*Ictonyx striatus*) of South Africa, which is the size of a ferret, and the muishond or Striped weasel (*Poecilogale albinucha*) of East and South Africa, both of which are terrestrial and feed on mice.

SKUNK'S "STINK-SCREEN"

The skunks are peculiar to America. Although related to stoats and weasels, they differ in certain striking characteristics. To begin with, they are all terrestrial, and are plantigrade, like the bears. Their tails are very bushy and the anal scent-glands are very highly developed. Using the discharge from these glands, they can put up a most effective foul-smelling screen, which forms an efficient defence against most creatures. As the result of generations of relying upon this means of defence, skunks do not run away if attacked, but stand their ground and put up a stink-screen. One consequence of this is that they often fall victims to cars when crossing a highway. Instead of getting out of the way of the approaching monster they throw out their screen and are run over. Perhaps one day they will learn better.

WARNING COLOURS

Another interesting feature of the skunk is its vivid black-and-white coloration. It is usually found that animals which are obnoxious, either by reason of their sting, poison bite, unpalatability or, as in the skunk, because of a foul-smelling discharge, are strikingly coloured as if to advertise their presence, instead of being so coloured as to harmonize with their background. It is a sort of "hands off" warning. Familiar examples are seen in wasps, poisonous lizards and snakes, and others.

The best known, the 2 ft. long Striped skunk (*Mephitis mephitis*) of Canada and the U.S.A., is black with a white stripe down each side, and most of the tail white. It is inoffensive, even playful and affectionate; but if roused to a sense of danger, it can eject a blinding spray of nauseous fluid to a distance of two to three yards. It is a useful mouser, and its diet includes other small mammals, small birds, insects, grubs and fallen fruit.

Slightly smaller, the Little Spotted skunk (*Spilogale putorius*) of the U.S.A., lives in burrows or in holes among rocks, particularly on the plains. Often

POLECAT IN ITS WELSH HAUNT

The polecat is the nearest wild relative of the domesticated ferret. Its defence against enemies is an evil-smelling fluid secreted from glands at the root of its tail. The animal is rare in Britain, being found only in the remoter parts of Wales.

ORIENTAL MARTEN IN SIAMESE JUNGLE

The martens are much like the stoats and weasels in appearance, but differ slightly in the formation of the teeth and in having a more squirrel-like body. They are much sought after for their fur and, in consequence, are dwindling in numbers over the major part of their habitat. The above picture shows a marten in western Siam.

found around farm buildings, it feeds on mice, insects and fruit. The Hog-nosed skunks (*Conepatus*), found from the southern U.S.A. to the Argentine, have pig-like snouts for rooting out insects.

The differences in outward appearance and habits of closely related animals are often considerable. Yet another example of this is seen in the badgers, so different from the stoats and weasels which can be justifiably described as their second cousins. Badgers are of heavy, stocky build, and measure about 3 ft. in length. Shy, cautious and entirely nocturnal, they spend the daytime in deep burrows. They can be numerous in a given locality without the human inhabitants being aware of them, except for the tell-tale "earths."

Although called the European badger (*Meles meles*), it ranges, with closely related forms, across Europe and northern Asia to China and Japan.

There is much of the quality of a bear in this animal, in addition to its build and the plantigrade feet. Although usually inoffensive, it is strong and tough, with powerful claws, normally used for digging, but capable of being used in defence. Like a bear, too, it is omnivorous, its diet comprising almost anything edible, including beetles, earthworms and grubs; its favourite food, however, is young rabbits, which it detects by scent and digs out of the nesting-chambers.

In spite of the ancient sport of badger-baiting (when the animal was tethered and dogs loosed at it) and the badger-hunts that still go on (the animals being dug out from their earths on suspicion of having raided poultry), badgers are still plentiful in England and Wales. Badger-baiting probably owed its popularity to the animal's ability to defend itself effectively, with its long, strong claws and powerful jaws and teeth.

The hair is a grizzled grey above, with the legs and undersides blackish. On the head are conspicuous black and white stripes, and it has been suggested that this is a warning coloration comparable to that of the skunk. If so, then it is strange that the badger moves about exclusively at night, and that there is no other aspect of its behaviour suggesting that it has any confidence in the effectiveness of this supposed danger signal to ward off its enemies.

The American badger (*Taxidea taxus*), found chiefly on the plains, where its holes are a menace to the horse-rider, is only two-thirds the size of its European relative and is less conspicuously patterned. It is, however, more active and more markedly carnivorous, feeding on ground squirrels,

OTTER ON THE BANK OF A RIVER

*Widely distributed throughout the world, the otters are graceful and agile creatures both on land and under water. Most species live near the banks of rivers or streams and prey upon fish. The young are born in deep burrows near the water's edge. The European otter (*Lutra lutra*) measures about 4 ft. from nose to tail.*

BADGERS EMERGING FROM THEIR EARTH

The badger is common throughout temperate Europe, America and Asia. It is of nocturnal habit and a powerful digger; its "earth," or den, is sometimes 16 ft. below ground. Here, two badgers are seen emerging from their earth for the nightly foraging expedition, during which they will devour worms, snails and roots.

prairie dogs and other rodents. If surprised in the open, it throws up a fountain of earth as it burrows for safety in double-quick time. The Hog badger (*Arctonyx collaris*) of South-east Asia has a pig-like snout which, like a pig, it uses for rooting.

VERSATILE HONEY BADGER

In South and East Africa, Arabia and India lives the ratel or Honey badger (*Mellivora capensis*). It has the size and appearance of the European badger, but lacks the black and white head-stripes. It also differs in certain details of the anatomy. In the Honey badger we have an example, when compared with the European badger, of the virtual impossibility of laying down rules—or even putting forward hypotheses—for living things. It has the powerful teeth and claws and the loose skin of its European relative and can beat off almost any enemy.

Moreover, it is also an extremely active beast, burrowing with great speed, climbing trees if necessary and, when it has no purposive action to perform, turning head over heels. Finally, in addition to its other defensive accomplishments, it can put up a stink-screen like a skunk. Surely here is a badger fully entitled to carry a warning coloration, a "hands off" sign, but it lacks the very striping which, in the European badger, a much milder animal, is said to have a warning function. Well, when you want to maintain a theory, you must look for the facts to fit it, and it has been suggested that the greyer back and more solidly black underparts of the Honey badger, which certainly contrast sharply, constitute a warning coloration.

Otters comprise the last group of the Mustelidae. There are a number of species distributed throughout the world, apart from Australia, but all are very much alike in outward appearance, for all are aquatic and have similar habits. The European otter (*Lutra lutra*), 4 ft. from nose to tail, has a thick, close fur which was at one time considered valuable but is not now so regarded. It is an expert diver and swimmer, with small claws and webbed feet, and small ears and nostrils which can be closed under water. It rests during the day in holes or holts in the banks of rivers and lakes, especially under the roots of trees, and hunts at night for fish. Here is another animal that is persecuted for its alleged interference with something which man regards as his monopoly. Some, who are in a position to judge, are strongly of the opinion that otters do no real harm to the fishing; that, on the contrary, by weeding out the sickly fish, they probably improve the stock. Such a view gains support from the knowledge we are accumulating of the role of predators in other parts of the world.

PLAYFUL OTTERS

All otters are playful in the extreme, whether young or old. Curiously enough, although so well adapted to life in the water, and although water is the perfect medium for indulging in antics, the otter seems to prefer the land for its play, which consists mainly of sliding down clay banks, or, in winter, sliding over snow.

Some idea of the small details of habit or structure distinguishing the various species of otter can be seen from the following. The Indian Small-clawed otter (*Amblonyx cinerea*), of South-east Asia, is smaller than the European otter and its claws are functionless. The Clawless otter (*Aonyx capensis*), of South and East Africa, is larger, more of a marsh dweller, and feeds on frogs and molluscs. The Giant Brazilian otter (*Pteronura brasiliensis*), of the Amazon, has the tail laterally compressed, and is the largest of all otters, measuring 6½ ft. in total length.

SEA OTTER

Otters sometimes forsake the rivers to hunt along the rocky coasts. They are then referred to by some people as Sea otters, but the true Sea otter (*Enhydris lutris*), of the coasts of the North Pacific, is a very different animal, more specialized for an aquatic life than any other otter. About 4 ft. long (including a 1-ft. tail), the hind-feet are long and broad, more like a seal's flippers, and the fore-feet are small pads with the toes hardly distinguishable. It lives among the dense kelp beds just offshore, where it finds shelter from its enemy, the Killer whale. Its ears are small, and hidden in a dense, glossy fur, which was always regarded as one of the two or three most valuable furs. A rich brownish-black, sprinkled with white-tipped hairs, the fur was known as "Kamchatka beaver," and to get it the Sea otter was hunted by the Russians in the Bering Sea, the Japanese in the Kuriles and, later, both the Russians and the Americans off Alaska and along the coast of California. Under such pressure it came near to extinction, but, fortunately, the interested governments agreed on its protection and it is now beginning to recover, especially off California.

Sea otters live on shellfish and sea-urchins, diving to the sea-bottom, sometimes as deep as 300 ft., to get them, and crushing them in their powerful cheek-teeth. They spend much of their time floating on their backs, and the females, when foraging, leave their young ones floating like this among the kelp where they look very like the large bladders on the seaweed. This, doubtless, gives them a measure of protection from enemies. Another curious habit, so it is reliably reported, consists in bringing up a flat stone from the sea-bottom with the sea-urchins. The Sea otter then turns on its back, places the stone on its chest, raises the urchin over its head between its fore-paws and crashes it down on the stone. This is one of the few examples of an animal using a purposive tool.

CIVETS AND GENETS

In the warmer parts of the Old World, the Mustelidae (stoats, weasels, badgers and otters) are largely replaced by the members of the family Viverridae (civets, genets and mongooses). To those who are familiar with countries in the northern hemisphere only, civets and genets are little known; to some extent this is true for those who have visited countries in the southern hemisphere. Doubtless they are sufficiently well known to the natives of these regions, but their habits being mainly nocturnal, and the fact that so many of them keep well to cover, means that our knowledge of them is somewhat scanty. Mongooses, on the other hand, are familiar enough, partly because of their habit of frequenting human habitations, partly because they have been introduced into other parts of the world, and partly because of the publicity which has been given to their exploits in killing rats and snakes.

The Viverridae are to some extent intermediate in character between the Mustelidae and the Felidae (cats, lions and tigers). Like the typical Mustelidae, they have slender muzzles and long tails, and, usually, non-retractile claws. Many have well-developed anal scent-glands. Most of them are striped or spotted, and all are active hunters of small vertebrates. They differ from the Felidae not only in their long muzzles, but in having a fifth toe on the hind-feet. There is one mongoose and one genet in southern Europe, but apart from these the Viverridae are confined to Africa and southern Asia. They are of no value as fur-bearing animals, but and striped with white, and the tail is ringed black and white. It is, in fact, a common animal throughout its range, though it is seldom seen, for it keeps well to cover, and hunts at night, feeding on almost anything edible. It often does much damage to poultry and young domesticated animals, as well as to

AFRICAN CIVET

The African civet has a range which extends over the greater part of tropical Africa. Like all the civets, it secretes a pungent, odorous fluid which at one time was in wide demand as an ingredient of perfumes. It is nocturnal and omnivorous in habit, devouring small mammals, birds and their eggs and even insects, as well as fruit.

some of them have been widely hunted for their musk glands.

The civets are comparatively large and heavily built, with a mane-like mat of hair on the back and a bushy tail. The African civet (*Civettictis civetta*), for example, which is found from south of the Sahara to the northern Transvaal, has a body-length of 2½ ft., with the tail 1½ ft. long. Its coat is ash-grey, spotted crops, having a particular liking for young maize cobs. In Abyssinia there used to be a thriving trade in musk, for making perfumes, obtained by removing the anal glands from the live animal. Fortunately, the chemist has now given us synthetic products which have greatly diminished this demand.

The African or Two-spotted Palm civet (*Nandinia binotata*), found from

PARTY OF AFRICAN LIONS

Lions, unlike tigers, prefer open country, for it is there that their natural prey—antelopes and zebras—abounds. They will often hunt in family parties, or in troops of several family parties, which may number up to ten, or even twenty, individuals. Lions are naturally indolent, and when searching for food will go to as little trouble as

GATHERED ROUND A KILL

possible. Thus they prefer to seize a small antelope rather than attack larger game, although there is no animal, with the exception of an elephant, a rhinoceros or some of the larger buffaloes, that they cannot pull down. However, lions generally avoid man, and, if wild game are plentiful, seldom venture to attack domestic cattle.

the Cameroons to Kenya, is typically a forest-dweller. It is a rich brown, with black spots, and with two pale spots on the shoulders from which its alternative name is derived. The tail is long and marked with rings, and the soles of the feet are pink and naked, the latter characteristic believed to be associated with its habits as a tree-climbing animal.

dwellers, with a body-length of some 2 ft. and a tail of similar length, feeding on small mammals, birds, eggs and fruit. In colour they are usually dark grey or brown, with indistinct spots and, often, a conspicuous pattern of dark and light patches on the face.

The Indian Palm civet or Toddy cat (*Paradoxurus hermaphroditus*), with re-

THE DISTINCTIVE SKUNK

The distinctive black-and-white markings of the skunk are considered by many zoologists to be a warning coloration or "hands off" signal to any would-be attacker. The secretion of a foul-smelling fluid has made it virtually immune from attack.

Among the civets of southern Asia is the Indian civet (*Viverra zibetha*), also found in Burma and southern China. It is very like the African civet in size, appearance and habits. The binturong (*Arctictis binturong*), of South-east Asia, lives in trees and has a prehensile tail. It has a short, broad head, tufted ears and a hairy tail; the whole 4-ft. body is covered with long black hair. The Palm civets are also represented in southern Asia. They are elegantly built tree-

lated races in Ceylon, southern China, Malaya and the Philippines, normally nests in holes in trees and in rocks, but it often lives near, or even in, human dwellings, or under the roofs of bunga-lows, feeding on rats—and on stored foods! It also has the unpleasant defensive habit of the skunk. Its second common name is derived from its habit of drinking from the cups, attached to tapped trees, in which the palm wine is fermenting. It is interesting to note that, even in its common names, this civet is recognized as a cat. Further, its near-domestication, as a voluntary action, is an indication of how easy it is to domesticate certain types of animals.

As in all groups of the Carnivora, some of the civets are far from being carnivorous. Owston's Banded civet, a rare animal of Indo-China, feeds on fruit and earthworms. The Otter civet (*Cynogale bennetti*), another rare animal of South-east Asia, has the sleek brown fur, broad flat head, well-developed whiskers, short legs and cylindrical tail of the true otter. It is believed to feed on fish and frogs, but very little is known of its habits.

MALIGNED FOSSA

Another carnivore that appears to have been maligned is the fossa (*Cryptoprocta ferox*), of Madagascar. It is 5 ft. long, and has the reputation of being a ferocious killer, but recent evidence suggests that this is an exaggeration.

The genets are far more exclusively African than the civets, only two forms of the Feline genet being found outside the continent, one in South-west Europe and one in Asia Minor. They are usually profusely spotted or blotched black or rust-coloured on a pale ground. Their legs are, on the whole shorter, and their tails longer. There are numerous species and races in Africa, of which some are found exclusively in the dense forests of Uganda and the Congo; others live in the scrub or grass. As a rule, they keep to thick cover, especially near rivers and streams, hunting small mammals, birds and frogs. Most genets make good pets if caught young, and, indeed, tamability seems to be a general feature of the members of the Carnivora.

The Feline genet (*Genetta genetta*) includes races outside Africa, the European genet of South-west Europe, and the Palestine and Arabian genets. Of medium size, with a black stripe of erectile hairs down the back, it is typical of the group, but the most numerous is the Blotched or Tigrine genet (*G. tigrina*), found all over Africa. The body of this last-named is marked with irregular rows of large rectangular blotches. Some of the species are, however, localized and rare, like the Abyssinian genet (*G. abyssinica*), a small pale-grey animal with black stripes.

In this group are several rare species. For example, *Osbornictis piscivora*, which lives in the depths of the Ituri Forest, has been known to us only since 1919. We know that it is the size of a cat, chestnut with white markings on the face and a black, bushy tail. Otherwise we know little about it.

VICTORIAN GENET

The Victorian genet (*Genetta victoriae*) allows the opportunity to point a moral and adorn a tale. When a new animal is found it falls to the lot of some zoologist or other to name it and publish a description of it. In choosing a scientific name it is usual to let the name be descriptive of some outstanding characteristic of the animal, or of the place where it lives; occasionally it may be named after the person who found it. Thus *Genetta genetta* is the genet of all genets; in other words, the typical genet. *Genetta abyssinica* is the Abyssinian genet. And so on. In 1911 Sir Harry Johnston sent to the British Museum (Natural History) from his headquarters at Entebbe, on the shores of Lake Victoria, the skin of a large genet, 3½ ft. in total length, and of a markedly rich and handsome colouring. It was recognized as a new animal and named *Genetta victoriae*. It has, however, never since been seen in the region of Lake Victoria and it is clear from Sir Harry's subsequent writings that the skin was obtained from natives who had collected it in the Ituri Forest. Except that it is nocturnal, practically nothing is known of its habits.

LINSANGS OF ASIA

The linsangs of South-east Asia are closely related to the civets and genets, but differ in the absence of the second upper molar. This may seem an extremely trivial character on which to separate species and genera, but the more we learn of animals as a whole the more we realize how variable are the external features, colour of hair and so on, and the soft parts. Consequently, it is to the skeleton that the systematist looks for the stable characters upon which to base his classification. Above all, the characters of the teeth are the most reliable.

Linsangs are of two kinds, Banded and Spotted. The Banded linsang (*Priono-don linsang*)—the name linsang is Javanese in origin—is found from Sumatra to Tenasserim. About 2½ ft. in length, its orange-buff coat is marked with broad bands. It lives in the trees, feeding at night on small birds. Similar in outward appearance and habits, the Spotted linsang (*P. pardicolor*), of Nepal to Indo-China, is marked with regular rows of dark spots instead of bands. The rare African linsang (*Poiana richardsonii*), about the same size, is a slender, active tree-dweller, with an ochreous coat beautifully patterned with small spots and a long banded tail. Alone among the Viverridae it has cat-like teeth and retractile claws. Practically nothing is known of its habits, for it lives in the dense forests of Liberia, Fernando Po and the eastern Belgian Congo.

The most numerous carnivores of many parts of Africa and southern Asia are the mongooses, of which there are many species. Weasel-like in form (though with longer tails), their grizzled grey fur unstriped, they range in size from that of a small squirrel to that of a cat. Terrestrial, with long digging claws, they are mainly diurnal and often, especially the smaller of them, hunt in troops. They are best known to us for their ability to kill snakes, though rats, too, and other small rodents fall to these active, fearless beasts. In many places the mongoose comes near to being a domesticated animal—as a voluntary action. That is, it frequents human habitations, feeding on any snakes or rodents it can find, accepting food from the human occupants and virtually taking up its abode with them. But although it will behave as a pet under such circumstances, will be playful and almost affectionate, it retains, nevertheless, its independence, and will readily resent any intrusion upon, or threat against, the latter.

CURIOSITY OF MONGOOSES

One of the outstanding characteristics of mongooses is their great curiosity, a quality which can be exploited in taming them. They show great interest in the actions of their human companions and will, if not disturbed, approach gradually closer and closer to see what is being done. Linked with this is a tendency to take and hide bright objects; if jewellery is missing when a mongoose is in the vicinity, the mongoose should be suspected rather than human associates.

The classical ichneumon or Egyptian mongoose (*Herpestes ichneumon*), found from Egypt to the Cape, as well as in southern Europe, is the largest, measuring 3½ ft., of which 1½ ft. is tail. It haunts the reed-beds by rivers, feeding

FEARLESS LITTLE SERPENT-KILLER

The Indian mongoose is renowned for its fearlessness in attacking and killing such deadly snakes as the cobra. Apart from its snake-killing activities, it is also useful in keeping down the numbers of such undesirable creatures as scorpions and mice.

on rats and, when occasion offers, poultry. This was one of the animals sacred to the Ancient Egyptians, who often embalmed it. Other African species are the White-tailed mongoose (*Ichneumia albicauda*), of East and West Africa, which feeds on termites and has feeble teeth; the Marsh mongoose (*Atilax paludinosus*), which lives on frogs and the like in the streams and marshes; and the Banded mongoose (*Mungos mungos*), patterned with dark bands, which lives in colonies in anthills on the arid plains of East and West Africa.

Then there are the many species of Dwarf mongooses, of the genera *Helogale* and *Myonax*. They are about 1 ft. to 1½ ft. long overall, and frequent the open grass and scrub of South and East Africa, often hunting in packs or living in colonies. They feed mainly on insects,

also eggs, lizards and other small animals.

The slender-snouted meerkat (*Suricata suricatta*), of South Africa, often frequents human dwellings, feeding on small rodents and insects. On the open plains, it lives in colonies, often sharing its burrow (dug with its long claws) with ground squirrels. About the size of a large squirrel itself, it is easily tamed and playful, and has a strong sense of curiosity, often sitting bolt upright to stare at intruders.

This short list by no means exhausts the numerous species found in Africa, and in Madagascar there are several others, most of them striped.

Several species are found in India, the best-known being the Indian mongoose (*Herpestes auropunctatus*), less than 2 ft. long, of which nearly a half is tail. It feeds on rats, lizards, scorpions and insects and, of course, snakes. This

SPOTTED HYENAS ON THE PROWL

Hyenas are fairly widespread throughout Africa and Asia. The massive jaws and stout teeth of these animals are admirably adapted to their carrion-feeding habits; they can, in fact, break bones upon which even the teeth of a lion have failed. Characteristic of the spotted hyena is its startling, almost hysterical, "laugh."

s the species that has been introduced into the West Indies and Hawaii to clean up the snakes and rats—and has become a menace to the native small mammals and ground-nesting birds. There is no truth in the idea that it is immune from snake-bite, nor that, being bitten, it seeks out certain herbs as an antidote. What immunity it has, in combat with a poisonous snake, is due to its agility and its long hairs which can be erected to act as a buffer against the striking fangs.

The Crab-eating mongoose (*H. urva*), of Nepal, Burma, southern China and Malaya, feeds on shellfish, crabs and the like, and will on occasion dive into water to catch fish.

There are many animals whose names are familiar to us, yet the animals themselves are so unfamiliar that we fail to

recognize them when we see them. In this category we may put the hyena, for "to laugh like a hyena" is in the nature of a household saying. Yet the animal is distinctive enough. Its heavy shoulders and fore-quarters slope down to the low hind-parts, short hind-legs and tail. Its grey coat is striped with black: its head is heavy and a mane, or dorsal crest, runs down the centre of the back. The Striped hyena (*Hyaena hyaena*) of North-east Africa, Arabia and India, 5 ft. long and 2½ ft. at the shoulder, is typical of the family Hyaenidae, which includes the hyenas and the aardwolf.

The Striped hyena is met with in almost any country but thick forest, where it forages at night for carrion, in pairs or in family parties. During the day it lies up in holes in rocks or in porcupines' old burrows. Its cry, a chattering laugh varying to a noise like the howling of the wind, together with its unlovely appearance and gruesome habits, do not recommend it. To describe it as cowardly is, however, a misstatement for, while it normally seeks carrion, it will kill and eat any living animal it can catch and often does much damage to livestock. It has even been known to attack sleeping villagers, though it has a wholesome fear of man when he is awake. This can be better interpreted, however, as deeming discretion the better part of valour. By contrast, if taken young it can be readily tamed and such an animal, even when fully grown, will be docile and companionable with smaller animals.

Whether it shows that the hyena prefers discretion to valour or not, the fact remains that it has been seen, on occasion, to " sham dead," when attacked with no hope of escape. So completely does it do this that it will allow itself to be worried by dogs without any sign of movement until such time as it sees an opportunity to bolt for safety.

HEAD OF THE HYENA

The hyena is very much a carnivore. Its teeth are very like those of the big cats, the head is massive, the skull short and deep with a high sagittal crest for the attachment of strong muscles needed to work the powerful jaws. In fact, the head is perfectly constructed to give the maximum biting power. The teeth, too, are stout, so that the animal is completely equipped for cracking the huge bones of carrion. Being a carrion-feeder, sight is not of great value to it; so its sight is poor, but its sense of smell is acute. And, judging from its large ears, so is its hearing.

The now scarce Brown hyena or Strand wolf (*Hyena brunnea*), of South Africa, is larger, with longer hair, no obvious dorsal crest and with indistinct stripes. It forages among marine refuse on the shore. The largest hyena is the Spotted hyena (*Crocuta crocuta*), of East Africa. Its colouring is yellowish-buff, tawny or grey, with brown spots. Locally, it is credited with magical powers.

The aardwolf (*Proteles cristatus*), of South and East Africa, has a somewhat misleading name, for it is only the size of a fox and looks like a miniature Striped hyena. Its jaws and teeth are weak, for it feeds mainly on termites. For defence it erects its mane, as if to give an impression of greater bulk, and discharges an offensive fluid from its anal glands.

THE CAT FAMILY

The family Felidae contains the cats, large and small, using the word in its strict and familiar sense. In them we see the most highly specialized of all the land Carnivora; and the members of this family are found throughout the world, except for Australia and, curiously enough, Madagascar.

It is of interest, in order to assess the relative values of anatomical details and the details of external appearance and behaviour, to compare the Canidae and the Felidae. If we examine the articulated skeletons of a number of Canidae (dogs, foxes and wolves) with a similar number of the Felidae (cats, leopards, lions and tigers), the first thing we notice is that, apart from size, there is a general similarity in the architecture of these skeletons. Indeed, take away the skulls and the bones of the toes, and it would be difficult for anyone, other than a specialist, to distinguish between them. The most outstanding difference in the toes is, of course, that the claws of the Felidae are retractile, as in the domestic cat. The skulls of the Felidae are noticeably shorter, the canine teeth are larger and the cheek-teeth are fewer in number and of them only the large carnassial is well developed.

If we leave the skeletons and consider the live animals, however, there is no general similarity. Rather the reverse. The Felidae reach their highest development, in size and in number of species, in the warmer parts of the world. The Canidae reach their greatest development in the northern half of the northern hemisphere. The Felidae are mainly solitary in habits, the Canidae tend to be gregarious. The Felidae rely on sight and hearing, stalk their prey and put all their energy into the final pounce, while the Canidae rely on smell and hearing, and run down their prey.

There are, of course, other differences; there are also exceptions; but these generalizations are correct as such.

A typical cat, which should be familiar to us but is not, is the European Wild cat (*Felis sylvestris*), formerly abundant throughout Europe, including Britain (but not Ireland). By the clearing of forests and the cultivation and general "taming" of the countryside, the Wild cat has been restricted to the wilder parts of Scotland and to the Balkans, eastern Europe and Asia Minor. It is a large tabby (3 ft. long including the 1-ft., blunt-tipped tail), living in rocky country, and feeding on hares, rabbits and small mammals and birds generally. In new plantations it is welcomed as a check on rabbits. Elsewhere it is assiduously persecuted.

WILD PROTOTYPE OF DOMESTIC CAT

The European Wild cat is probably one of the Wild cats from which domestic cats have been bred. Its numbers have dwindled in Britain, where it is now found only in the wilder parts of Scotland; it is still, however, quite common in certain parts of Europe.

LION WITH LESSER PREDATORS IN ATTENDANCE

The above picture, showing a lion feeding at its kill, was taken with a telephoto lens, which has the effect of foreshortening the foreground; the vultures and jackal were thus at a much more respectful distance from the lion than would appear.

The Wild cat, together with the yellowish-grey Jungle cat (*F. chaus*), of North-east Africa, and the Caffer or Bush cat (*F. lybica*), of Africa, have probably contributed to the various strains of domestic cat, but exactly how is not known. They, like most of the small cats, keep well to cover and are not readily seen in the wild. There are a number of other species of small wild cat in Africa and southern Asia. Of these, mention may be made of the Sand cat (*F. constantina*), of the western Sahara and Arabia, which is sandy-coloured with black markings on legs and tail. The soles of its feet are thickly covered with hair for moving over loose sand.

So many of the smaller Felidae are known well enough from their skins, but their habits are disappointingly little known to us. Thus, the beautiful Marbled cat (*Pardofelis marmorata*),

of South-east Asia, lives entirely in forests, is wary and nocturnal and, consequently, seldom seen. The Clouded leopard (*Neofelis nebulosa*), another beautiful forest cat, is equally little known, except that it preys on deer and has the longest canines, proportionately, of all the Carnivora.

The identification of some of these small cats is made the more difficult by reason of the colour phases presented by different members of a species. The Golden or Temminck's cat (*Profelis temminckii*), of South-east Asia, may be grey or reddish. Moreover, both the grey and the reddish phases may be unspotted or may be marked with conspicuous spots and blotches. The African Tiger cat (*P. aurata*), a similar animal, shows a similar variation. The position is made even more complicated by the fact that even the colour of a given individual is not constant.

JAGUAR CUB IN BRAZIL JUNGLE

Closely related to the leopard, the jaguar is found in the forests of South and Central America, where it preys upon the sloth and the capybara. The above photograph of a jaguar cub was taken in Brazil. The animal was chased up a tree by a party of dogs belonging to the hunter who took the photograph.

BENGAL TIGER GOES HUNTING

This study of an Indian tiger on the scent of its prey indicates the unswerving determination and merciless ferocity of this great cat. Note the projection of the shoulder-blades, so typical of the cats, as contrasted with the dogs. Few animals are robust enough to resist the force of the tiger's attack.

Thus a red Tiger cat brought some years ago to the London Zoo turned grey in six months. The jaguarundi (*Herpailurus jaguarundi*), of South America, an otter-like cat, may be a rusty-red or an iron-grey. Sometimes these colour phases have been marked by different names. For example, the serval (*Leptailurus serval*), of Africa, is normally tawny with black stripes and spots. There is, however, another colour phase, tawny with a fine powdering of minute specks. This second phase is known as the servaline, and at one time the two were thought to represent two distinct species, called respectively *Felis serval* and *F. servalina*.

The ocelot (*Leopardus pardalis*), ranging from South America into Mexico, is slightly larger than the serval, and without its large ears. It is better known, perhaps, because of the use of its skin for women's coats and collars. Its buff or grey hair carries a pattern of large black or dark-brown spots.

Finally, one of the most interesting of the smaller cats is Pallas's cat (*Otocolobus manul*), of Central Asia. The size of a domestic cat, with a soft pale fur, it lives on the mountains, feeding on pikas or mouse-hares. Pallas's cat has a broad, flat head on which the eyes are set high and the ears low. Thus, it exposes itself to the minimum when peering over the edges of rocks on hunting forays.

THE BIG CATS

The big cats are much more conspicuous and familiar, and while they keep largely to cover they are sufficiently big to be observed. Nobody but the most uninitiated would fail to think of lions, tigers and leopards as big cats, and to these we must add the jaguars and pumas, as well as the Snow leopards.

The first four of these have powerful vocal cords, permitting their owners to roar; but the pumas and Snow leopards, in which the hyoid or throat bones are more closely knit, cannot express themselves so loudly. The pumas and jaguars are found in the New World; the rest belong to the Old World.

HARD-PRESSED LION

Lions and tigers have markedly different habitats, and this has had an important bearing on the history of the two animals in relation to man. Lions prefer open country, with sufficient scrub thickets, reed beds or trees to provide adequate cover, and no more. Tigers, on the other hand, keep to the thickest jungle, which the lions shun. In India, lions were present in large numbers during the first years of the British occupation, but, as they could be easily ridden down on horseback and shot, they have been exterminated, except in a protected area in Kathiawar. Within historic times lions (*Felis leo*) ranged from South-east Europe through southern Asia, as well as throughout Africa, but are now exterminated throughout most of their range, though they are still numerous in certain parts of Africa. Even so, wherever the country is being settled they face extinction, and it is likely that the whole species will, in the measurable future, follow the Barbary and Cape lions into oblivion, except where they are in reserves and national parks.

The Cape and Barbary lions were merely races of *Felis leo*, which differed perceptibly in such things as colour, size and other external features. But then lions are variable, especially in the mane. In some this is well developed, in others it is poorly developed. It is noticeable that lions in captivity in northern climates tend to grow heavy

LION AND LIONESS ON SERENGETI PLAIN, TANGANYIKA

Lions are undoubtedly the most impressive of the big cats. Once widely distributed over Europe, Asia and Africa, they are now confined to Africa and a small area of India. They frequent open country and prey chiefly upon zebra and antelope; very rarely a lion has taken to man-killing, but when it has done so has proved itself a resourceful and dangerous enemy. In regard to presence or absence of mane, lions are very variable.

LIONESSES AND

Lions often do their hunting in family parties. As most lions have two mates, the usual family party consists of a lion and two lionesses. The cub is taken care of by both

manes, although in any one district within their natural range maned and maneless lions may be seen. The colour of the body is fairly constant, but the colour of the mane varies from tawny to black.

Their natural prey on the plains is, of course, antelopes and zebra. The lions often hunt in family parties, or in troops of several family parties which may number up to ten or even twenty individuals. The tiger, on the other hand, is very much a solitary hunter. For all that has been said of the ferocity of the lion, it will seldom interfere with domestic livestock if wild game are available. If, however, we exterminate its natural prey, then it is not surprising if it attacks cattle. In the same way, stoats, badgers, otters and other predators are likely to find their food among

man's preserves if their natural food has been thinned out. Occasionally, age or injury, in addition to desperate hunger, will drive a lion to prey habitually on livestock or even human beings. The building of the Uganda Railway, for example, was seriously delayed by a small number of lions terrorizing the labourers working on it. On the other hand, it is found that the lions in national parks and reserves develop a degree of tameness which is, perhaps, more embarrassing to the human visitors than to the animals themselves.

The tiger (*F. tigris*), still plentiful in India and Malaya, as well as Siberia and Manchuria, feeds on small game, such as deer and pigs, but will also attack larger animals, such as buffaloes. It is about the same size as a lion, both reaching up to 9 ft. in total length and a

34

CUB ON THE PROWL

females, and, as often as not, is taught by them how to hunt. The above photograph shows a cub being taken on a hunting expedition by its mother and foster-mother.

weight of some 500 lb. There are records of 10-ft. animals, but there is reason to believe that such records are obtained from skins—stretched in the curing!

Tigers will, like lions, attack cattle and even human beings, when driven by extreme hunger, injury or advanced years. Normally, however, they will avoid direct encounter with man.

Although we usually associate tigers with hot countries, there is reason to suppose that they spread into southern Asia from the north. Certainly, they are intolerant of great heat, seeking escape from the heat of the day by sheltering in dense shade, or lying in reedy swamps. Incidentally, they are quite good swimmers, and will often travel long distances by water to hunt on islands in lakes or in the estuaries of rivers.

The growl of a tiger will turn to a snarl or a short roar when angry, or to a loud whoof when surprised. The animal also makes a "belling" sound, like the call of the sambar deer on which it preys. It has been suggested that this belling is used to call up the deer, but this is a poor compliment to the sense-perceptions of the deer. Since human beings can readily distinguish between the belling of a tiger and that of a deer, it may be presumed a wild beast is even more readily able to do so.

Although lions and tigers enter into competition under certain circumstances with man, they have a value in acting as a natural check on deer and wild pigs which, if left unmolested, can increase to the proportions of a pest to agriculture. It cannot be stressed too much or too often that we have underrated this value in the past and, often too late, are discovering the fact that if the natural predators are killed off there is at first a natural increase in game followed, very often, by a diminution in numbers.

The leopard or panther (*F. pardus*), of southern Asia and Africa, is more numerous and widespread than its larger relatives. This is due to the fact that its keener senses, greater adaptability and wariness make it much more troublesome to hunt out and kill. It is able to live in almost any country, provided there is cover, and can climb trees with ease, even dragging its heavy prey with it out of reach of hyenas and jackals. As might be expected, its prey is varied, and includes all small game, pigs, deer, monkeys, young domestic livestock, and porcupines. In particular, it has a liking for dog and will even enter bungalows to carry away the dogs.

It is seldom a man-eater, but when it does turn on human beings it is an even greater scourge than the bigger cats owing to the difficulty of hunting the offender down. One leopard that turned man-killer is said to have accounted for two hundred human lives in two years. Like the lions and tigers, the leopard acts as a check on animals, particularly pigs and baboons, which ravage crops.

Leopards are more variable in size and colour than the bigger cats. The average length is some 7 ft. overall, but this varies from one part of its range to another, and lengths of up to 8 ft. have been recorded. The weight is, however, only up to 150 lb. The colour and the length of the hair vary also. The richest pelts are those from the colder parts of its range, from China; and in areas of heavy rainfall, such as Assam and Java, melanism—giving the colour to the so-

A CAT THAT LIKES WATER

The tiger, like all cats, is a hardy animal; its range extends from arctic Siberia to the torrid jungles of India, Malaya and Sumatra. Of a solitary disposition, it lurks and finds its prey deep within the jungle. However, the tiger has no dislike of water, but will swim long distances in order to cross rivers or hunt its prey on islands.

LEOPARD CAUGHT BY FLASHLIGHT AT ITS KILL

The leopard, about 2 ft. less in length than the lion and the tiger, is more dangerous and more feared than either of its bigger relatives. This is mainly due to the fact that its liking for dog's flesh brings it frequently to human habitations.

called Black panther—is not infrequent.

The Snow leopard or ounce (*Uncia uncia*), in contrast to the other big cats, keeps well out of human range—or, at least, endeavours to do so, for it is much sought after for its beautiful fur. It is not a true leopard, though its fur is blotched and spotted. It lives above the tree-line in Central Asia, Tibet and the Himalayas, going up in summer to 13,000 ft. or so. Its prey is small mammals, such as marmots, and the mountain sheep or ibex.

The jaguar (*F. onca*), of South and Central America, is about the size of a leopard and, like it, is spotted. Black jaguars, also, are not uncommon. It is a forest-dweller, though it is also found in swamps by large rivers. Its chief food is the sloth and the capybara, and although it will attack the smaller domestic cattle it is not normally dangerous to man. Like the tiger, it is a good swimmer and often adds to its diet by lying on an overhanging tree or rock and scooping fish out of the water.

Clearly, the jaguar occupies in the New World a similar ecological niche to that occupied by the big cats of the Old World. There are certain differences, naturally, but, taking it by and large, it is one of the large predators that keeps in check the smaller herbivores and omnivores. In this work, it has as a parallel the puma (*F. concolor*), also known as the cougar or Mountain lion. This ranges from the Canadian border southwards to Patagonia, and is as much at home in the plains and deserts as it is in the mountains and forests. Slightly smaller than the jaguar, the tawny-coated puma preys mainly on deer and used to be a check on their over-multiplication; with the advance of human settlement, however, the puma has suffered like all the large predators.

A PUMA UTTERS ITS UNCANNY SCREAM

The puma, also called the cougar or Mountain lion, has a wide habitat in the New World. Although a fierce and daring animal on occasion, and a scourge of sheep-farmers, it is not particularly dreaded by man. With a long, supple body and powerful limbs, it is one of nature's finest leapers, easily clearing 20 ft. or more in a single bound.

Hair-raising stories about the ferocity of the puma have been told since the early pioneering days in the U.S.A.; later, more calmly compiled evidence does not, however, support these stories. It certainly shows a lively interest in what men are doing, and will often investigate their camp-sites and other works; but this is the result only of curiosity. A cornered puma is, of course, apt to be dangerous, but it is noticeable that even in these circumstances it will often put up no fight. Imagination, aided by the animal's weird screams, its size and resemblance to the lion, were probably responsible for much of the exaggeration. An interesting point about this powerful and active beast is that it is a tremendous jumper. It can bound 20 ft. with ease, sometimes covering 40 ft. in a leap.

The lynx, some 3½ ft. in length, is another kind of cat, found mainly in the pine forests of the north or at high altitudes, and obviously adapted for life in the snow. Characteristically, the tail is short, the ears tufted and the cheeks ornamented with hairy ruffs. The most outstanding character is, however, the powerful limbs ending in broad feet which enable the animal to move over the snow-crust in search of rabbits, small deer and ground-living birds.

A good example of a natural balance is seen in the Canada lynx, which lives almost wholly on the Snowshoe rabbit. As is so often the case with rodents and their relatives, the populations of the

EUROPEAN LYNX IN SEARCH OF PREY

The lynx can be easily recognized by its facial ruff and tufted ears. The name of this nocturnal prowler is proverbially connected with keen sight; indeed, the name itself derives from a Greek word meaning "to see." The most important species are the European, or Northern, lynx (shown above), Spanish lynx, Canada lynx and bob-cat.

CHEETAH SPYING OUT GAME

The cheetah, or Hunting leopard, is normally considered to be the most speedy animal in the world—at least over short distances. In India it is held in high regard as a "coursing" animal, and is used for hunting very speedy game. It differs from the typical cats in its non-retractile claws and its preference for running down its prey.

Snowshoe rabbit rise and fall over cyclic periods. In the years when rabbits are abundant, lynx will be plentiful: when the rabbit population is at a low ebb the lynx is scarce. The lynx is hunted for its fur, which is grey, lightly spotted on the undersides, dense and soft in winter and thin and of low quality in summer.

Lynxes are found in Europe, northern Asia, and North America. In Asia, they go as far south as the Himalayas. The European lynx (*Lynx lynx*) is now scarce, although formerly its cater-wauling, a louder version of the call of the domestic cat, was heard over a large part of the continent. It has, however, been largely wiped out as a result of its depredations on domestic sheep and goats. The Spanish lynx (*L. pardellus*) was smaller, with shorter hair and more heavily spotted. The two North American lynxes include the Canada lynx (*L. canadensis*), and the Wild cat or bob-cat (*L. rufus*), of the southern U.S.A. It is of some interest to note how two related species can fare so differently under similar changes of circumstance, for whereas the Canada lynx has tended to disappear in the face of human settlement, the bob-cat continues to exist in fair numbers even where the country has been opened up. This is because, being smaller, it can live on smaller prey and make better use of scanty cover.

DESERT LYNX

The caracal or Desert lynx (*Caracal caracal*) is a slenderly built animal related to the lynxes. In pursuit of any mammals or birds that come its way it is swift and active. It is found throughout Africa (except for the tropical forest zone) and in southern Asia, from Palestine to northern India, though in certain parts of its range it is now extinct or nearly so. Some 3 ft. in total

length, the large black ears are terminally tufted, and the short hair covering the body is a rich reddish-fawn. The tail is short and the legs long.

SPEEDY CHEETAH

The last of the big cats, the cheetah or Hunting leopard (*Acinonyx jubatus*), is something of an anomaly, for it combines the characters of the typical cats and the typical dogs. Thus, although cat-like in build and outward appearance, it has the non-retractile claws of the dogs and, like them, hunts by running down its prey. At one time it was looked upon as intermediate between cats and dogs, but in the structure of its skeleton, apart from the claws, it is typically a cat. It is the fastest of all land animals, being credited, over short distances, with a speed of anything up to 70 miles an hour. It has been timed to do 100 yd. in $4\frac{1}{2}$ seconds—faster than any greyhound; it lacks the endurance, however, to maintain such speeds for more than a quarter of a mile or so, and can easily be run down over longer distances by a man on horseback.

Cheetahs, now scarce, were formerly abundant on the open plains of Africa, South-west Asia and India. Strangely enough, they are practically defenceless. Their crime, for which so many cheetahs paid the penalty, was that they sometimes killed sheep and goats. On the other hand, they can be readily tamed, and have for centuries been used by man for hunting the swift blackbuck. A hooded cheetah would be taken in a bullock cart as near as possible to a herd of blackbuck. The hood would then be removed and the cheetah released to make a terrific rush at the blackbuck. If, however, it caught no buck within the first quarter-mile, this living streak of lightning would just sit and wait for the hood to be replaced.

NORTH AMERICAN BLACK BEAR

The North American Black bear (Ursus americanus) *is treacherous, like all members of the bear tribe in the wild. It takes easily to human society, however, and is a great favourite in the National Parks, where it begs food from passing motorists. In a completely wild state, the Black bear is given to raiding farms and stealing food.*

Dogs, Wolves
and Bears

ABOUT the year 1500 the last wild wolf in England was killed—Little Red Riding Hood was able to visit her grandmother with safety.

It may seem unnecessarily facetious to mention a character from a fairy-tale on the first page of a serious article on natural history; yet it is not inappropriate, for the wild life of the world is fast approaching the point where its members will be little more than legendary figures to future generations, unless we show greater wisdom than did our forefathers. They will be as dead as the dodo, and, as with the dodo, we shall have people constantly asking if they ever did exist.

Certainly, few will lament the extermination of wolves in Britain; but there are other animals (and by "animal" we mean all living things except plants, so that birds, too, are animals), like the Great auk, Steller's sea-cow, the Barbary and Cape lions, the quagga, which we would gladly have with us now, but they are gone beyond recall, victims either of man's insensate greed, or of the cruel march of civilization. And many more are threatened with the same fate.

To return to wolves, however, it is of interest to recall that these large carnivores once ranged over Europe and northern Asia and, judging from the constant references to them in legends,

folk-lore, even nursery stories, they must have been sufficiently numerous and enough of a menace to impress very deeply the minds of men of long ago. Always they are alluded to as representing all that is cruel, cunning and sinister. Yet, even though they may have been numerous, even though they may have been a familiar menace, it remains the fact that we have to go to the pages of modern scientific literature dealing with the North American wolves if we want to know anything at all detailed of the lives and habits of wolves in general. It is as though the inhabitants of Europe and Asia were too scared to notice more than the danger.

Banished from England by Royal decrees—and a bounty for their scalps —at the beginning of the sixteenth century, they lingered on in Scotland until 1743; today, however, they are found only in the wilder parts of Scandinavia, France, Spain, Germany and eastern Europe. They are also found in China, India, Arabia (but not in Africa), and in Central Asia, where the inhabitants hunt foxes with eagles (using the birds as falcons were once used for hunting smaller game in Britain), and, it is said, hunt wolves with them also. If this is done, probably the most that is accomplished is the retardation of the wolf's flight through harassment by the eagle;

43

this delay might, however, allow the hunter to catch up with it.

What then is this wolf, this almost completely legendary animal? The European wolf (*Canis lupus*) may perhaps best be described as being like a large Alsatian dog, coloured yellowish to brownish-grey and brindled with black, with a drooping tail. To dismiss the description of its colour in these simple terms, however, would be to understate the variability present in all animals, though more marked in some than in others. Some wolves, for example, are nearly black.

Since wolves, like all wild dogs, are built primarily for the speed necessary for running down their quarry, we should not expect them to have great body weight, and the 110 lb. of an average wolf, compared with its total length of nearly 6 ft., could not include much spare flesh.

A LEGEND DISPELLED

A popular misconception about wolves which has been fostered by legend is the belief that they hunt in large packs—or is this just another example of our forefathers, being so scared of them that they indulged in exaggerated accounts of them? Certainly all the reliable information suggests that the largest hunting unit consists only of a few families, and that even this combination lasts only during the winter months. In summer, hunting is done by single family parties, the young remaining with the parents. The litters, born in dens among rocks, in burrows freshly made or taken over from other animals, or among thick cover, number from five to nine. At best, therefore, the summer family party would number less than a dozen, and the winter hunting troops well under fifty—numbers well below the hundred-or hundreds-strong pack which is the popular idea. From America, where the best descriptions have been obtained, they seem to have had a wholesome fear of man and there are very few acceptable records of unprovoked attacks on human beings—or of wolves hunting in packs. And so far as attacks on wild animals are concerned, the early accounts show that in attacking buffalo herds one beast was singled out, separated from the herd and attacked simultaneously from front and rear by two or, at most, four wolves.

WOLF'S HUNTING TACTICS

The usual tactics were for one, or two (as the case may be), to harry the buffalo from the front, snapping at the snout, tongue, eyes, or flanks, while the rear attack was directed to ham-stringing or castrating the hapless beast, until, fearfully mauled and weakened with loss of blood, the terrifically strong, well-armed ungulate fell to the smaller, more agile foe.

At the heyday of the American buffalo hunter, wolves learned to associate the crack of a rifle with a kill, and would gather around waiting for food. While the hunters skinned the beast and cut selected portions of the meat, the wolves would lurk about, ready to rush in and clean up the carcase as soon as the hunters left. This was a matter of little importance to the human population until the moment had arrived when the almost countless herds of buffaloes had been virtually exterminated from the plains. Then, as in Europe, the domestic cattle were attacked.

It was not always so easy to prevent this, for two reasons. First, some of the old wolves developed a great cunning in avoiding both traps and hunters. This cunning was most marked in certain individual wolves which had

ALMOST LEGENDARY WOLF

The European wolf, seen above, is very like a large Alsatian dog, being coloured yellowish to brownish-grey, brindled with black. An average specimen is about 6 ft. in length, from its nose to the tip of its tail, and it weighs about 110 lb.

45

BLACK-BACKED JACKAL
Jackals are found mainly in the warmer parts of the Old World. They are a little larger than foxes and, like foxes, prey on poultry and small domestic stock.

gained particular notoriety as cattle-killers and yet, although specially singled out for destruction, managed to outwit their pursuers for years. Further, all wolves had an advantage towards survival in face of an organized persecution because of the immense territory they covered. A wolf might kill at one place and be forty miles away by the next day, possibly not returning to the original place for weeks.

Field observations made in the U.S.A. of recent years have thrown an interesting light on this particular aspect of their behaviour. It has been customary to assume that wolves were nomads, ranging over vast tracts of territory in a quite inconsequential manner, following their noses, so to speak, and wandering where their fancy took them. Quite the reverse is the case. We now have a picture of them as creatures tied by habit, with regular beats and patrols. Indeed, it seems that this is likely to prove true of all animals, when the full story becomes known.

Certainly, the wolf has been found to follow a definite track; it dens up for the night and forages in various directions, but it ultimately resumes its beat, to den up again at another point for the following night, and so on. The total patrol may take several weeks, at the end of which it is "home" again. The circuit is then started all over again. The track is followed so faithfully that the beast does not deviate at any time more than a quarter of a mile either side of its well-trodden trail.

The variability of colour already noted for the European wolf is equally or even more marked in the North American wolf (*C. lupus*), which is usually regarded as an offshoot of the same stock. The various local races include that of the Arctic tundra of Canada, which is often white. This is of great size and preys on the musk-ox and caribou. To the south is the wolf of the plains, which preyed on the buffalo and later took to killing stock cattle. This has been cleared from the eastern states, but still survives in the wilder parts of the western states. Farther south are other races, in Florida (which are often black) and Mexico.

Wolves enjoy the generic name of *Canis*, and, as we shall see later, they contributed largely to the production of our modern domesticated dogs. Another North American wolf, also included under this generic name, but constituting a distinct species, is the coyote, or Prairie wolf (*C. latrans*), with its characteristic yapping howl. This is of smaller size, with a total length of 4 ft. and weighing only 35 to 40 lb. Somewhat jackal-like in size and habits, it has managed to hold its own in most parts of the U.S.A. Its survival has probably been due partly to its ability to live on a variety of small rodents, which makes it less of a threat to domestic cattle than

were the larger wolves; and partly to its small size, which enables it to hide easily in low cover.

Although, as we have seen, there are wolves even in India and Arabia, they are for the most part replaced in the warmer parts of the Old World by several species of jackal. These are little larger than large foxes, dog-like with bushy tails. Jackals are proverbially cowardly—or, rather, cowardly and treacherous human beings are often referred to as "jackals." The adjective seems largely undeserved so far as the animal is concerned, unless preying on any creatures they can overpower is cowardice. Certainly they follow lions and tigers to feed on their leavings, but that is because they have a taste for carrion. For the same reason they lurk about camps and villages, feeding on

AFRICAN WILD DOGS DEVOURING A ZEBRA

A pack of Cape hunting dogs, disturbed as they are about to begin their meal, snarl their defiance at the camera. This photograph was taken by Col. Sir James L. Sleeman from a range of only fifteen feet, without the use of a telephoto lens.

scraps and, it must be admitted, killing poultry, kids and other small domestic stock. Their eerie, yapping howl is, therefore, not a welcome sound to men living in the areas of their depredations.

The Indian jackal (*C. aureus*), found from Palestine and Arabia through India and Ceylon to Burma, is a dull, blackish-tawny colour. A closely related form is found in South-east Europe. In Africa there are several species. The Wolf-like jackal of Egypt (*C. lupaster*), measuring 50 in. from tip to tail and standing 16 in. at the shoulder, is the largest. In addition, there is the Side-striped jackal, found over most of the open country of Africa and deriving its name from the blackish band on its flanks; and the handsome Black-backed jackal of East and South Africa. The latter has a black "saddle" with white flecks and strongly contrasting reddish flanks and limbs. From the skins of the Black-backed jackal are made the karosses, the square rug-like garments worn by the natives of South Africa.

PUZZLE OF THE DINGO

The last of the Canidae to be considered is the dingo (*C. dingo*) of Australia. This is somewhat of an enigma. In the first place, the fauna of Australia is peculiar in that the native mammals are so primitive; there is nothing comparable with the big dogs and cats found in other parts of the world. It seems reasonable to assume that the first settlers in Australia, who were probably of Malay stock, brought the dingo with them as a domestic animal, and that it went wild again, increasing enormously in numbers, as a carnivore would be bound to do when it found itself without serious competitors in the midst of abundant food resources (in this case the numerous inoffensive, herbivorous wallabies and kangaroos).

The question might well be asked, and indeed has been asked, why we must so confidently assume that the dingo is a domesticated dog that has gone feral. As we shall see later, the mammalian fauna of Australia is marsupial; that is to say, it is composed of the sort of mammals which were formerly widely spread over the world and have been preserved in the island continent of Australia because it became severed from the main land-mass in Eocene times, when the large carnivores, the big dogs and cats, had not yet been evolved. That is the general picture.

BRIDGES OF LAND

However, we know from the geological findings that wherever a large mass of land has parted from the main mass the process has been slow, and there is always a period during which it has been connected by one or more land bridges. In the case of Australia, there was probably at one time, many millions of years ago, a land bridge with both Antarctica and the south-eastern corner of Asia.

The land-bridge theories are, however, difficult to sustain in the case of the dingo, and, although irrefutable evidence is not forthcoming, the sum total of possibilities is against it. If the dingo had come in from Antarctica we should have expected to find it in Tasmania, which formed part of that bridge; and it is not there. Had the land bridge from South-east Asia been maintained to a sufficiently late date to permit the dingo to come in that way, we should expect to find many non-marsupial animals in Australia. Again, although semi-fossil remains of dingoes are found in Australia, showing that its association with human beings goes back a long way, no fossil remains of this animal have yet been found there.

DINGO OF AUSTRALIA

The dingo is a fawn-coloured dog about the size of a foxhound. It is believed that early settlers in Australia brought it with them as a domesticated animal and that it went wild again. Although capable of semi-domestication, it is very untrustworthy.

Anatomically, there is a close comparison to be made between the dingo and the northern wolf; and its skeleton is essentially the same as that of other domesticated dogs of comparable size and build, except that the canine teeth are larger and more wolf-like. In like manner, the erect ears and bushy tail also point to a close affinity with the wolf.

Consideration of the dingo leads very naturally to the subject of domestication, and, although in this book we are dealing primarily with wild animals, it must be recognized that the frontier between wild and domesticated animals is very ill-defined. Man has domesticated the dog and the cat. It seems, for example, that almost any species of wild animal can be domesticated and equally

that any domesticated animal can go feral. In addition, not only do we get varying degrees of submission to deliberate attempts at domestication, but a voluntary acceptance by some species of a partial domestication—or, at least, a close association with man. We see examples of this in the behaviour of the mongooses and a species of skunk, to mention two more of the carnivores. Finally, it must not be forgotten that on many occasions people have had tame cheetahs, leopards and, up to a certain age at all events, lions.

The early history of most domesticated animals is lost in the obscurity of time. Man must have domesticated them at a time, probably in the Neolithic period, when he himself was little more than a wild animal. In some

49

cases the wild species from which the domesticated animal was derived appears to have died out completely and we are left without a clue. In others we can do little more than conjecture, for under domestication, with its selective breeding, such great changes in the appearance of the animal are brought about that any evidence we have of ancestry is largely of a supplementary or circumstantial nature. There are, however, a few general principles that may be mentioned. When man domesticated an animal it meant that he found it useful to him in one or more ways—as food, as a source of clothing, as a beast of burden, as a companion or as an assistant in his hunting. Dogs, without doubt, come into this last category. On the other side, we must suppose in the animal some quality, a tamability, which permitted it to accept domestication and to live with man.

ORIGINS OF DOMESTIC DOGS

Our domesticated dogs have probably been derived from several sources: from the wolf and the jackal, and possibly other wild dogs. The Alsatian and the dingo point directly to a wolf ancestry, and it is significant that in Arctic Canada, where the husky is the favourite for pulling sledges, the bitches are often tethered in the open, at the appropriate time, in order that they may be mated with wolves. In this way the stock is revitalized by the infusion of wild blood.

Under domestication something seems to happen to the personality of an animal which it is difficult to define or to account for. In the first place, diet may have something to do with it. Certainly there is considerable evidence in support of the theory that diet does affect personality. We are apt to conclude that character is a thing solely of the mind,

that is, of the brain. But this is only one of the factors contributing to the sum total of behaviour. The physiology of the body, in which may be included the tremendous contribution of the ductless glands, undoubtedly plays a major part. To restrict an animal equipped with strong, sharp teeth and a shortened intestine, designed for a mainly carnivorous diet, to a mainly vegetarian diet must involve far-reaching consequences in its physiology, with resultant changes in its personality. Secondly, there can be little doubt that many animals brought up from infancy among human beings seem to take on something of the personality of their human guardians, even if their parents were totally wild. At the Prague zoo in recent years a Polar bear cub fostered in the flat of the superintendent of the zoo was "almost human," whereas a cub from the same mother fostered by a Boxer bitch retained a great deal more of its native personality. There must be many such examples known to those who have first-hand contact with animals.

DEGREES OF TAMABILITY

It must be admitted, however, that the example of the Polar bear cubs must be accepted cautiously, for Young and Goldman, in their book *The Wolves of North America*, have shown that in a given litter the degree of tamability varies not only with the age at which adoption occurs, but from one young wolf to another. Wolf cubs are best tamed if taken just as their eyes are opening. If taken at three to four weeks they can be trained only with difficulty. Further, in any litter there is a steady proportion of those which respond to training and those which resist it completely. In the early stages of domestication man must have selected the amenable individuals from which to

FOXES AT THE ENTRANCE TO THEIR EARTH

Compared with the wolf the fox is of small proportions. An average specimen measures about 3 ft. from nose to tip of tail, about one-third of which is tail, and weighs only about 15 lb. Foxes have evaded extinction in Britain largely because they provide sport and can avoid capture and death by their habit of burrowing and by their native cunning.

51

breed his tame strains, and would quite clearly have destroyed any that proved refractory or untamable.

It is apparent, therefore, that the fact that dingoes can be tamed (and, being tamed, will forsake their notorious habit of killing sheep) is not necessarily evidence that they are tame dogs gone wild again. But it does show how readily dogs, and probably all animals, can be tamed and can revert.

ANTARCTIC WOLF

An interesting commentary on this question of tameness and tamability is provided by the story of the Antarctic wolf (*Dusicyon antarcticus*). The first white men to visit the Falkland Islands found there a large wolf-like animal with a shaggy coat. The name is apt to mislead, for the Falklands are not in the Antarctic proper, and the animal was restricted to those islands, where it fed on the abundant sea-birds and their eggs. When first seen, it did not run away when the men went near it—so they clubbed it! What a marvellous story we have to tell of the human race! "It's a fine day—let's go out and shoot something." Darwin, in his *Voyage of the Beagle*, tells how in 1833 the Antarctic wolf was very abundant and very tame. He also predicted that it would soon be extinct, which it was by 1876. Darwin was not only a great naturalist, but he evidently knew his fellow humans well.

In fairness, however, it ought to be admitted that some justification can be found for its later persecution. By taking to killing sheep when sheep-farming had become the staple industry of the Falklands the wolf sealed its own doom. Nevertheless, the story of wanton killing is a long one.

The Antarctic wolf left two relatives —the Crab-eating fox of the Argentine and Paraguay and the Maned wolf of southern Brazil. The second of these is like a giant fox on stilts, with a shaggy reddish coat and large erect ears on a fox-like head; it measures 5 ft. from tip to tail.

Common names are bestowed intuitively—one might almost say impulsively—and have little relation to scientific knowledge. As a consequence they are apt on occasion to conflict. Thus, of the three closely related carnivores just discussed, two have received the designation "wolf" and the other "fox," though they are neither fox nor wolf. It is perhaps excusable that the layman may sometimes feel sceptical about the niceties the scientist maintains in classifying animals. The foxes, for example, the next group of carnivores to be considered, are certainly dog-like; or, alternatively, they could be described as small wolves. Yet they are neither the one nor the other. In general build and appearance, in their anatomy, physiology and psychology, they are very distinct from either wolves or dogs. Stories are sometimes current of a fox having mated with a bitch, or a dog with a vixen, but there is no authentic case of this having happened. If there is, in fact, any relationship between dogs, wolves and foxes, both dogs and wolves refuse to recognize it and they lose no opportunity of killing and eating a fox.

THE FOXES

The history of the foxes would doubtless have paralleled that of the wolves, if not that of the Antarctic wolf, but for three things: they provide sport, they are a source of valuable furs, and they can evade capture and death by their habit of burrowing and by their native cunning. Of the less than a dozen species distributed over

SILVER FOX

To trappers of the past the Silver fox was a rarity, and such high prices were offered for its skin that in 1894 experiments were tried in breeding these foxes in captivity. The first "farmed" furs, from Prince Edward Island, sold for £500 a skin.

Europe, Asia, North America and Africa, the best known is the European fox (*Vulpes vulpes*), which, despite its name, is found through Europe, northern Asia and North America. Its bright rufous coat, white underparts, black-backed ears and white-tipped tail are well known from story and picture. Compared with a wolf it is of small proportions, 3 ft. from tip to tail, of which one-third is tail; its average weight is only 15 lb., although an old dog fox may weigh up to 29 lb. The small size means, too, that it will feed on much smaller creatures, such as rabbits, rats, mice, ground-nesting birds, frogs and insects. Some fruit is included in its diet—not necessarily sour grapes! So the fox is not tempted as a regular habit to attack stock, apart from poultry and lambs; otherwise it is doubtful whether, in spite of its nocturnal habits and a natural cunning, it would have been allowed to survive as well as it has done.

Students of animal psychology could do worse than collect as many stories as possible of the behaviour of foxes, sift and analyse them, and see where they lead in this very vexed question of animal intelligence. For it seems that the mentality of the fox—of the wild fox, not of the mentally degenerate beast we find on fox-farms—has a radically different quality to that of the domesticated dog or even the wild wolf, much as these show advanced mental traits. Hunted foxes, for example, especially old and experienced animals, will adopt many stratagems to throw hounds off the scent, such as running through a herd of sheep or cattle, through farmyards, along the tops of narrow walls where the hounds would find difficulty in following, or even leading the hounds up to a fresh fox whose scent they will follow.

There is the story of the three old dog foxes who, when the hunt was on, would take it in turns to lead the hounds a dance. When the first was tired, he would lead the pack to the second fox, who would take up the game until, weary, he led the hounds to the third fox, and so on. If true, this behaviour comes remarkably close to co-operative thought.

THE FOX AND THE FLEAS

Then there is the story of the fox and the fleas, which has been repeated often enough and by reputable field naturalists. If it be true that a vermin-laden fox will gather sheep's wool from the bushes, wade into a stream with it in his mouth, submerge until the fleas have escaped on to the wool, and swim away from the wool, leaving the fleas to a watery grave, then we have a truly remarkable story. Is it true ? One would dearly love to know; for, if true, it would again betoken something very near conceptual thought.

Foxes are one of the mainstays of the fur trade, particularly those of Scandinavia, Siberia and North America. In the wild, colour phases or mutations are not infrequent, especially in North America. The Cross fox, for example, is distinguished by a handsome black band across the shoulders and blackish underparts; otherwise, it is red. A more valuable catch is, however, the so-called Silver fox, its rich, lustrous coat relieved on the back by the white tips to many of the guard hairs.

To the trappers of the past the Silver fox was a rarity, a choice and valuable prize, but avaricious man had to improve on nature, so in 1894 experiments were tried in breeding these foxes in captivity. Success came quickly, and the first farmed furs, from Prince Edward Island, in the Gulf of St. Law-rence, sold for five hundred pounds a skin—a fantastic price. Soon a major industry developed in Canada and the U.S.A., which spread to Norway and other parts of Europe and to Japan. The annual output of first-class skins soared, and the price slumped to ten pounds a skin.

Practically all Silver fox skins are now obtained from farming, a highly skilled job which demands a knowledge of and attention to diet and hygiene, the selection of the right climatic conditions, and freedom from disturbance for the animals. Recently, sports or mutants with white face-blazes have been selectively bred to produce the white-face and platinum foxes for the luxury trade. But civilization must press on: so experiments are being made in the control of light and temperature in order to bring pelts to prime condition earlier than under natural circum-stances, so as to capture early markets and high prices.

THE LUCKLESS KIT FOX

The story of the Kit fox (*V. velox*) of the open plains of the western U.S.A. affords a poignant contrast with the care and attention devoted to its northern relatives. It is smaller than the Red, Common or European fox (you can take your choice of the names). Its fur, yellowish-brown, sprinkled with black-tipped hairs, and with a black-tipped tail, has no market value. So the Kit fox, in common with other small and harm-less carnivores, has been almost wiped out in some of its haunts by the inten-sive poisoning campaign against the wolves.

The Arctic or White fox (*Alopex lagopus*), with its colour phase the Blue fox, which lives in Arctic regions, is also farmed, though less extensively than the larger Silver foxes. A successful experiment in fur-farming has been the stocking of the small, uninhabited islands off the Alaskan coast with breeding Arctic foxes which have been allowed to multiply under natural conditions, except that food has been provided. In its native haunts, the rocky coasts, the Arctic fox feeds largely on nesting birds or their eggs, or on stranded fish and other carrion. In winter it feeds on large numbers of dead lemmings which it has caught and stored up in crevices in rocks against the time when food will be scarce. Also, during the hard weather the fox will follow the Polar bear, jackal-like, to feed on the remnants of seal the bear may leave after satisfying his appetite.

The Grey fox (*Urocyon cinereoargen-*

teus), of the eastern and Pacific states of the U.S.A., has fur of little value, so we can ignore this fox, except to remark that it is able to climb trees quite well, and that it is an omnivore (that is, will eat a wide range of animal and vegetable matter).

The remaining foxes, of Africa and Asia, are smaller and include the Bat-eared fox (*Otocyon megalotis*), of South and East Africa, which has large erect ears, feeds on insects and lives in colonies on the sandy plains. Two other foxes live in the semi-desert regions of North Africa and Arabia. These are the Sand foxes (*Vulpes ruppelli*) and the Fennec (*Fennecus zerda*). The latter is 2 ft. in total length, is slender and possesses very large ears; the hairy soles of its

LITTER OF BAT-EARED FOXES

Bat-eared foxes are found in South and East Africa, where they live in colonies on the sandy plains. They have large, erect ears and live mainly on insects. They make charming pets, but attract leopards, which are very fond of Bat-eared fox meat.

BLACK BEARS IN THE
*The American Black bear is smaller than its European relative, and less formidable.
Once a valuable source of food to the early pioneers, it now leads a peaceful life within
the protection of national preserves. Naming animals by their colour can be mis-*

CANADIAN ROCKIES

leading, for, although the glossy black of the American bear is typical, it is not un-common to find brown or cinnamon varieties. This Canadian Film Board photograph was taken in the Jasper National Park, which has an area of 4,200 square miles.

feet enable it to run over loose sand. Like most desert animals, it lies up during the heat of the day, coming out at night to feed on small rodents and insects, especially locusts.

No account of foxes should end without reiterating the lamentable result of taking the Red fox to Australia. It would be easy enough to label the action of those responsible for its introduction as iniquitous; but to do so would be somewhat hypocritical when, even in this enlightened age, we are still committing similar acts of vandalism. Whether the fox was taken to Australia by early settlers to provide them with sport, or whether to counteract the menace of the rabbit, the result has been serious for the native fauna. According to all accounts, the foxes in Australia disdain rabbit when they see

such a glut around them, preferring to take other things, such, for example, as the glorious but fast-diminishing lyrebird.

All things being considered, therefore, dogs in the wild (using the word "dog" in a broad sense) have a bad conduct sheet wherever they come into competition with the human race. This is in striking contrast to their record under domestication—and therein lies a moral. We are much too prone to ask: "What is the use of this animal? What is the use of that animal?"—as though the universe were made solely for man's benefit. We are late-comers on the scene and it is for us to recognize that there is such a thing as a natural balance, and that it is through our upsetting this that animals, and plants, in the main, become a nuisance. The

FENNEC FOXES

Fennec foxes live in the semi-desert regions of North Africa and Arabia. They are slender little animals, about 2 ft. long, with long ears and hairy-soled feet that enable them to run over loose sand. Nocturnal, they feed on small rodents and insects.

CAPE HUNTING DOGS

Cape hunting dogs stand about 2 ft. high at the shoulder and have broad, hyena-like heads, with large, erect ears. They will travel great distances, and a pack will clear the countryside of game for miles. Outstanding is their curiosity in human affairs.

natural predators, the wild dogs and cats of all descriptions, have a definite role to fulfil. Paradoxically enough, the predators actually benefit the species whose numbers they decimate. This is a principle we are only just beginning to recognize.

The short-haired, reddish Indian wild dog or dhole (*Cuon javanicus*), made familiar to us by Kipling in his Jungle books, feeds largely on deer, which are run down by small packs of dholes. The dogs are powerfully built (38 in. in head and body, with an 18-in. tail), and possess an unusual stamina and great persistence in hunting. Scouring the forests and jungles, they scare away game for miles around. Even tigers and leopards are sometimes forced to give up their kill by these redoubtable dogs.

The Cape hunting dog (*Lycaon pictus*), no very near relative of the dhole, rivals it in hunting prowess. Slightly larger, its body, blotched black, white and yellow, bearing a broad hyena-like head and large, rounded, erect ears, is carried on unusually long legs, so that

the animal stands 2 ft. high at the shoulder. In the open grass country, where its soft hooting voice may be heard keeping members of the pack in touch, it will clear the countryside of game for miles around. Though outlawed, its high birth-rate (up to ten in a litter), as well as its vitality and audacity, ensures the persistence of this troublesome species. In common with all wild dogs and wolves, the Cape hunting dogs will travel great distances, only to reappear in the same area some time later. Like wolves, they probably have a well-trodden itinerary, though this has not been studied as fully as that of the North American wolf.

This wide-ranging hunter is afflicted with an extraordinary curiosity. A pack of these dogs will stand gazing at a human intruder for a long time, until dispersed by shots. Is a sense of curiosity a concomitant of such extravagant hunting over wide areas—a desire to explore and search out?

By contrast, the Raccoon-like dog (*Nyctereutes procyonoides*) of the river

BLACK BEAR TAKES A STROLL

The tameness of the American Black bear is well illustrated by this photograph, taken in the Glacier National Park, U.S.A. These animals frequently sit in the road and hold up motor-traffic, refusing to move until they have been fed with tit-bits. In their purely wild state, however, they can be extremely destructive of crops and stores.

valleys and willow-studded grassy plains of China, Korea and Japan is solitary, eats almost anything and is particularly partial to fish. It is very like the North American raccoons, being 2½ ft. long, including the bushy tail, and having short, dark-brown legs, a pale ash-coloured head and neck, and dark patches round the eyes. Known to the fur trade as "Japanese fox," it has been introduced to several parts of the U.S.S.R. for the sake of its fur.

An even more unusual dog than the latter is the Bush dog of the tropical forests of Brazil and the Guianas. Badger-like in colour, and with badger-like short legs, it is pale above and blackish below, a reversal of the usual obliterative shading. The Bush dog calls to mind the Red Sea fish that has a silver back and coloured belly, a reversal of the usual colouring—but it swims upside down! What, then, is the significance of reversal of colouring in the Bush dog? This is another problem to which the field naturalist will have to give attention in the future.

VARIETY OF CARNIVORES

To the academic zoologist the order Carnivora presents few, if any, anomalies. To the non-zoologist this group contains a bewildering array of cats, dogs and cat-like and dog-like animals, such as civets and genets, foxes, jackals and raccoons. But it also contains the bears, pandas, stoats, weasels, otters, badgers, hyenas and so on, all of diverse habit, appearance and mode of life.

It is easy to understand the grouping together of cats and dogs, and their like. But what about the rest? Now, the foundations of different houses look very much alike. They may differ in details but not in principle. The resulting buildings will, however, differ considerably. They may be bungalows, cottages, villas, two-, three-, four-storeyed. The roofs may be slated, tiled, or flat and have sun-parlours. The walls may be of rough-cast, half-timbering or plain brick. To the architect they all belong to the order Dwelling-houses, and the one common feature is the foundations. (Architects may disagree with this analogy, but it will serve.)

TELL-TALE SKELETONS

To anyone privileged to wander around the study collections of a large museum, to examine the rows and rows of skeletons set up, there will be much difficulty (if he ignores the labels) in telling whether a particular skeleton belonged to a cat, dog, wolf, bear, mongoose, civet, badger or panda, except in size. There are details which differ, and to the skilled eye are quickly apparent—just as foundations have tell-tale differences for the architect. The big differences, certainly the more obvious differences, appear (as with dwelling-houses) when the bare bones are clothed. In these basic skeletons, however, there are certain constant features which serve as a basis for comparison and classification; such are the bones of the skull and of the feet, and more particularly the teeth.

Now let us pass to the nearest relatives of the dogs—the bears, the largest of the Carnivora and among the least carnivorous. Except in Africa and Australasia, bears have been found almost everywhere in the world, though over wide areas, as in Britain, man has eradicated them.

Heavily built, almost tailless, with broad, flat feet, each with five toes bearing non-retractile claws, they follow, on the whole, the policy of live and let live, at least as far as the larger animals are concerned. Berries, wild fruits, any small creatures living under stones and logs form the bulk of their diet. Fish, scooped out of the shallows with a flipping action of the paws, are not disdained. They will eat other animals if opportunity affords, and occasionally a rogue has taken to stock-killing.

In the rare cases where a man has been attacked, it was usually under provocation and in defence of the cubs. (A comparable action in human beings would be acclaimed as heroic: the dumb brute, however, gets a bullet!) On such occasions grievous injuries may result from blows of the strong claws, but the time-honoured belief that a bear attacks by hugging its enemies seems to be without foundation. The enormous power of a large bear can be illustrated by the ability of an old grizzly to smash a bison's skull with a blow of its paw, to pick up a pig and walk away with it— even biting the pig's head off without halting in its progress!

HABITS OF THE BEAR

Other than man, bears have few natural enemies; a troop of hungry wolves may attack an ageing bear, but even this is rare. It is a general feature of the behaviour of all wild animals that they prefer to avoid a fight unless they are driven to it either by hunger or in self-defence.

The time-honoured belief that to lie motionless is the best defence against a bear is, however, correct. Its sight is poor and a still object will remain undetected at a hundred yards. On the other hand, hearing and smell are acute.

Bears, as a rule, live in wild mountainous country, in forests or whatever cover is readily available, and roam about, either alone or in family parties. Most bears can climb trees, slowly and deliberately, but the grizzly, perhaps because of its great weight, will not do so readily. In the northern regions they accumulate fat in preparation for their hibernation in caves, rocky hollows, large hollow logs or under the roots of fallen trees. They emerge from hibernation, thin and hungry, in the spring. During the hibernation period the two young are born. The cubs are friendly and playful, but as they grow up they are of uncertain temper. And at all times, whether in play or in temper, their sharp claws are a constant menace.

TYPES OF BEARS

There are fourteen different kinds of bears in the world, excluding the Polar bear, and some of them, at least, illustrate a modern trend in the study of zoology which is worthy of some attention at this point. Eight of them may be referred to collectively as Brown bears; the rest are characterized by black or white coats, or a mixture of the two. Originally they were regarded as representing distinct species. Now four of them are looked upon as races or subspecies, and at least two other so-called "species" may eventually be grouped under a single species. It is not possible to enter fully into this point here. It is rather a technical matter and one for the specialist, but something of its implications will become apparent as the various kinds of bears are dealt with.

It is natural, since the first zoologists, in the strict sense, were Europeans, that the European Brown bear (*Ursus arctos*) should be our starting-point. This bear, abundant up to the eleventh century in Britain—and now found there solely in captivity—is rare in most parts of Europe. It is found in small numbers in the wilder parts of the Pyrenees, Alps and Carpathians; in Scandinavia, Finland and the Balkans; and more plentifully in the U.S.S.R. Local forms of it are, however, found

WISTFUL EXPRESSION OF A BROWN BEAR

EUROPEAN BROWN BEAR

The European Brown bear is today rare in most parts of Europe, being found mainly in the wilder parts of the Alps, Pyrenees and Carpathians, Scandinavia and the Balkans and, more plentifully, in the U.S.S.R. It roamed Britain in Saxon days.

in Siberia and eastern Asia, with one such in Hokkaido, the northern island of Japan. It often happens that animals that we normally speak of as "European" range from the British Isles, across Europe and Asia to Japan. Typically, this Brown bear averages 6 ft. in length, but may reach 7 ft., varies in weight with the season from 450 to 550 lb., and has a brown shaggy coat.

There is, however, the Blue or Snow bear, of western China and Tibet, which, although having a coat of blackish-brown hairs "frosted" (i.e. tipped) with silver or slate-grey, is now accepted as no more than a subspecies, its scientific name being *Ursus arctos pruinosus*, the second name indicating its species, the third its subspecies. Similarly, the Red or Isabelline bear, of Kashmir and the western Himalayas, with a pale brown coat, is *U. arctos isabellinus*; and the Syrian bear, of Asia Minor, the smaller, ash-brown animal of Biblical fame (it killed forty-two children that mocked Elisha), is *U. arctos syriacus*. The Syrian bear is also famous as the dancing bear which formerly was led on a chain by wandering musicians, a spectacle which happily can no longer be seen in Britain.

The three North American Brown bears are still accorded specific rank, though some zoologists are inclined to regard them as giant races of *Ursus arctos*. The Grizzly (*U. horribilis*) may

NORTH AMERICAN GRIZZLY

The Grizzly bear may measure up to 8½ ft. in length and weigh as much as 880 lb. Because of its uncertain temper it is one of the most respected of America's big game. It is found mainly in British Columbia, the Yukon and Alaska.

ISABELLINE BEARS

Known also as the Red bear, because of its light reddish-brown coat, this is the most southerly member of the Brown bear group, living above the tree-line in the Himalayas and hibernating throughout the winter. Its food is varied, from grass, grubs and fruit to cattle, sheep and ponies; but it is seldom dangerous to man.

measure 8½ ft. in length and weigh up to 880 lb., and the Kenai bear (*U. kenaiensis*) and Kadiak bear (*U. middendorffi*) are even larger, the latter reaching 9 ft. or more and up to 1,650 lb. Although so large, they are inoffensive, and are now protected. The Grizzly, on the other hand, is of uncertain temper and, particularly in the early days of white settlement, when firearms were less reliable, was the most respected of America's big game. The name "Grizzly" refers to the grizzling due to the pale tips of many of the body hairs, and has nothing to do with "grisly," meaning fearsome. The animal is now gone from most of the western U.S.A. and southern Rockies, but is commonly seen in British Columbia, the Yukon and Alaska.

It is always misleading, although it is often done, to name animals by their colour, as we know only too well by the frequent occurrence of white, or partly white, blackbirds. So with the smaller American Black bear (*U. americanus*), for although it is typically a glossy black, brown or cinnamon varieties are not uncommon, and in the coastal areas of British Columbia there is a white bear (nothing to do with the Polar bear) which may be an albino Black bear. At the moment, however, it is known as Kermode's bear (*U. kermodei*).

The Black bear was a valuable source of food to the early pioneers, especially in autumn, when it had laid on its fat for the winter. Today it is a favourite in the National Parks, begging food of passing motorists and invading camps to search the garbage. In the purely wild state it can be a nuisance, raiding farms or stealing cached food laid up by backwoodsmen and trappers.

South America has only one bear, the Spectacled bear (*Tremarctos ornatus*), living high up in the mountains of Venezuela and Chile. Very little is known, however, concerning its habits.

SLOTH BEAR

The Sloth bear of India and Ceylon lives on termites, which it digs out with its claws and sucks up with its mobile lips. Contrary to its name, it can move with surprising speed, and although generally mild in temperament, will charge an intruder if surprised. The whiteness of its long, dog-like muzzle contrasts strangely with its rough black coat.

Bears are associated in our minds with the temperate and more northerly regions, and this conception is generally true. Hence the farther we go south the greater the likelihood of finding them living in high, cool areas. Moreover, with the exception of the South American Spectacled bear, they are confined to the northern hemisphere. There are three species still to be considered. These are the Himalayan Black bear (*Selenarctos thibetanus*), the Sloth bear (*Melursus ursinus*) and the Malayan or Sun bear (*Helarctos malayanus*). All three are black, the first having a prominent V-shaped white patch on the throat, the second a white chest-patch, and the third species a yellowish chest-patch.

The Himalayan Black bear, in spite of its name, is found on high ground from northern Persia to China, and on the South Island of Japan, living in summer as high as 12,000 ft. and in winter hibernating at high altitudes or coming down to the lower altitudes. It is the largest of the southern Asian bears, 6½ ft. long, with a 3-in. tail, and weighing up to 265 lb. It is said to have little fear of man, and maulings by it are not uncommon, especially if it is wounded. A favourite trick, when alarmed, is to roll downhill in a ball—so hunters keep on higher ground than their quarry!

The Sloth bear, of India and Ceylon, a slightly smaller animal, digs out termites with its powerful claws, blows

66

the earth from around them and sucks them up with its mobile lips. Living on so soft a diet, its teeth are poorly developed, very unlike the teeth of most Carnivora. Its temperament, too, is mild, but being, like all bears, short-sighted it will charge in the direction of the intruder, when surprised in cover, lashing out with its powerful claws. The Sloth bear, contrary to its name, can move at speed, despite its short legs. At such times a cub will ride its mother's back like an expert jockey.

The Malayan bear, the smallest of all bears, is an expert climber, with a passion for honey and syrup; its playful antics make it a favourite in zoos.

The Polar bear (*Thalarctos mariti-mus*), which rivals the Kadiak bear for size (up to 9 ft. long and 1,600 lb. in weight), is the most markedly carni-vorous of all bears. This is to be expec-ted, since it inhabits the Arctic where vegetation is scanty. Moving freely over the ice on its broad, hairy-soled feet, with the head swinging from side to side, as if continually smelling out its prey, it stalks the seals, its favourite prey, amid the snow hummocks. It will also approach a seal, asleep on the edge of an ice-floe, by water. There is, however, no foundation for the story that it covers the black tip of its nose with its paw, so as not to give its position away to a seal; nor that it buries its nose in the snow so that the seals shall not smell its evil breath—and so be warned of its approach! Equally, there is no foundation for the story that a Polar bear, when it misses a seal, will pound its paws on the ice in a frenzy of temper, smashing the bones of the paws.

If these stories mean anything at all they are indicative of the usual prin-ciple that, where knowledge is scanty, legend and superstition fill the gaps, for it is a fact that our knowledge of these bears in the wild is compara-tively scarce. We do know, however, that Polar bears are expert swimmers and divers, and are often seen swimming strongly miles from land. Their acute sense of smell is evidenced by the way the bears will leave the land and travel on drifting ice to pursue their prey, and by the way a dead whale will attract numerous Polar bears from miles around.

MALAYAN BEAR

The Malayan bear is the smallest member of the bear tribe. It is an expert climber and has a passion for honey, which it obtains by opening wild bees' nests and licking out their appetizing contents.

GIANT POLAR BEAR

Polar bears are the most carnivorous of all bears and, with the exception of the Kadiak bear, the largest. They may measure up to 9 ft. in length and weigh as much as 1,600 lb. They are expert swimmers and divers, plunging readily into the sea to pursue and capture a passing fish. Moreover, for all their size, they are unexpectedly agile on land.

FASTIDIOUS RACCOON

Raccoons are cat-like in size and nocturnal in habit. They feed in the main on fish, frogs and shellfish, and always wash their food in the water before eating it.

Polar bears have little fear of men, as well they might, with their powerful, heavy build, great limbs and claws, and their conspicuous agility on land and in the sea. So long as they were hunted by Eskimos, with dogs and spears only, they were difficult to kill, but modern firearms have altered this. Even so, they often visit encampments or ice-bound ships and, when impelled by hunger, can be a considerable nuisance; they will destroy explorers' food caches even when protected by heavy stones.

The two young are born in the depth of winter, the mother burying herself deep in the snow for the event. This is not hibernation, only a retirement from active life to bear and suckle the cubs.

Broadly speaking, the Carnivora can be divided into the Dogs and their relatives and the Cats and their relatives, but in this rough-and-ready grouping we have to include the bears and the seals, both of which have an obvious relationship to the Dogs and Cats. Certainly, so far as bears are con-

cerned, they are intermediate in a large number of ways, in outward appearance and habits, and more especially in their internal anatomy. There are, however, members of the Carnivora that are even less obviously related to the typical Cats and Dogs, and the next family to be considered is, to all appearances, an anomaly, yet it is a good illustration of the wide view the zoologist must take in these matters.

The family Procyonidae includes the raccoons, the coatis, the kinkajous and the pandas. The first three of these are cat-like in size and in the possession of long hairy tails; these characteristics are, indeed, shared by one of the pandas. Yet all are related, by stable anatomical characters, both to each other and to the Giant panda, which is so bear-like in form. Moreover, none has a true carnivore's teeth, although it is easy to see that their ancestors must have had them.

The raccoon (*Procyon lotor*), like the coatis and the kinkajous, is found in the warmer parts of North and South

GIANT PANDA

Giant pandas live in the densely forested hillsides of Tibet and south-western China, where they feed mainly on bamboo shoots. Shy, secretive and inoffensive, they live very much on their own, and practically nothing is known of their habits in the wild state.

America. It is 2½ ft. long, including the 10-in. bushy tail ringed brown and white. Its dense fur is greyish-brown and much sought after. The value of the fur and the fact that its flesh is good to eat make the "coon" hunt a popular sport, especially in southern U.S.A.

Raccoons are nocturnal and live close to wooded streams and lakes; they draw their livelihood from water, feeding on fish, frogs, shellfish and turtles, which they catch with their long naked fingers, paddling in the shallow water to get them. They are in no sense aquatic, however, and when hunted will readily take to trees or the shelter of rocks. A strange feature of their behaviour is that they always wash their food in the water before eating it!

Closely related to the raccoon, the Ring-tailed cat or cacomistle (*Bassariscus astutus*) is unlike it in appearance, and is smaller. The mere fact that it is called a "cat" is yet another expression of the divergence between strict zoological classification and outward appearance; there is, certainly, something essentially cat-like in its build, for the body is lithe and slender, with a 17-in. tail ringed black and white, and in spite of its size it weighs a mere 2½ lb. Moreover, its paws are well furred and its claws semi-retractile. On the other hand, like the raccoon, it is marten-like in general appearance, and is, like the marten, nocturnal and an active tree-climber.

Within this group of oddly assorted animals come the coatis (*Nasua*), of which there are several species, found from Mexico to Peru. The size of a raccoon, though longer and with a longer tail, they live communally in the trees of dense forests, searching, so it is thought, the holes in the trees with their long, mobile snouts for insects, young birds and eggs.

The reddish-brown kinkajou (*Potos caudivolvulus*) lives in the same regions as the coatis, and also inhabits trees. It is another oddity among carnivores, for it has a prehensile tail, and it feeds on fruit, scooping out the soft pulp with its long, mobile tongue.

Finally, we conclude the heterogeneous collection with the pandas, which by common consent as well as by zoological precedent are closely related. Yet the one, the panda (*Ailurus fulgens*), is cat-like, while the Giant panda (*Ailuropoda melanoleuca*) is bear-like. Only the last-named is well known in Britain, having been popularized in picture and story in recent years; yet it is the least known of the two in their native Asia, and was not made known to European zoologists until 1869. A further complication has arisen directly from this popularity, for we commonly call the bear-like creature the "panda," when it should be "Giant panda." As a consequence it is becoming necessary to call the cat-like panda the Lesser panda.

The panda (or Lesser panda) lives in the forests of Nepal, Sikkim, Yunnan, Szechwan and Upper Burma, at altitudes of 7,000 to 12,000 ft., feeding mainly on fruit. It is a rich chestnut in colour, with a white face, black underside and limbs and a long, brush-like tail, with dark and pale rings.

The Giant panda, known to the Chinese as beishung, or "White bear," is a striking animal with a 6-ft. bulky body, the merest stump of a tail and a conspicuous black-and-white coat. Its home is the densely forested, precipi-

tous hillsides of eastern Tibet and south-western China, where it feeds on bamboo shoots, occasionally taking small mammals and fish for a change. It lives very much on its own, is shy, secretive and inoffensive, so much so that natives living near its haunts may be often unaware of its presence. Apart from its bear-like build, its teeth are so obviously derived from the typical carnivore pattern that there can be little doubt that its ancestors subsisted mainly on flesh. In the present-day panda, however, the cheek-teeth are very broad and the skull is deep and strong, with powerful muscles for actuating the jaws, all adaptations for masticating the fibrous bamboo shoots. Practically nothing is known of the Giant panda's habits in the wild. It may be worth drawing attention, however, to its most uncarnivore-like characteristic, the small pad on each fore-foot, which acts like a thumb so that the Giant panda is able to grasp its food with it and lift it to its mouth.

LESSER PANDA
Though related closely to the much rarer Giant panda, the Lesser panda has a quite different, cat-like appearance.

AN OLD BULL ELEPHANT AT A SALT-LICK

The largest of all existing elephants, full-grown bulls of Loxodonta africana *average about* 10½ *ft. in height at the shoulder. The old bull shown here was photographed in Kenya by Sir Geoffrey de Havilland, from a "hide" only fifteen yards distant. It spent a long time in dosing itself at a salt-lick, digging up the potassium-laden earth with its right tusk and conveying it to its mouth with its trunk.*

The Elephant family

THERE are only three living species of elephant, the Indian, (*Elephas maximus*), the African or "Bush" elephant, (*Loxodonta africana*), and the Lesser African or "Forest" elephant (*L. cyclotis*). It seems possible, in view of the recent researches of Sir William Gowers in North Africa, that the first elephant to become well known in Europe was the Lesser African elephant; in all probability it was the one first brought to Rome, and the species which furnished Hannibal with the famous elephants which crossed the Alps with his army from Gaul into Italy. This elephant, now rare, must at that time have been numerous; its habitat would have been the vast forests which covered the Atlas Mountains, but which have long since vanished.

The name given to the Indian elephant—*Elephas maximus*—may appear somewhat confusing in view of the fact that the African elephant—*Loxodonta africana*—is the largest of the three species. It may well be, however, that the Indian elephant, which became known to Europeans after the Lesser African elephant but before the African elephant, was mistakenly regarded as the largest species extant.

Again, the "trivial" names of the two African species are not sound: "Bush" and "Forest" elephant infer an incor-rect summary of their habits. For the larger beast, which averages about 2 ft. higher at the shoulder than *L. cyclotis*, is found just as much in dense forest as in bush, while *L. cyclotis* is at times found in open bush, and even in company with *L. africana*.

India and the elephant have long been associated in many western minds. This association is, of course, due to the many services which the elephant per-forms in that country, and the respect in which it is held by Hindus, to whom it is a religious symbol of wisdom, pros-perity and riches.

Much of this respect shown to ele-phants has been due to the fear engen-dered by their size, power and alleged intelligence. Their intelligence has, however, been the subject of many exaggerated stories; for instance, their famed knowledge of which bridge or patch of quicksand is dangerous is largely undeserved, or they would not be caught in pitfalls or be fatally bogged so often. However, if elephants had all the intelligence with which they are credited they would never work for man in a state of domestication.

They have poor eyesight, very good power of scent, and good hearing. But they are very nervous beasts, stamped-ing, even after many years of domestica-tion, for the most trivial of causes.

ELEPHANTS AT A POOL IN CEYLON

*In the daily life of India, Burma and Ceylon the elephant has always been prominent
—whether living wild in the jungle, toiling in the timber forests, or striding majestically
amid the splendour of the courts of kings. To the Hindu it is a symbol of wisdom and
prosperity. Here, elephants have been ridden into a pool to drink.*

Their habitat has not shrunk greatly of recent years, though they are much scarcer at their western limits in Lower Garhwal and the forests of Oudh, and have vanished from the Central Provinces. But there are still plenty of them in eastern Bengal and Assam, in the forests of peninsular India, in Burma, Siam and Malaya. In Ceylon they have been greatly reduced in numbers by export for zoos, and there are said to be few survivors in Borneo or Sumatra.

INCREASING HERDS

At one time the standing of the ruler of an Indian state was judged largely by the number of elephants he could display on ceremonial occasions and the richness of their trappings. Nowadays the princes ride about in motor-cars and the "kheddahs" for catching wild elephants to fill vacancies in royal stables are so much reduced that the herds have increased and do damage in the forests which outweighs their potential usefulness. Even forty years ago the Forest Department of Madras was offering rewards for the shooting of elephants, whose death at the hands of a sportsman ten years before would have meant a fine of anything up to two thousand rupees. They were so numerous in southern India at the beginning of this century that herds of as many as eighty were sometimes seen at the foot of the Nilgiri Hills, and the damage they did was colossal.

It will be realized that their existence in such numbers was dependent on protection by man. Even when hunted remorselessly, however, elephants still remain numerous. This is mainly due to the vastness of their sheltering forests, the greater security from attack gained by a herd existence, and the awareness of approaching danger communicated by the elephant's keen sense of smell.

In habits the Indian elephant is entirely forest-loving, and is not found where the concomitants of forest and humidity are absent. In captivity it is unwise to work them in the sun in hot, dry weather.

They feed on trees and bamboos, occasionally eating much coarse grass for medicinal purposes, and usually drink water at dusk or soon afterwards. They make a joyful din when drinking water, trumpeting, squealing and dousing each other.

The period of gestation is nineteen months for a female calf and twenty-one for a male, according to native information, which seems accurate as far as it can be checked. In Burma and Siam, where elephants are kept in a much more natural state than in India, being sent out to browse instead of being artificially fed, many calves are now born in captivity; in Lower Burma a mother and her five young were all working for the same timber firm at the same time, just before the Second World War. On the eastern side of the hills which divide Burma and Siam, twin calves are quite common.

The males go *musth* in seasons of sexual excitement, the usual sign being an enlargement of the eye-gland, with a discharge which trickles down the face, and they are then dangerous.

VALUABLE SOURCE OF IVORY

The size of the tusks of Indian elephants varies greatly in different areas. The tusks of elephants towards the northern parts of their habitat never grow large, 6 ft. in length and 50 lb. apiece being the maximum; but in southern India they may go to $8\frac{1}{2}$ ft. and 90 lb. In Burma the tusks are not large, a 5-ft. length and 50-lb. weight being about the limit for a bull. Cow ivory hardly goes beyond the toothpick

THE EVENING BATH

Trained working elephants are valuable animals, and every care is taken of them by their mahouts, or drivers. After work they are allowed to wallow indolently in pool or stream, where their drivers bath and scrub them until they are quite free of grime and insects.

stage at any time. In Ceylon most males are tuskless, and it seems probable that these are indigenous, while those which bear tusks are the offspring of elephants imported from India.

Living as it does in close proximity to man, and raiding village crops with persistent regularity, the Indian elephant acquires tolerance, contempt or even hatred of man; the last-named attitude is often due to wounds received when raiding crops at night.

It is reasonable, therefore, that there should be many more dangerous "rogues" in India than in Africa: in fact, the *Gazettes* of Madras and Assam are seldom without several such declared pests, rewards being offered for their destruction. They will even come into a village and break down huts, killing or maiming people as they run out; will overturn bullock carts, or charge out from the forest at innocent passers-by.

They have few enemies, and tigers rarely attack even the young ones; guinea-worm, suppurating wounds from fighting or from broken tusks, and snake-bite are the main causes of natural death. The snake usually responsible for fatally biting an elephant is one of those great hamadryads which run to 17 ft. in length, and are the most poisonous and aggressive of all snakes. The bite is not always fatal, for now and then an elephant is met with convalescent from such a bite; its leg is dead white for two feet up and the nails drop off. Whilst recovering it leads a solitary life, feeding up in some small valley.

When catching wild elephants for domestication young cows and half-grown males are the principal quarry. Old males either lose heart and die while being trained, or remain hopelessly vicious.

There are four methods used in catching elephants, or were, for the first two are now forbidden by law. They are: (1) the staked ring; (2) the pitfall; (3) the pursuit with tamed elephants and noosing of calves which fall out of the herd, and (4) the well-known kheddah, or circular timber stockade.

The staked ring is a very ancient and cruel practice in which a stout ring about 30 in. wide, made of twisted rattan or other strong wood, is placed, slightly sunk, over a hole 18 in. deep in an elephant path. The inside of the ring is armed with sharp spikes which do not quite meet in the middle; when an elephant puts its foot through the middle, the spikes are depressed and stick into the ankle all round it, going deeper in when the victim tries to withdraw the foot. The whole ring, covered with leaves and grass when the trap is set, is tied by a strong rope to a heavy log so that when the elephant tries to

HAULING TEAK IN BURMA

The Indian elephant is a forest animal and thrives best in shade and humidity. It is harmful to captive elephants to work them in the open sun during very hot weather, and in teak-yards, such as the one above, this practice is avoided as far as possible.

go off it drags the log with it. The trapper can thus follow up the very clear trail. Many elephants so trapped died from gangrenous wounds, after suffering agonies, and few of those caught were ever any use for training.

The pitfall, also dug in an elephant path and covered lightly with leaves and branches, caught many elephants— calves most frequently. Calves so caught would be fed in the pit for a short time, and the pit gradually filled in; when they could get out two domesticated females would be waiting to secure the captive. The shock of the fall was so great that many of the captives died of "broken heart," and this method has also been forbidden.

The pursuit of wild elephants with a team of domesticated elephants, known as *mela shikar*, is a most exciting and effective method of catching young elephants, but the ground must be fairly favourable and not hilly. Three or four tame elephants usually work as a team, one of them a male which can be counted on if the wild ones become aggressive.

CATCHING YOUNG ELEPHANTS

Each domesticated elephant has two riders, one on the neck who guides it and throws the noose, the second who lies flat on the pad near the tail and prods the mount into greater speed: he has cross ropes to hang on to, but both riders are usually considerably scratched and bruised by branches at the end of a hunt. Accidents through the agency of the wild elephants are very rare. The noose is attached to the biggest *koonki*, as the tame females are called. Sometimes the team can make its way into a wild herd and noose a calf without a chase, but only when the herd has not been hunted for a considerable time.

This method of catching is adopted in similar form in Siam, but by men on foot without the assistance of tame elephants. The skill is in getting into a herd without being seen and noosing a calf by a hind leg, then throwing a loop around a tree with the rest of the rope and startling the herd into flight. The mother will usually leave her calf, expecting it to follow. If the nooser is detected before the operation is completed it will probably go hard with him.

THE KHEDDAH

The kheddah method is well known. A great circular stockade is built, usually in some small valley through which elephants commonly pass; at each end of the stockade two halves of a huge gate are hung between trees; the two halves swing to as soon as a retaining rope is cut.

The men who do the driving, sometimes several hundreds strong, may begin operations a fortnight before the herd is expected to enter the kheddah, bivouacking at night and moving the herd a little every day. When approaching the stockade, torches are lit and a terrific din drives the elephants towards it; the leaders dither at the entrance, then partly from panic and partly from pressure from behind they rush in; the retaining ropes are cut, the huge gates swing to and the catch is made.

The big males have usually got away before the stockade is reached, slipping off to a flank or breaking back; this is much to the pleasure of the drivers, for they are not only useless commercially but most undesirable in the kheddah. It is only they who may charge the stockade, smash it to splinters and lead the herd out through the gap.

Elephants caught in the hills between Burma and Siam are not kept in the same way as they are in India, where they are fed daily and housed in great

AN ELEPHANT HERD AT PLAY

A small herd of African elephants is seen here at play in a forest clearing in Kenya, taking turns to paddle in the diminutive pool in the left-hand foreground. Elephants are of a sportive disposition, and love gambolling about. They are particularly fond of playing with water, squirting it over one another with joyful squeals.

79

brick stables. Some of the elephant-stables used by either pack or draught elephant-batteries in the nineteenth century are still to be seen in the cantonments of central India. In India the elephant's ration is 18–20 lb. a day of great flapjacks made of coarse wheat-meal, supplemented with *gur*, the almost solid molasses of India. In Burma and Siam they get no such delicacies, being turned out to browse in the forest with a long chain round the off-forefoot to hamper movement and prevent them straying. In these last countries they are very sketchily trained and are often dangerous when out browsing.

For pack-transport the Indian elephant has great nets slung across its pad, holding over half a ton of gear. In Burma such a contraption is only of use in fairly open country or on properly constructed roads; it would be scraped off against the trees in the dense forests of Lower Burma and Siam. They carry, therefore, a shallow, wooden basket of split bamboo or other strong woven wood, which is perched on top of their backs and does not project on either side. It will only carry loads of small bulk, such as rice bags, and the limit is 700 lb., while the normal load carried in these baskets is about 300 lb.

HAULING TEAK LOGS

The Karens of Burma and their elephants are the mainstay of the timber trade; they haul the great teak logs through forests where there are no roads, and then dump them into rivers to be carried downstream by monsoon floods. They are also amazingly clever in clearing jams of these logs, some of them 70 ft. long; picking out the key log, they lever it about until the whole colossal mass breaks up into a whirl of white foam and wildly bucking trees.

The African elephant (*Loxodonta africana*) and the Lesser African elephant (*L. cyclotis*) differ greatly in size, the bulls of *africana* averaging 10½ ft. in height, while those of *cyclotis* barely touch 9 ft. The cows of both species average 1 ft. less than the bulls.

ELEPHANTS OF AFRICA

Africana is now plentiful in the Sudan, East Africa, Uganda and the Congo, while many are still found in Portuguese East Africa. They have been much reduced in numbers in the Rhodesias, and have almost vanished from the Union of South Africa. The smaller species, *cyclotis*, is almost restricted to the French and Belgian Congo, though some are found in British West African colonies, and small parties wander over into Uganda. They are distinguished by long, thin tusks in the male, which point more directly downward than those of *africana*, a straighter forehead with the frontal bump reduced in size, and a greater height of leg in proportion to bodily size. Local Africans also assert that they are bad-tempered, though they have proved to be quite tractable in the Belgian Congo.

Though for many years African elephants have been the object of ruthless persecution because of their ivory, they have yet managed to survive in large numbers. Their bare survival in bush areas would, no doubt, be ensured by the protection which they have been given in recent years. But it is far from obvious why such slow-breeding animals should have continued to thrive numerically in bush country where they had, until recently, been under constant attack by man, and where there is no natural protection such as the forests provide. Merely to keep their numbers under control has involved quite heavy and officially organized killing.

However, in big and difficult forests like those of Mt. Kenya, the Aberdare Range and the Congo, such steady maintenance of their numerical strength is understandable.

The best ivory is now found in Kenya, particularly on either side of the Tana River, where bulls with tusks nearly 9 ft. in length are still to be met with. This is thornbush or *nyika*

they dose themselves with the potassium-impregnated earth and coarse grass, ensuring a thorough cleansing of their insides. Some go as high as 11,000 ft. to eat the berries of the mukaita tree (*Raponoides rhododendrensis*), which is also prized for medicinal purposes by the local tribesmen. There is the frozen corpse of a cow elephant at nearly 15,000 ft. on Mt. Kenya, and they

"FOREST" ELEPHANTS OF CENTRAL AFRICA

The Lesser African elephant is sometimes known as the "Forest" elephant, although, like the pair above photographed near Lake Edward, western Uganda, it also frequents open bush country. It was probably with elephants of this species that the army of Hannibal made its celebrated crossing of the Alps into Italy in 218 B.C.

country, where the vegetation is mainly flat-topped acacias and thick-leaved succulents. Both of these are much eaten by elephants, and the moisture of the succulents, such as sansevieria, acts as a substitute for water between the elephants' periodic visits to the river.

In the forests they live on various trees, but are particular in their choice of food, and occasionally during the rains make their way to a salt-lick, where

undoubtedly cross the shoulders of that mountain at over 14,000 ft. in the course of local migrations.

Herds usually consist of anything up to a hundred individuals, though larger herds are sometimes met with on ground where the feed is good. The great Lorian Swamp herd in East Kenya is said to have been over six hundred strong at times. When the Lorian Swamp dried up in 1945 the herd dispersed to the fifty-mile strip of forest by the Tana River, where many magnificent bulls were shot.

When tracking a bull of the Indian species it is fairly easy to estimate its size by the diameter of the fore-foot. With Indian elephants, the rough rule-of-thumb is that the height at the shoulder equals twice the circumference of the fore-foot. But this rule does not apply with the African species, for big African bull-elephants of 11 ft. and more have been found to have the same-sized fore-foot as those 1 ft. smaller. The record height for an African elephant is 12 ft. 3 in.—the height of an elephant shot by Major Anderson, a well-known big-game hunter.

The weight of tusks is usually greater in elephants living in bush than in those living in heavy forest; the contrary is the case with the horns of rhinoceroses living under the same conditions. A different diet is probably responsible for this.

The period of gestation is about the same as in the Indian species and calves stay some three years with their mothers, who are dangerous while they are with them. The trunk is tiny in a new-born calf, but reaches normal proportions inside two years. The birth is a very noisy affair, other elephants gathering around and trumpeting almost throughout the night. The calf is born in a great caul which hardens to board-like stiffness and is left behind; this caul is never attacked by hyenas or jackals.

It is usually mothers with calves which are responsible for the worst crop-raiding, and render the Control

ELEPHANTS STAMPEDE
A herd of elephants in the Great Rift Valley, Tanganyika, startled by the aeroplane from which this photograph was taken, is just beginning to stampede.

AFRICAN ELEPHANTS

Elephants are very fond of bathing. The picture shows a group about to enter a shallow pool near Nyeri, Kenya. Although normally elephants and rhinoceroses are

Officer's work difficult and dangerous at times. The raiders will often retire into the forest for the day, raiding at night. Searching for them in thick cover, with cows ready to charge an intruder from behind dense cover, needs a cool head and straight shooting. The greatest danger to the hunter is often when the herd stampedes; for they are then likely to run in almost any direction and may well overrun the hunter.

In some districts where the elephants have been shot at and wounded by Africans armed with inefficient weapons a whole herd may become vicious and ready to take the offensive on finding a hunter or hearing the first shot. They have even been known to follow up by scent, tapping their trunks on the ground along the trail of the retiring man. Their power of scent and their hearing are very good; their eyesight,

however, is poor, being incapable of distinguishing a motionless object at more than thirty yards, or detecting a moving man at fifty. They are very difficult to see even in light forest, blending with the trees and patchy sunlight, and can move with soundless stealth even in dry weather, with many loose sticks lying about. When in a herd a hunter may find that a big bull has come up noiselessly behind him and is standing within a dozen yards, blocking his way out, so that he may have to shoot to get away.

The head shot is that most often used by professional hunters, as, properly placed from the side halfway between eye and ear, it penetrates the brain and drops the bull on the spot: the brain is about the size and shape of a rugby football, placed obliquely. The heart shot is often used owing to the head being hidden by branches, or because

AT A WATER-HOLE

aggressive when they meet, they will, in times of drought, wait their turn together at a water-hole with remarkable docility, while natives and their cattle slake their thirst.

the elephant is restless and is swinging its head from side to side. The shot should be placed just behind the point of the shoulder, for the heart lies unexpectedly low down. After a heart shot an elephant will probably go from two hundred to a thousand yards before eventually collapsing.

DETERMINED RAIDERS

When they have taken to crop-raiding a particular area they are most persistent, returning again and again; if unsatisfied, they may break open grain-stores in a neighbouring village. If one is shot it does not necessarily mean that the others will take heed and cease raiding that particular crop. It seems paradoxical that licences should be required for shooting these great beasts, while a large staff is kept up mainly for the purpose of killing several hundred

crop-raiders every year in several different territories; but ivory is valuable and the big bull-elephants which carry it are rarely among the raiders, keeping themselves to themselves, except when the sexual urge sends them to look for a herd and consort with a cow.

A curious noise made by elephants is "tummy-rumbling," which is probably expressive of satisfaction with their food; it is controllable, for when a man goes into a herd the first intimation he gets of its being aware of danger is the cessation of this tummy-rumbling, even though the herd be spread over several hundred yards of forest.

They are noisy feeders, their trumpeting and crashing of branches being easily heard a couple of miles away. They are very fond of the woody fruit of the Dom palm (vegetable ivory) when ripe; and so are monkeys, which, in addition to throwing down much fruit for the elephants, act as sentries.

An elephant walks, when undisturbed, at about seven miles an hour, so no hunter on foot can keep up with them for any length of time; they may stop to feed, however, and so allow their pursuer to come up with them.

CRUEL TRAPS AND SNARES

Trapping by Africans used to be mainly by pitfalls in remote forests, or by a heavily weighted spear embedded in a mass of wood and suspended from a branch over a forest path, which dropped on to the elephant's back when it tripped over the trigger-rope. Horrible suppurating wounds in shot elephants give evidence of the cruel inefficiency of such traps.

During drought elephants and rhinoceroses will wait their turns at waterholes, while the natives and their cattle assuage their thirst. At one set of waterholes in the Northern Frontier District of Kenya, fifteen rhinoceroses died through sticking in the narrow rocky entrances to the wells; the elephants were more fortunate in that they could reach the water with their trunks, and none died.

Elephants and rhinoceroses do not agree, the larger animal driving away the smaller, which is contrary to the manner of their meeting in India, where the elephant is much afraid of the rhinoceros.

In big swamps elephants, otherwise invisible in 15-ft.-high grass and reeds, are often spotted by having egrets riding on their backs. These birds are either bent on extracting parasites from their hosts or, more probably, catching the large insects put up by the passage of the pachyderms through the greenery. Often, when perched on some rocky outcrop above a marsh, every part of which he has examined without result, the hunter may see a flock of snow-white egrets come flying over, wheel around and drop into the grass in graceful curves to alight on the backs of a herd of elephants.

Elephants are very fond of bathing, and will at times stay right under water for several minutes, with only the tip of the trunk showing above water. They are apt to have differences with hippopotamuses, which resent their presence with loud grunts and yawns, exhibiting their formidable incisors; it is seldom that the hippo dare any really aggressive movement, and if they do they are soon driven off.

Elephants have, in fact, no serious enemies in Africa other than man; and although man has lived for many centuries in this great continent he has only comparatively recently been armed well enough to make serious attacks on them. More recently still man has become their preserver, and there are many who think that, even should this protection be withdrawn, the elephant, and in particular the elephant whose habitat is the dense and wide forest, will be the last of the large mammals to become extinct in Africa.

PROBLEM ANIMALS

For a long time it was the practice to include elephants and hyraxes, horses, rhinoceroses and tapirs, together with hippopotamuses and pigs and all the other cloven-hoofed animals, in one large order, the Ungulata. This was no more than a convenient taxonomic litter-basket. Today these animals are separated into distinct orders, of which the Proboscidea (elephants) and Hyracoidea (hyraxes) are typical examples.

The hyraxes, the "conies" of the Bible, found all over Africa and also in Syria, have presented a difficulty to the

TINY RELATIVES OF THE ELEPHANT

A pair of dassies, or Rock hyraxes, sunning themselves outside their home among the rocks. A noisy but inoffensive little animal with greyish-brown fur, the hyrax is identified with the "coney" of the Bible. It is related anatomically to the elephant.

systematist for many years. At first they were classed among the rodents, then in the order Ungulata, and now are placed tentatively near the elephants in a separate order, the Hyracoidea. There is a single family of them, the Procaviidae, containing the terrestrial hyraxes or dassies, so named from their South African species, and the Tree hyraxes, *Dendrohyrax*. The front teeth are like those of rodents and the back teeth like those of ungulates.

Hyraxes are small animals, up to 15 in. long, with short tails and medium-length fur, usually greyish-brown in colour. There is a gland in the centre of the back, marked by a black spot in the terrestrial species, and a small patch of white fur in the arboreal. The white patch of the Tree hyrax is flicked open and shut when the animal is excited. The ears of both types are small, rounded and lie close to the head.

They are all known more by their voices than their appearance, for they are noisy little beasts. The dassies utter a staccato "bom" from their holes

among the rocks (and from this they get their Somali onomatopoeic name), while the arboreal species have most raucous voices, their rattling screams making night hideous in the forests where they are plentiful. The arboreal species usually live in holes inside hollow trees, but sometimes come down to spend the day inside a thick bush, where they often fall victims to a passing dog or jackal. All species are given to sunning themselves at the mouths of their rock retreats or in front of a hole high up a tree which catches the sun.

These animals make pleasant pets, but are apt to get rather too inquisitive, pushing into places where they are not wanted, while they voice their objections to other noises in a competitive effort to drown either human conversation or the sounds emitted by a wireless.

They have plenty of natural enemies, but their retreats render them fairly safe; and man takes little interest in them, except when hunting for skins to make a kaross, or when they raid gardens in their search for fruit.

ZEBRAS AT A WATER-HOLE

Zebras are greatly given to associating with other animals, particularly the larger antelopes such as the eland, hartebeest and wildebeest or gnu. Here zebras are seen drinking at a water-hole in company with brindled gnu, water-buck and impala. From these antelopes their boldly striped coats make them easily distinguishable.

Horses, Rhinoceroses
and Tapirs

IT IS a remarkable fact that all present-day wild horses have their habitat in the Old World, although there are fossil remains of their long-extinct ancestors in various parts of the American continent. Seeing that the horses imported by the Spaniards and the English into both halves of the New World flourished and increased into great semi-wild herds, it seems probable that some great change of climate accounted for the extinction there of earlier horses in Miocene times.

The earliest horse probably had five toes, but these have been reduced in modern wild horses to a single one, with traces of two others (the splint-bones). Their bodily size has risen from about that of a fox to the 14 hands of the Grevy's zebra, and, under domestication, to the 18 or 19 hands of our bigger breeds.

It is probable that the original wild horses were dun-coloured with stripes or bars, as such markings are apt to appear in domestic breeds. In zebras and the extinct quaggas such markings are the rule, although the young of these animals are born with a dull-brown body colour.

Przewalski's, or the Mongolian Wild, horse is the nearest type to our domestic breeds, but, living as it does in the Gobi Desert, little is known about its habits.

It has a large head, a Roman nose and a long tail, and is pale dun in colour.

The chigetai and the kiang, which are races of the same species, have been called wild asses. The kiang, which is much the better known of the two, is often called the Tibetan Wild ass, but is really more closely allied to the horses than to the asses. It stands about 12 hands, is of a reddish-brown colour fading into light brown underneath, and has a stiff, upright mane of black hairs which is carried along the spine in the form of a thin black stripe. The chigetai is an inhabitant of Turkestan and is little known; but the kiang of the Great Tibetan Plateau, which is to be seen in many zoological gardens, is only too familiar to the traveller and sportsman on the north-east fringes of India.

Kiangs live on high ground, rarely coming below 15,000 ft., and are found in the same country as the Great Tibetan Wild sheep (*Ovis ammon*), the bharal (*Pseudois nahura*), the Tibetan antelope (*Pantholops hodgsoni*) and the Tibetan gazelle (*Gazella picticaudata*). The sportsman in pursuit of these wild animals suffers much from the curiosity of the kiang, which is even more highly developed in this species than in the rest of this most inquisitive family.

The first view of a kiang is usually of a brown fiddle head, darker on the face

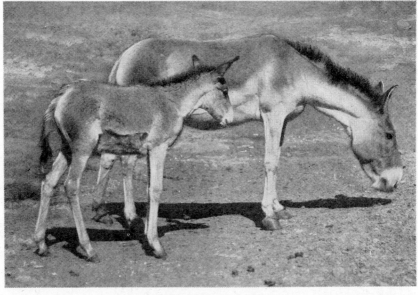

KIANG AND FOAL

The kiang, or Tibetan Wild ass, lives at an altitude of 15,000 ft. and above. It is reddish-brown in colour, stands about 12 hands high, and is extremely inquisitive. Out of sheer curiosity, it closely follows hunters and so betrays their presence.

and topped by a coarse black mane, staring over the top of a ridge at the passing traveller or sportsman. This matters little to a caravan moving along the Central Asian trade-route, but to a sportsman it usually means the end of his stalk, for the beast will then come forward to the crest to get a better view, and will almost certainly be joined by others of its kind. As the hunter moves along the whole troop will keep parallel with him along the top of a ridge, now and then trotting and capering around while they bite and kick each other playfully. Then, quite suddenly, they will vanish, leaving the sportsman on his own once again. One would imagine that the inquisitive nature of this animal would make it easy to photograph it. This, however, is not the case, for its caution outweighs its curiosity and it will seldom approach within

camera range. Much careful and patient stalking is required before success crowns the efforts of the photographer. It is seldom shot, as its hide is of no value; and it is quite intractable in domestication.

Kiangs have no enemies in the adult state; for, though a party of wolves may kill a solitary beast, they are usually in herds of from three to twenty, and even two of them will attack a solitary wolf, striking at it with their fore-feet.

As they can find a good living at great altitudes, it would seem that there is little check upon an increase in their numbers; but probably wolves and Snow leopards get a good many foals or even adults in winter, when snow restricts the free movement of the kiang. Normally their country has a rainfall of about 4 in. a year, and the permanent snow-line is about 18,000 ft. high.

The onager of the western Indian deserts is slightly smaller than the kiang. It has a broad black dorsal stripe, is generally grey in colour with very little rufous, and in general appearance is much more of an ass than a horse.

The Somali wild asses (*Equus asinus somalicus*) were once found in northern Abyssinia, but are now said to be extinct in that region and are only to be found in the northern plateau country of Somaliland, on stony ground covered with light bush and seamed with small ravines. They are true wild asses, long-eared, short-maned and grey in colour with no rufous tinge. They are independent of water, using thick-leaved succulents to supply the deficiency of liquid. They fall frequent victims to lions, which fact would very likely account for their disappearance in country where they have few other enemies. Being without means of defence, and living in light bush forming the best possible cover for carnivores, they may easily die out altogether. They have been protected in British Somaliland for the last forty years, but show no signs of increase.

To the south of these wild asses live the most northerly of the zebras, the Grevy's, a species with very definite characteristics distinguishing it from others of its tribe. Its ears are large, rounded and heavily fringed with white hairs; it is bigger and more closely striped than other zebras, and has a stiff, upstanding mane.

Its voice, a loud strangled neigh, contrasts sharply with the high barking of Burchell's zebras, when the two species are together and the herds are alarmed. The voice of Grevy's zebra is typical of the horse tribe, while those of the True

KIANGS GRAZING

In spite of its curiosity, the kiang retains some caution, and this picture of a small party feeding was taken only after patient and skilful stalking. The adult kiang is seldom molested by other animals, for it is quick to take defensive action.

ONAGER, OR ASIATIC WILD ASS

The onager is grey in colour and slightly smaller than the kiang. In summer it lives in hilly country, but descends to the plains during the colder months.

zebras and Burchell's have no relation to the voices of others of the family.

Grevy's zebras associate with Burchell's in the southern part of their habitat, notably in the region just north of the Tana River, and in the bush and sandhill country of the coast near Lamu. They do not, however, cross the Tana, though there would seem to be no real reason why they should not do so, particularly as Burchell's zebras are common on both banks of the river.

They are the only tamable members of the genus *Equus*, so are much sought after by zoos. But they suffer from the want of stamina common to the wild members of their tribe.

Burchell's zebras average about 4 in. less at the shoulder than Grevy's, and have fewer and broader stripes. They are greatly given to associating with other animals, mostly the larger antelopes such as eland and hartebeest, and are found in suitable country anywhere between the Sahara and the Zambesi. The Grevy's are rarely found above 4,000 ft., but these "bonte-quagga" zebras go much higher, up to 8,000 ft. at least. The National Parks of Kenya are well stocked with these very ornamental animals, but farther west, in Uganda and the Belgian Congo, the moister and hotter climate does not suit them and they are much rarer.

The Mountain, or True, zebras live in South Africa, and are remarkable for the "gridiron" transverse striping of the hind-quarters. They have been much shot down and, though they have not yet come to the fate of the extinct quagga, they are now only to be found within the protection of national preserves. The quagga, which was striped only on the neck and shoulders, has been extinct since 1875: it lived in the same country as the Mountain

92

zebra, being at one time particularly plentiful in the Cape Province.

The speed of wild horses is not very great compared with that of the larger antelopes, though they can gallop at about 30 miles an hour for a couple of miles. Tried out with a motor-car, the onager has been found to travel at 26–28 miles an hour.

When a large mixed herd of zebras and antelopes stampedes, the zebras make off first but are overtaken by the others. They will all canter fast, keeping level with a car going at about 30 miles an hour, then accelerate to cross ahead of it at nearly 40 miles an hour.

There have been many theories about the usefulness or otherwise of zebra markings, which are never exactly the same in any two zebras, or even on the two sides of any one zebra. Many of these theories have been propounded by those who have never seen zebras in their natural wild state. One popular theory is that the striping renders them invisible at close quarters at night, various hunters having stated that they have been unable to see zebras at ten yards on a starlit night. But man, being a very late comer in the development of mammals, can have had no influence on their protective coloration; and such protection by night would be useless against the real enemies of zebras, the large carnivores, whose senses are so much more acute than those of man.

It is by day and at about two hundred yards and over, in light bush such as is most favoured by them, that the striping of zebras merges with the background and affords them protection against being seen by carnivores at long distances and a stalk begun without their being aware of it. At night zebras

ZEBRAS SCRATCHING FOR WATER

Zebras have acute senses of smell and hearing, and these, rather than their "dazzle" type of camouflage, give good protection against attack by large carnivores.

93

ZEBRAS AND WILDEBEESTS

The Common, or Burchell's, zebras are still quite numerous, unlike the Mountain zebras, whose numbers have dwindled so that they are now found mainly in national reserves. This photograph shows a mixed herd of zebras and wildebeests at Ngong Hills, Kenya. The acute development of their hearing and sense of smell makes zebras

AT NGONG HILLS

very difficult to approach and constitutes their greatest protection against attack.
Whether or not their distinctive marking has the function of making them invisible
to their enemies in dim light is doubtful. It is certain, however, that in daylight,
in light bush, the striping helps to conceal them from stalking carnivores, notably lions.

COW RHINOCEROS WITH HER CALF

When in season, usually after or during a rainy period, the cow rhino will wander off in search of a mate. The period of gestation is about fifteen months, and the calf stays with its mother for about three years, before being driven away to fend for itself.

are protected by their sense of smell and acute hearing, the latter being their chief defence; so efficient is their hearing that lions are more likely to attack when zebras are on the move, drowning other sounds by the noise of their own hoofs.

Photographing these large mixed herds containing zebras is far from easy, as they must be approached upwind and the dust they raise drifts down on to the photographer unless he be clear to a flank; and such a position is not always available, owing to difficulties of light and cover. He has frequently to spend a couple of hours in futile search for a point from which to make his exposure. When zebras are alone he can sometimes trade on their inquisitiveness and draw them nearer by a slight flutter of a handkerchief; but their curiosity seldom goes so far as to bring them within reach of either a camera or a lurking enemy.

Summing up the present status of the Equidae, it would seem that they are steadily decreasing in numbers, for although Burchell's zebra, Grevy's zebra and the kiang are holding their own (though without any noticeable increase), the range of the chigetai, the onager and the Mountain zebra is steadily being reduced, while the Somali wild ass is threatened with extinction.

The cause of this steady downgrade must be attributed to the agency of man, except perhaps in the case of the Somali wild ass; the quagga is already extinct through his efforts, and the Mountain zebras would vanish if not protected.

RHINOCEROSES

It seems strange, at first sight, to include rhinoceroses and tapirs in the same section as horses, but in the structure of the skull these three show obvious relationships. In addition, the tapirs bear a superficial resemblance to the earliest ancestors of the horse.

Formerly there were many species of rhinoceros distributed over the whole of the Old World, even as far north as Siberia, where lived the only species bearing a single horn in the middle of its forehead. All were large and clumsily built, but, judging by modern survivors, sufficiently active to be a match for most enemies and efficient in the use of their horns, both in defence and attack. The five surviving species, three Asiatic, two African, are long-bodied, with naked skins of great thickness. Their hides are soft in life, so that when a rhinoceros is killed the skin can be cut with a small knife and taken off in large sections without difficulty. When dry, however, the skin hardens to board-like consistency and this fact has given rise to the legend that it is impenetrable by a rifle bullet.

There are three toes on each foot, with a small but stout hoof-like nail on each, the whole foot being almost round and the toes projecting only a little beyond the margin.

There is considerable difference between the various species of rhinoceros in regard to size and weight. The two largest species, the Great Indian rhinoceros and the White rhinoceros of Africa, stand a little over 6 ft. at the shoulder and weigh about 2 tons; the smallest species, the Sumatran rhinoceros, is only 50 in. high and weighs under 1 ton. The dimensions of the Javan rhinoceros are intermediate between these limits.

The three Asiatic species differ conspicuously from their African relations in having their loose skins arranged in several folds; those in the Great Indian rhinoceros are particularly deep, the fold on the front of the shoulder continuing right across the neck. This species also has its skin thickly covered with round tubercles, like the flat heads of large nails.

Both sexes of the Great Indian rhinoceros carry a single horn, but only the male has one in the Javan species, while the Sumatran has two small horns, the front one up to 1 ft. long and the rear one about half that length. The greatest length that has been recorded for a horn belonging to the Great Indian rhinoceros is 24 in.

It is easy to distinguish the three species, even a piece of skin providing the necessary evidence; for that of the Javan has no tubercles, but is marked with a network of fine cracks, like a mosaic, while that of the Sumatran is smooth and more hairy than are the skins of the other species.

"MEDICINAL" VIRTUES

The Asiatic rhinoceroses are steadily dying out, being relentlesly persecuted for the supposed medicinal value of every part of the body. A dead rhinoceros may be worth two thousand rupees to the poacher who kills it. The blood is cupped into small phials while it is still warm, and each phial may later

RHINOCEROSES

Despite their size and apparent clumsiness, rhinos can be quite playful, and will roll together on the ground like puppies. In this they are somewhat hampered by their

be sold at a price between fifty and a hundred rupees. Yet it is the horn, sold in solution as an aphrodisiac, which is in actual fact the most valuable part of the rhinoceros.

STRANGE SUPERSTITIONS

The horn of a rhinoceros is an agglutinated mass of hairs, which even falls apart when left lying too long in water or mud; yet nothing will persuade the average oriental that he will not be cured of many ills by drinking it in solution, swallowing it powdered, or even holding it in his hand for a prescribed number of hours. The Chinese are mainly responsible for these superstitions, and the horns fetch great prices all over the Far East, most of them coming nowadays from East Africa. The ammonia content of the rhinoceros horn is probably the foundation of the greatly exaggerated belief in its powers of medication.

The great Mogul emperor Babar often hunted rhinoceroses in the Peshawar Valley in the first half of the sixteenth century, but by the beginning of the eighteenth century they had vanished from this area and the Punjab. At the beginning of the nineteenth century they were still to be found in the marshes of Rohilkhand and Kheri, but only an occasional straggler remained on the western border of the United Provinces by the end of that century. They are now confined to Assam, Bengal and Nepal, where they live in elephant grass 15–18 ft. high; like huge rabbits, they make runs through the tall grass and are rarely seen except when hunted with elephants.

A recent attempt to estimate their surviving numbers gave a total of about two hundred and fifty of all ages, and it was thought that, as they are still being killed off by poachers, they would die out in a few years. Since then they

AT PLAY
horns, which prevent them from rolling right over. In the Square-mouthed species the horns reach a length of 5 ft. or more, females having longer horns than males.

have been discovered in one or two remote places, one traveller in an out-of-the-way spot having seen eight in a morning, so they may yet survive for some years. Their chief protection is the abundance of tigers, which readily take to man-killing.

Like all rhinoceroses, they have the habit of depositing their ordure in the same place day after day; the habit is very marked in this species, which makes large piles, sometimes belonging to several individuals. This makes the poacher's work far too easy, as he has only to wait under cover beside one of these piles.

When hunted with elephants, the Great Indian rhinoceros is by no means a passive victim, for it will make a furious charge, attacking the under-parts of an elephant with its horn and large incisors to such effect that some elephants will not face up to them in a beat, but bolt on getting their scent.

They are long-lived beasts, even in captivity, and are reported to have lived for fifty years in a zoo. They have bred at least twice in the Calcutta zoo, the period of gestation in each case being a few days over nineteen months.

JAVAN RHINOCEROS

The Javan rhinos are in an even worse plight than their larger cousin. They have vanished from the Sundar-bans, where they were common less than a century ago, and the few survivors in Upper Burma may well have been killed off during the Second World War, when conditions there were un-settled. There may be one or two still left in Lower Burma, and both this species and the Sumatran were living in the same valley in an uninhabited part of the Siamese hills a few years ago. There seem to be none left in Malaya, and few survive in the densely-forested hills of Sumatra and Java.

99

BLACK OR HOOK-LIPPED RHINOCEROS

The Black rhinoceros is still found in considerable numbers in Kenya and in Tangan-yika. It frequents high country, often ascending to a height of over 12,000 ft., and abounds in the forests of Mount Kenya. It is also called the "Hook-lipped" rhinoceros, from the peculiar shape of its upper-lip, which overhangs the lower-lip. Rhinos of the remote mountain forests are usually much larger than those of the plains.

The smallest of the Asiatic rhinoceroses, and the only one with two horns, the Sumatran, was in much better case up to the end of the Second World War. Shortly before Burma was given self-rule, one or two Englishmen had visited some of the preserves and national parks created in the middle 1930's largely for this species, in which they had flourished and increased, and these visitors had found that the Japanese occupation had had little effect on their numbers. But since then there has been no news of their status. The uninhabited stretch of the hills between Burma and Siam may still harbour a few, but poachers range far in search of such valuable quarry, and they are unlikely to last long.

They are fond of the forested tops of ridges, and even in cold weather may be found at an altitude of 4,000–5,000 ft. It is on the upper slopes of these hills that they make their wallows, to which they frequently return, so giving the poacher an easy chance of shooting them. In the wallow, and usually at night, they make a curious bubbling sound on a baritone note.

They are said to be very vicious at times, charging without provocation in thick undergrowth, and they have a curious objection to camp fires.

Altogether the history of the Asiatic rhinoceroses is a sad one of unending persecution by man and gradual extinction.

AFRICAN RHINOS

There are two species of rhinoceros in Africa, the "White" or "Square-mouthed" (R. simus) and the "Black" or "Hook-lipped" (R. bicornis). To distinguish these species by colour is not really very satisfactory, for the colour of both is fundamentally a dull grey; their colour at any given time is dependent upon the colour of the soil, rock or dust which is used for dustbath or wallow, and upon whether a recent rainfall has washed their bodies clean. Thus a Black rhinoceros met with in the hills of Somaliland may appear a brilliant white owing to its dustbath being in a hollow stamped out in the gypsum rock. On the plains of Kenya it may be red or black, and ochre on the top of the Aberdare Range, where the soil happens to be yellow clay. The same applies to the White or Square-mouthed rhinoceros, except that, not having such a wide range, it is not found on the same variety of soil.

SQUARE-MOUTHED RHINO

The Square-mouthed or White rhinoceros is so named because it has the upper lip horizontally straight and parallel with the lower; in the Hook-lipped species the upper lip protrudes downwards and overlaps the lower.

The Square-mouthed is the bigger beast, being about 6 ft. at the shoulder, some 6 in. more than the Hook-lipped, and normally carries a longer horn. Neither of these species has the folds in the hide which distinguish the Asiatic species, and they are almost hairless except for fringes on the ears and the tuft at the end of the tail.

Only seventy years ago the Square-mouthed rhinoceros was plentiful between the Zambezi and the Orange River, though it had been nearly wiped out farther south early in the eighteenth century. It would have vanished altogether if protection had not been given to a small colony which still flourishes in Zululand. Early in this century another colony was discovered in the Lado Enclave, given immediate protection, and has now increased and overflowed southwards into Uganda, where it is also rigidly protected by the law.

The Square-mouthed rhinoceros is, as a rule, inoffensive, though one is recently reported to have killed several people; but it is often to be found quite close to villages, even entering them at times.

Females of both species usually carry the longest horns, though they are thinner than those of the males; the record for the Square-mouthed is 62¼ in.; that for the Hook-lipped is 9 in. less.

HOOK-LIPPED RHINO

Hook-lipped rhinoceroses are still plentiful in some parts of Africa, especially in Kenya and Tanganyika; they frequent high country of moderate rainfall, where there is plenty of cover. They are equally at home in thorn-bush or forest, and ascend the mountains up to a height of 12,000 ft. and above. They are fond of grazing on the giant heath which is found above the tree-line at about 11,000 ft. on Mount Kenya. Recently the government of Kenya, wishing to open up new country, sent out a professional hunter who killed over a thousand rhinoceroses in a year. They do not like a very wet climate, so are only found in the drier parts of Uganda and West Africa.

In the forests of Mount Kenya and the Aberdare Range there are still many, mainly because the trapping of them in pitfalls is now forbidden; moreover, it is far more difficult to poach them and export the horn than it is with the rhinoceroses of the plains. Yet the finer horns are found in these remoter forests, growing to such dimensions that they would seem seriously to incommode their owners in thick cover. The forest rhinoceroses are also considerably bigger than those of the plains and thornbush; in the extreme north-east of their habitat they are more than twice the weight of the plains beast.

In Somaliland and just north of the Tana River the bush-dwellers are, as a rule, small and very bad-tempered. This is due to the former Somali habit of surrounding the animal and then throwing cloud after cloud of spears at it, until the unfortunate creature died of multiple wounds. The object was to get the hide for making shields, but, intertribal warfare having now largely ceased, and the tribes being mostly armed nowadays with rifles, the horns are the only valuable trophy to be gained, and these are usually very small in the rhinoceros of this part of Africa.

The Hook-lipped rhinoceros has a very uncertain temper, and its behaviour is eccentric in the extreme. More often than not it will go away peaceably if disturbed, but one can never be sure that it will not make an unprovoked charge, even at the sound of a shot not aimed at it. A cow rhinoceros and her young calf, when met suddenly in thick cover, are dangerous and a charge is most probable. Fortunately they are not very difficult to kill, a bullet in the chest accounting for one quite quickly.

BREEDING HABITS

A rhinoceros of either sex will take up a piece of territory, including a patch of thick cover, and may be very difficult to dislodge : if this territory is on the edge of a settler's farm serious trouble may result, for the rhino may break fences, scare the herd-boys and even take to chasing and killing cows.

When in season, usually after or during a rainy period, a cow will wander off in search of a mate, bringing the bull back to her bit of country. The period of gestation is about fifteen months, and the calf stays with the mother for some three years; the bull will sometimes remain with them for

BLACK RHINOCEROS WITH HER CALF

The "Black," or "Hook-lipped," rhinoceros is the smaller of the two African species.
It has a very uncertain temper, and will often make an unprovoked charge, especially
if it happens to be a female animal accompanied by her calf.

this period. When the cow comes in season again the calf is driven away to find its own living and annex its own bit of territory. The calves have better eyesight than the adults, their range being quite double the fifty yards usually assigned to the older beasts.

When an enemy is located rhinos give loud snorts, and there is always a lot of grunting and snorting when they are fighting for a female. When alarmed and searching for an enemy, they sometimes utter a squeaking noise like that of a toy trumpet.

They are mainly browsers, but eat grass after a drought, and sometimes leaves and grass within a few minutes. They are surprisingly independent of water in some parts of their habitat, notably in the hills of the interior of Somaliland, where they chew the thick-leaved succulents, such as sanseviera, to supply the deficiency.

A curious habit is that of spreading their dung about with the front horn, often returning to the place specially to do this, and even spreading the dung of another rhinoceros which has not yet returned for the purpose. If undisturbed they may use the same place, usually a stretch of several yards beside a game track, as their latrine for a fortnight or more.

Many of them have a wound behind the shoulder, most often on the right side, the cause of which is not known for certain. It is said to be the result of fighting, or of a cow horning a bull after mating, but may be made by tick-birds (Red-billed oxpeckers) pulling out ticks from this tender part of the hide, then enlarging the wound by pulling pieces off its edges. Whatever the cause, the beast so marked becomes a dweller in dense cover to avoid the attentions of these birds.

It seems probable that forest-dwelling rhinoceroses, especially those living high up on mountains, will survive for many years yet. Their horns are not sufficiently valuable, and their readiness to retaliate is too much favoured by thick cover, to make hunting them easy or profitable; moreover, they are not as easily found as are elephants, as they do not live in herds. Even with their slow rate of increase, they still maintain their numbers in such places, and where they have been much shot for destroying forest plantations there seem to be just as many after a while.

TAPIRS

The tapirs, curious in structure, appearance and distribution, have four front and three hind toes, and have the snout elongated into a short trunk. They are of a rather pig-like appearance, with the rump higher than the withers, and carry their heads low. They are akin to the rhinoceroses, but are smaller animals; the largest species, the Malay tapir, is 40–42 in. at the shoulder, with a length on the curves from nose to root of tail of about 8 ft.

The Malay tapir (*Tapirus indicus*) is curiously coloured, being black on the front half of the body and light grey behind the shoulders and on quarters and rump. Its legs are all black. It is the only Asiatic species and is found in Tenasserim and Mergui (Lower Burma), Siam, Malaya, and the island of Sumatra. The young are born striped and spotted with yellowish white, these markings persisting for the first three months of their lives.

The Malay tapir is found mainly on both sides of the spine of hills which runs from north to south between Burma and Siam, but not farther north than latitude 18 deg. It must have evergreen jungle within easy reach, and spends most of its time in thick cover, its colouring giving it such good protection that it is most difficult to see at even a few yards. It usually stands with head and shoulders under a thick canopy of leaves, while the light through the big trees above patches its grey hindquarters with wavering shadows.

HABITS OF THE TAPIR

Tapirs seem to be stupid animals, or else rely on their protective colouring to an abnormal extent, for they will stand head down and motionless within a few yards of a man. But when found on the upper slopes of the hills, they can move at a fast pace across them and, except in evergreen foliage, take no undue risks.

They have a habit of making wallows high up on the hillsides, where some small spring comes out of the earth. They trample it into a muddy basin and lie there, at night as a rule, making a curious bubbling noise which is very like the sound emitted by the Sumatran rhinoceros under the same circumstances.

That such stupid animals, with no apparent means of defence, should continue to maintain their numbers is most remarkable, for there are more tigers in their habitat than anywhere else in the world. It may partly be due to the fact that these big carnivores do most of their hunting—for sambar and other deer—in other parts of the forest, for these animals do not like evergreen jungle. Also the tapir's flesh is not

TAPIR OF PERU

The Common tapir of South America stands 4 ft. high at the shoulder and is 7 to 8 ft. long. Although clumsy in appearance, it shows great activity when necessary.

palatable to man, and it is, therefore, not hunted by the natives—a major cause of extinction in so many other species.

Tapirs are solitary animals and, except for a female with a single young one, two are rarely found together. Though fond of water, they or their tracks are seldom seen beside the many small rivers which flow at the bottom of their hills, and all their drinking and bathing seem to be done high on the slopes.

Little is known of South American tapirs other than the fact of their existence, that they are coloured a rather dark brown, and that the young are striped and spotted just as in the Malayan species.

The Common tapir (*Tapirus terrestris*) has a short upright mane on its neck. Roulin's tapir comes from the hills of Ecuador and Colombia. They

are shot and eaten whenever the opportunity presents itself to the natives; this is normally only when they come out on to the bank of a river, though a few are killed by hunting with dogs. But they have such enormous stretches of impenetrable forest in which to live and feed that such encounters are mostly accidental, and very little is known of their habits.

They would appear to have only one serious enemy, the jaguar, which probably kills a few immature tapirs; but as the jaguar preys largely on smaller beasts, such as peccaries, which are more plentiful and more easily found, it cannot be considered a serious threat to the existence of tapirs.

In fact, until their great sheltering forests are much reduced, and this is unlikely in the foreseeable future, these large and almost defenceless beasts seem likely to flourish for many years.

INSIDE A HIPPO'S MOUTH

Yawning, the hippo discloses the vast cavern of his mouth, set in the lower jaw with keen-edged teeth as much as a foot in length. The canine and incisor teeth, prominent in this photograph, grow continuously, replacing the edges that are worn away by cropping the coarse herbage on which the hippo feeds. Though naturally inoffensive, the hippo can be roused to great ferocity, and then is capable of biting a man in half.

Cloven-hoofed animals

AT one time the vast assemblage of hoofed animals was lumped together in the order Ungulata. Today they are separated into a number of separate orders, which better express their affinities. Apart from the elephants (order Proboscidea) and hyraxes (order Hyracoidea), and the horses, tapirs and rhinoceroses (order Perissodactyla), there is the order Artiodactyla, which includes all the even-toed ungulates, the pigs, hippopotamuses, camels, llamas, cattle, sheep, goats, giraffes, antelope, deer and others less well known.

The Artiodactyla are conveniently subdivided into three sub-orders : the non-ruminants or Suiformes (pigs and hippopotamuses); the Tylopoda (camels and llamas); and the Ruminantia, including all the rest.

The Suiformes, or non-ruminants, have simple stomachs and four-toed feet, although the pigs walk on two only of these toes.

The true pigs (*Sus*) are distributed in seven species over Europe, Asia and North Africa. They are crop-destroyers of the worst kind, and are most difficult to keep down. The best known are the European and Indian wild swine, which are much alike and are famous as the quarry in hog-hunts, when they are pursued by mounted men armed with long spears. These animals sometimes reach 36 in. at the shoulder, although a boar of 32 in. is considered a big one, and may weigh as much as 400 lb. The largest specimens are found in Mesopotamia and in the Indian jungles. They are brown-grey or brown, with stiff, rather scanty hairs and an upstanding dorsal crest about 9 in. high. No more courageous animals exist ; when hunted they frequently turn on their pursuers, and many a hog-hunter and his horse have suffered from a determined charge by one of these animals.

There is a curious little species, the Pygmy hog (*Porcula salvania*), under a foot in height and found only in north-eastern Bengal; it is fond of very thick cover. An even more eccentric member of the family is the babirusa (*Babirussa babirussa*), of the Celebes, in which the upper canines grow straight up through the skin of the face, curving backwards at the top.

In Africa the European pig inhabits the hills of Morocco and the Atlas, but farther south and east there are three species peculiar to the continent. These are the warthog (*Phacochoerus aethiopicus*), the bushpig (*Potamochoerus*) and the forest hog (*Hylochoerus*). The first two are found all over Africa south of the Sahara, but the forest hog, which is much the largest, is confined to equatorial Africa. In West Africa forest hogs

A WILD PIG WITH HER YOUNG

The wild boar, supposed ancestor of our domestic pigs, became extinct in England in the Middle Ages, but is still found in France, Spain, Russia and Central Europe, as well as in Asia and North Africa. The young have handsome striped coats, such as are shown above, but they lose these markings as they grow older.

live on flat or low ground in rain forest; but in East Africa they were until recently confined to the forests at high altitudes. Lately they have come down much lower and combine with the other two species in destroying crops. They will leave an acre of ground after a night's visit covered with furrows which they have made when grubbing up potatoes. Bushpigs are most destructive in maize, where they knock down a cob

haired, reaching 32 in. in height and 250 lb. in weight, while forest hogs may attain as much as 38 in. and 600 lb. Both are very low on the leg, and being heavily built they look more like bears when on the move in forest, which they rarely quit. Warthogs may be seen in the open at times, but spend most of the day in holes which they enlarge from the diggings of ant-bear and hyena.

Bushpigs stick to thick, low bush or

WARTHOGS AT HOME IN KENYA

The warthog is the most hideous of the pig family, with a huge head carrying formidable tusks and a face decorated with warts, knobs and gristly excrescences. Inhabitants of Africa south of the Sahara, warthogs live in holes and tunnels in river-banks.

and devour only half of it before passing on to another.

The old male forest hog grows a big, flat, semicircular excrescence under each eye, but has no warts, while the bushpig has no facial adornments. Warthogs are, however, distinguished by up to three conical warts on each cheek and a long gristly excrescence on each upper jaw. The forest hog has a high back instead of the concave one of the warthog.

Warthogs are grey and sparsely

reeds as a rule, have high-ridged backs and are well-haired ; they are brown to red in colour, often with white faces, and, in the case of some of the hill animals, a broad white band all along the spine.

The peccaries are an indigenous group of several species but very similar habits, which are spread over Central America and the northern half of South America. They go about in large herds, sticking largely to the cover of forest and marsh, damage crops and are said to be very dangerous. They have been known to kill and eat a man.

The hippopotamuses, related to pigs, are much larger and have a broad muzzle. *Choeropsis*, the Pygmy hippopotamus from West Africa, is only about 6 ft. long, and is little known in the wild state owing to its retiring ways. It is a pleasingly tame species when in captivity, where it breeds quite freely.

THE PONDEROUS HIPPO

The Common hippopotamus, on the other hand, may reach 14 ft. in length and a ton and a half in weight, and is found in almost every suitable large area of water, lake or river south of the Sahara, even appearing unexpectedly in remote little crater lakes and partially dry streams. It may even be found walking overland in apparently most unsuitable country, hilly and covered with rocks and thorns, as it makes its way from one pool or river to another. In some lakes and rivers, such as Lakes Edward and George, it is found in great numbers, several thousand living in Lake Edward alone, while in some rivers, notably in parts of the Nile, it is dangerous, attacking canoes and killing the occupants. On Lake Edward one fishery lost thirty-two men in five years, about half of them being killed on land. Adult hippos wander as much as six or seven miles inland at night in search of food, and may be encountered by day during rainy weather, when they lie up in a puddle under bushes. They are particularly dangerous if their disturber gets between them and the water. Yet on Lake Victoria attacks by them are very rare, and in some rivers they live side by side with humans almost in amity.

The biggest bulls usually annex a piece of territory along the bank of river or lake and fight fiercely with rivals for possession, slashing each other terribly with their great incisors, sometimes with fatal results.

They also assemble in herds of fifty or even more at times, and may be seen huddled together in a black mass until an hour after sunrise, when they usually disperse. They are noisy animals, grunting and bellowing day and night, and in some places, such as the lower Tana River, do much damage to crops on land, to rice in particular. Being very inquisitive, a lamp is an attraction at night, and Africans are sometimes killed at night among their huts by running into hippos in the dark. Hippos and elephants are most unfriendly towards each other. Elephants, when bathing, are always demonstrated against by hippos, and will chase hippos when they find them on land.

Hippos stay under water for about two and a half to four and a half minutes as a rule, but it is sometimes asserted that they can remain under without breathing for more than a quarter of an hour. Such records have to be accepted with care, for, on coming up for air, they often protrude only their nostrils above the surface—frequently in a patch of weed or behind some floating debris which makes it hard to detect them.

TWO SPECIES OF CAMEL

The Tylopoda (camels and llamas) have two-toed feet, with nails instead of hoofs, and a complex stomach. The two species of camel, the one-humped Arabian and the two-humped Bactrian, are too well known to need description. They are now entirely domesticated animals. There is a herd of so-called wild camels in Spain, on the Guadalquivir plains, but these were brought over from North Africa by the Moors centuries ago. The wild two-humped camels of the Gobi Desert

RIVER MONSTERS OF AFRICA

The hippopotamus is found only in tropical Africa, where it inhabits pools and river-banks, spending most of its time in the water. Huge and cumbrous as it is, the hippo is an inoffensive creature if left alone, although it often pillages crops by night. Note the white egrets perched unconcernedly upon the backs of two of these huge beasts.

may well be of recent origin, having probably escaped from domestic herds and caravans.

Camels are Old World beasts, famous for their carrying powers and resistance to thirst over long periods in desert country. Selected breeds can carry 300 lb. for forty to fifty miles a day for ten days without a drink. They are one of the few beasts of burden which will literally go on until they drop dead. Camels are mostly bad-tempered, and at times even savage, beasts: they have been known to kill men during the rut, knocking them down with their necks and tearing out their entrails.

The Bactrian camels of Central Asia are comparatively little used for riding, being used mainly as pack animals on the Central Asian trade-routes. They are a fine sight in winter, when in condition and carrying masses of dark hair on shoulders and thighs, as they come in long caravans through the Khyber Pass, or into some bazaar of eastern Asia Minor.

The llamas, which are grouped anatomically with the camels, are entirely South American and are of two species, the guanaco of about 42 in. at the shoulder, and the vicuña, which is nearly a foot shorter. Both have been domesticated, the guanaco as a transport animal and the vicuña for its fine coat, from which blankets and coats are woven. They look like small and slender camels without humps, but have neither the stamina nor the relative carrying power of the bigger beasts.

CAMELS AT A WADI
Camels, found only in the Old World, are widely used as pack-animals. The one-humped Arabian no longer exists in the wild state, but the two-humped Bactrian is still found wild in small numbers in the Gobi Desert of Central Asia.

The Ruminantia have hoofed feet, with either two toes (giraffes and okapis) or four toes, no incisors in the upper jaw and—the character by which they are best known—a complex stomach. The main families are: the Tragulidae (mouse-deer), Bovidae (cattle, sheep, goats, antelopes and goat-antelopes), Giraffidae (giraffes and okapis), Cervidae (deer), and Antilocapridae (prong-buck).

The chevrotains or mouse-deer (Tragulidae) are small ruminants, brightly coloured and slender, with tusk-like upper canines and without horns or antlers. The True chevrotains (*Tragulus*) of South-east Asia include the meminna (*T. meminna*) from South India and Ceylon. The former are 10 to 12 in. high, delicately built, and usually rufous-grey in colour, with white stripings on throat and chest, while the meminna is splashed and spotted with white on the body. The latter is found in plenty on the trap-rock plateaux of central and southern India, spending the day in holes (where the female also produces her pair of young), feeding at night, or in the early morning and about sunset.

The Malay mouse-deer or kanchil is rarely seen, but if one sits beside some rocky jungle stream about sunset one may see a few of them, treading delicately as they pass by the edge of the water and nipping off hanging roots and fresh shoots from the bushes.

The African Water chevrotain (*Hyemoschus aquaticus*) is hardly known even to residents in its habitat, so much does it stay in reedy marshes, while its olive-brown coat merges with the cover and is further broken by splashes of white to give protection. It is an equatorial species, about two inches higher at the shoulder than its Asiatic relatives, and is most common from the west coast to western Uganda.

In the Bovidae the horns are hollow, seated on bony cores, and are never

LLAMAS OF BOLIVIA

Llamas flock in the streets of Potosí. These beasts, in the same anatomical group as camels, are smaller, without a hump, and have woolly coats. The name is applied particularly to the transport animal of the Andes. Another domestic form is the alpaca.

LONG-HAIRED YAKS OF CENTRAL ASIA

In Tibet and on the lofty, desolate tableland between India and China the yak is unsurpassed as a surefooted beast of burden. Strong, hardy and hard-working, it yields meat, milk and the long, shaggy hair from which the tribesmen's clothing is made.

shed. There are no face or foot glands. There are six genera of living wild cattle—the aurochs (*Bos primigenius*) of Europe, the typical member, being now extinct—of which the gaur (*Bos gaurus*) and the banteng (*B. sondaicus*) form the first; the rest include *Bison* (the North American buffalo), *Poephagus* (yak), *Syncerus* (the African buffalo), *Bubalus* (the Indian buffalo), and *Anoa* (the Dwarf buffalo).

The gaur is a fine beast, distributed over the hills of southern and central India, through Assam, Burma, western Siam and Malaya. The old males are black with white stockings, the cows a duller black or occasionally brown, while the young are chestnut red. They live in forests, with a preference for those with much bamboo, on whose new shoots they feed in the rains. The old bulls run to 6 ft. at the shoulder, and are wary and dangerous when wounded. The horns are very massive and of a peculiar olive-green tint, often over 40 in. in span, 30 in. in length and as much as 20 in. in girth at the base.

They were fairly plentiful in many parts of India, but they have been much hunted of late, and in some places have also suffered from rinderpest. In Assam they grow to their greatest size and in Burma are often associated with the equally fine wild ox, the banteng or tsaine, which, though a little shorter, is an upstanding and active beast, noted for its wariness and savagery when wounded. The cow tsaine (both sexes have a big white patch on the buttocks) are nearly always rufous-khaki in colour, though sometimes individuals occur of darker shade; the bulls vary greatly. The most usual body colour is dead-oak-leaf khaki, but deep copper-beech bay is also common, with French grey, chocolate brown and black rarer; the last is very rare in the north of their habitat, but is the usual colour for adult bulls in the East Indian Islands, where they are also found.

EUROPEAN IBEXES—AGILE, SUREFOOTED

The ibex, or Alpine wild goat, is distinguished by its splendid, backward-curving horns, which measure as much as three feet along the curve. They are deeply ridged in front. At one time very common in the Alps, the European ibex has been severely reduced in numbers by indiscriminate hunting. It is now found in limited areas of the

NATIVES OF MOUNTAIN PEAKS AND CRAGS

Swiss and Italian Alps and in the Carpathians, where the group seen above was photographed. Ibexes congregate in small herds, with an old male in charge. They are timid animals, and post sentinels to give warning of danger. Closely allied species are found in Central Asia, Abyssinia (only rarely seen), Arabia and the Caucasus.

AFRICAN BUFFALOES FACE THE CAMERA

Buffaloes are plentiful throughout most of Central, East and South Africa, and, owing to their ravages among crops, are regarded as a serious nuisance. When wounded, they become dangerously savage and cunning. This picture shows the outpost of a herd scenting the photographer and ready for trouble.

The gaur is a slow-moving, rather slow-thinking beast, but the tsaine is ever on the alert, and, being without the heavy forehand and hump of the gaur, is rather more impressive, the longer leg and lighter body making for activity. The horns of the tsaine are set apart at the base by a solid mass of naked gristle, whereas those of the gaur have a hairy boss between them.

Also Asiatic is the yak (*Poephagus grunniens*), which is a high-altitude dweller in the mountains and plateaux of Central Asia. It is black all over and covered with masses of long hair. The average height at the shoulder is about 52 in. Yaks have acquired their specific name by their habit of grinding their teeth and grunting, which is most annoying when in camp with tame yaks as transport. They are the stock transport animals of the great Tibetan plateau. The domesticated animals are much smaller and often marked with white, while their horns never reach the sturdy 30 in. and more which a wild bull carries.

They are mainly found in northern Tibet and in the Kuen Luen Mountains and are still plentiful in those barren regions. In late summer they sometimes enter Indian territory, most commonly in north-eastern Kashmir, but also round some of the central Himalayan passes. Their country is barren of trees (most of it being over 15,000 ft. above the sea) and only carries low vegetation, so that it is remarkable how such large animals manage to find sustenance, yet they show no sign of decreasing.

Then come the European and American bisons, which are almost extinct as really wild animals. Some of the European species are still found in Lithuania and other parts of eastern Europe. The American bison, which once covered the prairies of North America in vast uncountable herds, are now reduced to semi-tame park herds in the western U.S.A. and in Canada. They have to be regularly shot down to reduce their rapid increase.

There are three species of Asiatic buffalo: two small island forms, the anoa of the Celebes (*Anoa depressicornis*), which is only about 3 ft. high with horns a foot long, and the Mindoro

buffalo (*Bubalus mindorensis*) of the Philippines, which is a small form of the great Indian buffalo (*B. bubalis*). The Indian buffalo may stand $5\frac{1}{2}$ ft. at the shoulder and is the most savage of the wild oxen, often attacking without provocation and, when wounded, fighting it out to the death.

This species, from which are derived the domesticated water-buffaloes of the East, is found truly wild in central India, Orissa, Assam, and the Sundarbans. Both sexes carry immense horns, which are sometimes over 70 in. long and 20 in. in girth at the base. They live mainly in country of marsh and high grass.

The buffaloes of Africa (*Syncerus*) are found from the southern Sudan to the

A NOBLE ANIMAL SAVED FROM EXTINCTION

In the days of the early white settlers, bison covered the plains of North America in vast numbers, but, as a result of unrestricted hunting, they became almost extinct in the late nineteenth century. Today they are carefully preserved amid wild surroundings.

Zambezi, with a few south of that river, and from coast to coast, in various races and sizes from about 45 in. to 54 in. at the shoulder.

In South Africa the adults are black and the calves red. Farther north both adults and young are black in East Africa and Uganda, but in western Uganda, near the Belgian Congo border, there are often red youngsters in a herd of black adults. North and west from Lake Albert comes the "bush cow," a small species of the Congo and West Africa, which is red throughout life, and there is a small black race in the Sudan. The bush cow is reputed to be very savage, probably owing to persecution by spear-throwing natives.

Buffaloes are still very plentiful between the Sudan and the Zambezi, and are often a great pest owing to their crop-raiding habits and rapid increase.

They probably account for more deaths among hunters of all races than any other wild animal; they are mainly kept down by lions, which will tag along after a herd for hours, trying to pick up a stray calf in thick cover.

SHEEP AND GOATS

The Caprinae, the wild sheep and goats, the second sub-family of ruminants, are all mountain-dwelling and of smaller size than the oxen. Both sexes have horns, though those of the ewes are small, while the rams have large curving horns. There are three main types of horn: those that spiral outwards (sheep), those that show a single backward curve (ibex and all true wild goats), and those spirally twisted and directed backwards (markhor).

The larger wild sheep belong to the ammon group (sometimes called the bighorns), which stretches from the northern Himalayas, through the Thian Shan and Altai ranges, to Kamchatka

and across to North America, where the bighorn sheep are found all down the mountain spine of the Rockies, from Alaska to Mexico. There are various races intermediate with the well-known Pamir argali (*Ovis poli*), whose horns, measured on the curve, run to 75 in., and the argali (*O. ammon*) of the Altai and northern Himalayas, while the bighorn has also been divided into several races. All of these are rufous dun, with the rufous much reduced in the winter, and they range in size from the 46 in. height of the argali down to the 38 in. of the Kamchatkan and American bighorns.

KEEN SIGHT AND SCENT

Everywhere they live on great barren, open slopes, their eyesight and sense of smell being their chief means of protection from leopards and wolves. All of them shed their coats in summer; those of the argali are so dense and come away in such large lumps that they may be seen rolling over the hilltops, driven by the howling wind which usually rages in Tibet. They are brown in summer, but much lighter in winter.

The mouflon group range from Corsica and Sardinia, the island homes of the true mouflon, eastward through Crete and Asia Minor, Persia and Afghanistan, to northern India and the Himalayas, though they are not found there south of Kashmir. They range in size from the 28 in. of the Corsican animal to the 36 in. of the Ladakhi shapu of eastern Kashmir.

Nowhere is sheep country in any way as hard going as goat country. When hunting the wild sheep of the great Tibetan plateau, it is the altitude—usually over 15,000 ft.—and the vast rolling ridges, barren of cover and ranged by the wonderful eyesight of the quarry, which make the difficulties. These are

A BARBARY WILD SHEEP WITH ITS LAMB

There is only one species of wild sheep in Africa—the so-called Barbary sheep, which is found across the north of the continent, in rocky, desert country, from Morocco to the Red Sea. It is a large animal, with somewhat goat-like horns. Note the long tufts of hair fringing the chest and upper part of the fore-limbs.

increased by the varying winds off the glaciers that bear scent to the sensitive nostrils of the big rams, which are usually in small parties of up to six in the summer hunting season.

The only wild sheep of Africa is the Barbary sheep, or arui (*Ammotragus lervia*), which is found in hills from Morocco to the Red Sea, and even in rocky outcrops in the deserts of North Africa. It is a large beast—about 38 in. at the shoulder—covered all over with long hair which hangs in bunches from throat, shoulders and thighs. Its horns may be over 30 in. long, curved strongly backwards, but ridged like those of the mouflon. It will probably survive in its desert hills as it is wary, and the absence of water deters hunters from pursuing it into its native fastnesses.

The largest of the goats is the Himalayan markhor (*Capra falconeri*), which is about 44 in. high and weighs up to 240 lb., with smaller races found all down the North-west Frontier and in the vicinity of Quetta. The spiral of the horns becomes tighter as one goes farther south, and they are measured straight from tip to base and not along the curve as in the Himalayan race.

Goats and ibexes inhabit such awe-inspiring precipices as the 8,000-ft. sheer cliffs of the middle Indus valley or the equally daunting rotten rocks of the North-west Frontier hills of India. Even the rare Abyssinian ibex has managed to survive because its refuges are almost inaccessible.

On similar ground are found the Asiatic ibex (*C. sibirica*), in the northern

TAHR OF SOUTHERN INDIA
In contrast with its shaggy, warmly clad relative of the cool Himalayas, the Nilgiri tahr has a smooth coat, suited to the heat of southern India.

Himalayas, with horns curving back over the shoulders to a length of 50 in., a shoulder height of 40 in. and 200 lb. weight. It is even hardier than the markhor, which is driven much lower by the winter snow and so falls to the guns of poaching villagers, while the ibex remains up in the snow, scraping a living from scrub and grass uncovered by its feet.

The European ibex (*C. ibex*) is a native of northern Italy, but the other five species live in low hills on either side of the Red Sea and from the Indo-Persian border to the Taurus Mountains. All these species are about the same size as the Himalayan ibex (*C. sibirica*), except the Sind Wild goat, which is only 34-35 in. at the shoulder and quite independent of water in its barren hills; yet its horns run to 50 in. and are the longest proportionately of any of the group.

Goats and sheep have very different habits, for the sheep graze on big open slopes and lie down on their feeding-grounds, whereas goats both browse and graze on slopes where grass and bushes are growing, then climb up on to some precipice to spend the rest of the day or night safe from attack.

Three species of tahr (*Hemitragus*) form the third group of the wild goats, and are widely separated in appearance and habitat. The Himalayan species is 38 in. at the shoulder, with a long coat of wiry hair and an under-coat of *pushm*. They live in even worse country than the markhor, the great gorges cut through the outer Himalayas by the big rivers, notably the Chenab, and bearing pine forests on the easier slopes.

The Nilgiri tahr of south India is a little larger, but is smooth-coated and, like the Himalayan one, brown to coffee-colour. The old bucks have a light-coloured saddle, which indicates their age and makes them fit quarry for the hunter.

They also live on big cliffs of the mountain ranges south of Mysore, but come up to the easier ground on top to feed.

Only a very few specimens of the third species, the Arabian tahr, are known—from the hills west of the Gulf of Oman. It is a much smaller beast, and its 11-in. horns are more slender than those of its Indian relations.

The sub-family of Rupicaprinae, or "goat-antelopes," contains the chamois, goral, serow and takin, Rocky Mountain goat and musk-ox.

The chamois of Europe (*Rupicapra rupicapra*) is found in mountain ranges from the Pyrenees eastward to the Caucasus, and is distinguished by its upright horns with their downward and backward hooks at the tips. It is small, a little over 30 in. at the shoulder, and its horns are up to 12 in. in length. It varies in colour seasonally, and also locally, being usually dark brown in forest country and lighter in colour in open and rocky precipices.

With much the same habits, the gorals (*Nemorhaedus*), which inhabit the Himalayas, have been called the Asiatic chamois. They are smaller, 26–28 in. at the shoulder, and are fonder of big grassy slopes than the chamois, though they are quite at home on the worst ground. The coat of brown to grey is lighter in winter. They have a white patch on the throat and a black line down the front of each fore-leg, a short tail, and their horns, at the most 9 in. long, curve back slightly over the head and are ringed for about half way. They have great powers of concealment, and a big grassy slope which has been examined with glasses unsuccessfully for an hour or more may suddenly be found, as the sun leaves it, to hold half a dozen gorals.

The Burmese gorals are very similar, but have a good deal of yellow in the coat in the north, though farther south and in western Siam there is little difference between them and the typical *Nemorhaedus goral* of the Himalayas. The great cliffs of the big river gorges are their favourite haunts, and this also seems to apply to the Chinese gorals, which are sparsely distributed across that great country as far as Korea.

The distribution of the serows (*Capricornis*) is much the same as that of the gorals, but they are much larger, up to 40 in. at the shoulder. They are coarsely haired, black when young, with rufous gradually replacing the black on the underparts, and have the inside of the legs white and a white blaze down the face. With age they also develop white spots on the throat and cheeks.

There is an entirely rufous colour phase which stretches westward from the Burma-China frontier, across Arakan and throughout the eastern Himalayas, as far as Naini Tal. The Siamese-Malayan races are almost entirely black, with a curious bloom on the coat.

They are most retiring, living on bush-hung cliffs and being rarely seen; while they have a reputation for being dangerous when wounded, and, owing to their habits and the precipices on which they live, are very rarely shot by Europeans.

The Rocky Mountain goat (*Oreamnos americanus*) is white all over and all the year round, and has long hair with an erect dorsal crest. It is about 40 in. high, but its horns are small, the record being $11\frac{1}{2}$ in. It is found in precipitous country, but does not stick to bush as much as the serow of Asia.

The musk-ox (*Ovibos moschatus*) is a strange beast whose horns are close to each other on the skull, then droop downwards and have an upward turn at the

SHY SEROW OF EAST ASIA

The serow frequents bush-clad mountain slopes, from Tibet as far east as Sumatra. Solitary and retiring, it is seldom seen by man, but can be dangerous when wounded.

tip, being nearest in appearance to those of a takin. It measures about 4 ft. at the shoulder. Musk-oxen are inhabitants of the Arctic; they live on mosses, which they get at in winter by scraping the snow away with their feet. When a herd is attacked by wolves they form a close phalanx, with their calves inside, and their 25-in "meat-hook"-shaped horns are efficient weapons. Musk-oxen are covered with long brown hair, and their feet are expanded and have hair on the undersides, giving a firm grip on ice or snow.

THE RARE TAKIN

Takin (*Budorcas taxicolor*) are little known, living as they do in the tangle of mountains round northern Burma, Assam and western China. A few explorers have brought back specimens with great difficulty, owing to the constant rain, the reluctance of the natives to furnish transport, and the want of supplies.

Averaging 44 in. at the shoulder, they are heavily built, with stout limbs and a curved profile which is distinctly reminiscent of a gnu. The horns also curve in much the same way as those of a wildebeest.

Farther east, in Chinese territory, this species is replaced by the Golden takin (*B. bedfordi*), in which the body colour is orange, grey or intermediate shades. The horns of both species may be up to 24 in. long.

Golden takin often visit the warm mineral springs at some seasons of the year, and may then be found in herds of fifty strong. They are reputed to be dangerous when alarmed, ready to attack man or beast, even when unwounded.

Though the typical antelope, the blackbuck (see below), is Indian, by far the greater number of this big group,

containing twelve sub-families, are African. There is none in America or Europe, though plentiful fossil remains have been found in Greece.

The Bubalinae, or hartebeests, are all large; the true hartebeests, of which there are eight species, are lovers of open bush and plains from south of the Atlas Mountains to the Cape. They are notable for their high withers and sloping hindquarters, for speed and stamina. Their horns are mounted on a big bony pedicle, greatest in the lelwel, and are annulated, with the points turned back. In body they run from 44 in. at the shoulder of the bubal of North Africa, to the 53 in. of the lelwel of East and Central Africa, and their horns from 15 in. in the bubal to 26 in. in the lelwel.

With them are grouped the hirola (*Damaliscus hunteri*), found in a limited habitat between the Juba and Tana Rivers only; and also the bontebok and blesbok, none of which has the exaggerated horn pedicle, while the high withers and sloping hindquarters are much moderated. The last two of these are plum-coloured, with white face-markings, and the horns are more upright, running to 30 in. in the hirola. Also grouped with them is the korrigum or topi (*D. korrigum*), from Equatorial Africa, which is chocolate-brown with, in the coastal race of East Africa, a rich bloom like that on a plum.

THE WILDEBEESTS

In the same sub-family, but of very different conformation, are gnus, or wildebeests, of which the Black wildebeest is the smallest and now only exists under strict preservation in Cape Colony. The larger Brindled gnu (*Gorgon taurinus*), dark grey, with black lines on the sides, and masses of hair on the neck and throat, is still very plentiful

COVETED GAME ANIMAL OF THE ALPS

The elusive, nimble-footed chamois is the principal quarry of Alpine hunters. Much of the fascination of tracking this small animal arises from its extreme wariness and agility, which make it very difficult to come within close range of it.

in Tanganyika and southern districts of Kenya. Standing 52 in. at the high withers, its smooth horns curve outwards, up and inwards, with a width of up to 30 in.

A very different group are the duikers—all small animals—of which there are thirty or more species. The largest of these is the Yellow-backed duiker (*Cephalophus sylvicultrix*), which is about 30 in. in maximum height. They are divided into forest, bush and blue duikers; the bush duikers, living in the more open country south of the Sahara to the Zambezi, being those most frequently met with. The Grey duiker, a typical example of these, may be put up in low scrub to run away in the diving and ducking manner which gives them their name. Most of the forest duikers are bright red in colour. Their horns, but a few inches long, are found in both sexes and are stout, sharp and usually buried in a tuft of coarse hair.

The little klipspringer (*Oreotragus oreotragus*) is the only member of the next sub-family and a most interesting one. About 26 in. at the shoulder, it is squarely built, and has coarse, pithy hair; its feet are so fashioned that it goes about on the tips of its toes, each toe having a hollow point with a soft centre, which gives it a sure grip on the rocks of the cliffs where it is always found. Klipspringers live in pairs, and are often seen on top of a commanding rock, one lying down, the other standing and keeping watch. The horns of the buck are 4-in. spikes, slightly ringed at the base and standing up straight from the head.

Any rocky hill in country with a moderate rainfall, from Nigeria and Abyssinia southwards, may hold these quaint and pleasing little beasts, which are independent of water.

Their nearest relatives, the oribis

steinbok has a curious trick of running hard in a semicircle when disturbed, then suddenly lying down flat, often without sufficient cover to hide it, so that one would think that it would be easy prey for eagles and jackals; but there seem to be as many of them today as there were fifteen years or so ago.

BIGHORN SHEEP OF THE CANADIAN ROCKIES

The bighorns of western U.S.A. and Canada, with their massive outward-curling horns, are among the most handsome of all wild sheep. Their keen sight and scent warn them of the approach of enemies from far away over the wild Rocky Mountain country.

(*Ourebia ourebi*), live on grassy plains, mainly in East Africa, and have smooth, short coats. Their horns are short and vertical and are ringed at the base. They nearly always go about in pairs.

The grysbok (*Raphicerus melanotis*) is found in South Africa only, and the steinbok (*R. campestris*) from South Africa to Kenya. Like the oribis, they are fawn-coloured, with upright horns slightly smaller than the oribis'. The

The sunis (*Nesotragus moschatus*), of East Africa, are pretty little forest-dwelling antelopes with neatly ringed 3-in. horns. They are only about a foot high at the shoulder. When disturbed they run off, making a noise like " chock, chock, chock," which can be heard a long way off and warns other animals of danger. Their relative, the Royal antelope, is only 10 in. at the shoulder and is entirely confined to West Africa.

The dik-diks (*Madoqua* and *Rhynchotragus*) are most attractive little animals, found in dry country from the Red Sea to Tanganyika, with a slightly larger species in South-west Africa. They are among the smaller of the antelopes, about the size of hares, with an elongated snout (the so-called "trunk"). They have a big tuft of hair on the forehead, almost hiding the laid-back 2½-in. horns, with which they fight fiercely at times. The horns are ringed for half their length and are only found in the males. Dik-diks are so plentiful in some parts of North-east Africa that fifty to sixty are caught in an afternoon, in nets by driving. About 3,000 ft. is their altitude limit.

Related to the dik-diks is the beira, a beautiful little slenderly built antelope, standing about 23 in. and living on rocky hillsides in Somaliland, from the Maritime Range behind Berbera to at least two hundred miles south, in the Bur Dab Range. They are most graceful, with large leaf-like ears, and the buck has thin upright horns with a slight forward bend, up to 5 in. long. They are found in parties of two to four, and on being alarmed will jump on top of rocks to look around for the danger.

WATERBUCKS

The reedbucks and their relatives form a very different group of larger animals. The waterbucks, the first of them, are 4 to 4½ ft. at the shoulder, with sturdy lyre-shaped horns, much ringed and up to 40 in. long in Western Uganda, though 30 in. is a big head in other parts of Africa. They have a coarse dark-brown coat with a splash of white on the throat and a tinge of rufous where it joins the white of the belly. Some of the Uganda ones are rufous all over.

In the true waterbuck (*Kobus ellip-siprymnus*), the common species of the East African coast and three hundred miles inland, there is an oval white ring on the buttocks, which in the Defassa (*K. defassa*) is a big white patch with diffused edges. These two cross at times, and in the Nairobi National Park they have done so and the offspring are midway in appearance between them.

LYRE-SHAPED HORNS

Lechwes are smaller than waterbuck. They have long, lyrate horns of over 30 in., heavily ringed. They are swamp-dwellers, ranging from the Sudan to the Zambezi and congregating at times in large herds, the handsome bucks being either red or black. Unlike the waterbucks, which may be found up to 10,000 ft. on the East African hills, they prefer flat ground.

The kobs (*Kobus kob*) are again rather smaller than the lechwes, with shorter and more sturdy horns curved in much the same way, and are found in Equatorial Africa and Rhodesia. The Uganda kob, of the eastern Belgian Congo to Lake Victoria, is the best known.

Reedbucks (*Redunca*) are usually found in the neighbourhood of big rivers and lakes, and are of varying size and appearance. They range from 37 in. at the shoulder, in the bohor of the Nile, to 27 in. in the little Chanler's reedbuck of East Africa, and the Mountain reedbuck of the East African hills, which delights in grassy hillsides at an altitude of 5,000 to 8,000 ft. The normal colour is yellow. All reedbucks have a shrill whistling snort as their alarm note.

The strange dibatag, or Clarke's gazelle (*Ammodorcas clarkei*), of Central Somaliland deserts, stands 33 in. at the shoulder and has extraordinarily long

A HERD OF SABLE ANTELOPE GATHERS

This party of male and female Sable antelope, with a few young ones, was photographed as they came to a water-hole to drink. Behind them, awaiting their turn, were several other animals not fully shown in the picture, including a zebra. The home of the Sable antelope extends from the Transvaal, where this scene was photographed, northwards

ROUND A WATER-HOLE TO DRINK

to Kenya and Tanganyika. This fine animal is chiefly black, with underparts and face-
markings of white. The strong yet slender horns curve backwards like sword-blades
and can be as dangerous, for, when wounded or at bay, the Sable antelope will turn
boldly upon large carnivorous animals. The horns may attain a length of over 4 feet.

and slender neck and legs, with horns of 10–12 in. curving forward above a chestnut face. The colour is warm grey, matching the twisted stems of the bushes on whose bark these animals mainly feed. They are quite independent of water, chewing thick-leaved succulents to obtain the necessary moisture. The long black-tipped tail is raised above the back when they flee, tail and neck bobbing backwards and forwards, like scissors opening and shutting.

The beautiful chestnut-red impala (*Aepyceros melampus*) lives usually in herds of up to twenty-five, with a herd buck in charge. Sometimes the herd buck's supremacy is challenged and a fight takes place, with much hoarse grunting and head-on pushing, while the does stand round unmoved. The older bucks with the longer horns, to 30 in., rarely win these battles, and the herd is nearly always under a male in his young prime, but with horns four or five inches less in length.

In very fine specimens the horns may run to 33 in., which is also the body height. Their elegant bright-red forms are best shown off when they display their wonderful jumping powers. They are found from northern Kenya south to the Transvaal.

NASAL AIR-FILTERS

The ugly saiga and quaint chiru, or Tibetan antelope, both have swollen muzzles with numerous small nasal channels through which the bitter cold air of Central Asian winters is filtered and warmed before reaching the lungs.

The saiga (*Saiga tatarica*), of southern Russia to Turkestan, is almost sheeplike in appearance in its winter coat, being, in spite of its 28 in., rather short-legged. Both it and the chiru (*Pantholops hodgsoni*), of the Tibetan plain, acquire what looks at first to be a dense eiderdown, smooth on the outside but composed of intertwined fine hair which is the best of protections against intense cold. This coat is gradually pushed off in summer by the new growth coming up underneath. Both coats are pale buff in colour.

GAZELLE-LIKE HORNS

The horns of the saiga are only 14 in. long, of pale amber colour and gazelle-like in bend and ridging. They do not compare with the upright ones of the chiru. These last may stand 25 in. above the head, and are ridged on the front. They often reveal the presence of their owner when he has scraped himself a trough in the ground in which to lie and shelter from the bitter winds. Gravelly plains at an altitude of 16,000 ft. are their usual haunts; though they may ascend the hills to 18,000 ft.

The Indian blackbuck (*Antilope cervicapra*), if it had not been common, would have been one of the most treasured trophies of the big-game hunter; for its ringed and spiral horns run to 30 in., and the glossy black of the upper two-thirds of an old buck's coat contrasts sharply with the pure white of the underparts. The young bucks and the does are fawn-coloured, and in the hot weather the old buck fades to dull buff. Some bucks never acquire the full black-and-white coat. The does are 4 in. less in height than the bucks.

The gazelles are a group of antelopes very uniform in build and colour, spread widely over Asia and Africa, from Mongolia to southern India and the Atlas to the Cape, mainly where there are broken stony and gravelly plains. They are all buff, reddish buff or fawn on the upper parts, usually with a dark lateral line between the fawn and the white underparts. Many of them have a white patch on the buttocks and a dark streak down the nose. The females of some species have horns, always thinner and shorter than those of the males.

The goa, or Tibetan gazelle (*Gazella picticaudata*), is remarkable for the great altitude at which it lives, over 15,000 ft. throughout the year. Goas are slender little animals, with rather long, coarse coats developing a *pushm* or undercoat in winter. Their horns, up to 15 in. long, are curved sharply backward and closely ringed. They are, like most of their group, about 25 in. in height. They have wonderful eyesight, which contrasts with their poor scenting powers. Wolves are their chief enemies, and they suffer much from them if there is a heavy fall of snow.

The chinkara, or Indian gazelle (*G. bennetti*), is found everywhere up to 4,000 ft. where there is scrub and plain broken by ravines, and in the deserts of the western Punjab to Kutch. Its horns run to over 15 in. and it is much hunted with dogs in northern India, greyhounds or salukis being used. On the plains of the Peshawar Valley it is hawked with golden eagles, which slow down and confuse the gazelle by gripping its nape until dogs and horsemen arrive.

The Arabian gazelles are very like the Indian in appearance and habits, even being found on some of the Red Sea islands where there is no surface water. Several other species are found in North-east Africa, including the curious Speke's gazelle, of Somaliland, which has a skin pouch on its nose inflatable to the size of half a tennis ball in moments of excitement. Others are found in the Sahara.

Western Egypt, Tunisia and Algeria

WHITE-BEARDED GNUS IN KENYA

Distinctive among the larger antelopes are the gnus, or wildebeests, of East Africa, with their somewhat horse-like build, mournful, elongated faces, savage temper and grotesque antics when excited. Their necks and throats bear long, thick hair.

KIRK'S DIK-DIK—ONE OF THE SMALLEST ANTELOPES

The dik-diks, which are among the smallest antelopes—some of them being no larger than a hare—inhabit dry country, from the Red Sea to Tanganyika. The diminutive horns are concealed by a tuft of hair, while a curiously lengthened snout further distinguishes this dainty animal from other diminutive antelopes.

hold the slender-horned rhim or Loder's gazelle, and still farther west and south comes the Red-fronted gazelle, passing into the Mongalla gazelle and Thomson's gazelle (*G. thomsoni*), which is found all over East Africa; very plentiful in many parts of the country, it bears a strong resemblance to the chinkara of India.

Grant's gazelle (*G. granti*), of the southern Sudan and East Africa, is the finest of the tribe, in colour, shape and horn measurement. It stands 34 in. at the shoulder, is the usual gazelle buff, and has horns which sweep up and back in a graceful curve to as much as 30 in. in length.

The aoul, or Soemmering's gazelle (*G. soemmeringi*), is very like Grant's in body-size and colour, but with the points of the horns turned inward almost at right-angles to the beam. These horn points may actually cross in specimens of the aoul from the Maritime Plain fifty miles east of Berbera.

The largest of the gazelles is the addra of North Africa, from North Nigeria to the Sudan, but its horns are only up to 15 in. long, the tips curving sharply forward.

The springboks (*Antidorcas marsupialis*) were once found in immense numbers on the plains of South Africa, and are still fairly common in parts of the Union and in Angola. They are allied to the gazelles, having the same body-colour, but with the face all white; while their great peculiarity is a fold of skin on the back which can be turned inside out in moments of excitement, so that its lining of white hairs stands up like a white brush.

The gerenuk, Waller's gazelle (*Lithocranius walleri*), is unique in appearance and habits. It has long legs and long neck, and is often known as the giraffe gazelle. It stands 3 ft. or so at the shoulder and lives largely in waterless country, chewing succulents and small wild gourds for needed moisture. Its length of limb and neck enables it to reach fresh leaves on the tops of acacia bushes. Half a dozen gerenuk standing on their hind legs round a flat-topped acacia are a quaint sight. They are very wary animals, and when running away in bush they lower their bodies by sprawling their legs.

SABLE ANTELOPE

After the gazelles come a great variety of large antelopes, with horns present in both sexes. The Sable antelope (*Hippotragus niger*), with its long annulated horns curving back over a black-crested neck and jet-black body, is thought by many to be the handsomest. It has a white belly and its face is streaked with white. The adult sexes are alike, but the young are reddish. It is found from the Transvaal northward to Tanganyika and the coastal hills of Kenya, and is famed for its courage when attacked by carnivora. It is extremely dangerous when wounded. In the northern parts of its range the sweeping horns are rarely more than 40 in. long, but in Rhodesia may be a foot longer.

The spear-like horns of the oryx group, which make even a lion think twice before attacking, are carried by both sexes, and those of the cow may be longer than the bull's, though not so stout. The horns are annulated at the bottom, up to nearly halfway in bulls, but only for a few inches as a rule in cows. Oryx are very pugnacious, only the abnormally thick skin of the

shoulders saving them from serious injury. This skin was much prized by Somalis and Arabs for making shields. The horns reach their greatest length in the gemsbok (*Oryx gazella*), which is also the largest of the group, up to 4 ft. at the shoulder. The horns curve slightly backwards from the plane of the face and may be 4 ft. long. Like all the group, they prefer desert country, the Kalahari and the barren parts of Portuguese West Africa being their home. The beisa (*O. beisa*) of Northeast Africa is slightly smaller, but has the same type of markings and coloration. In both it and the gemsbok the body colour is warm rufous-grey, and the face is marked with black bands on the cheeks and a long black spot on the nose. There are black bands on the fore-legs above the knees, in line with the black flank band and patch on the lower thighs.

The Arabian oryx (*O. leucoryx*) is the smallest of the group—only 30 in. at the shoulder—and is dingy white in colour with black spots on face and cheeks. The horns may reach 27 in., but this very rare animal is hardly known to Europeans.

THE SABRE ORYX

The White or Sabre oryx (*O. algazel*) gets its second name from the strong backward curve of the scimitar-like horns. A little smaller than the beisa, its whitish colouring contrasts handsomely with the suffused chestnut markings of the chest, neck, face and flanks. It ranges from Nigeria eastward to the Sudan, where it has lately been much shot down by Arabs, even though it is usually found in waterless desert.

With the Sabre is associated the addax (*Addax nasomaculatus*), which has a smaller range over the more desert areas. The addax might almost be termed an oryx with spiral horns, ringed nearly to the tips. It stands 42 in. at the shoulder, and has coarse brown hair on the neck, shoulders and forehead, the rest of the body being grey. The hoofs are splayed out and very wide, enabling it to travel easily over loose sand.

The four-horned antelopes or chousingha of India, in general appearance, and especially when on the move, could easily be mistaken for chinkara or Indian gazelles, but they have no black on the face. They are 25 in. high and have two pairs of upright horns, the rear pair 4 in. long and the front pair 2 in. The front horns, which are often mere knobs just above the eyes, may be missing entirely in specimens from southern India. Chousingha are found on low rocky hills and outcrops anywhere in Peninsular India, are solitary or in pairs, and drink in the hottest hours of the day. They are very fond of wild figs and may often be found under a gula tree, devouring the fallen fruit in the early hot weather.

THE BLUE BULL

They are classed as relatives of the much bigger nilgai or Blue bull (*Boselaphus tragocamelus*), which is also a relative of the African tragelaphines. A big, clumsy beast, 55–56 in. high, the male is dark blue-grey and the cows brown. The horns, in the male only, are quite small—up to 9 in. long—with a half-twist and a slight frontal keel. Blue being the sacred colour of the Hindus, the nilgai is classed as sacred by them.

The finest and most interesting of the antelopes are the tragelaphine antelopes, mainly with spirally twisted horns. The bushbucks or harnessed antelopes (*Tragelaphus scriptus*) show great difference of colour between the sexes. The

males become mahogany-colour to black as they grow old, with rufous on the limbs and a variable amount of white in splashes and spots on the body; the females are always rufous, as are immature bucks. The males range from 30 to 36 in. at the shoulder, the females a little less.

The horns grow to 21 in., but 16 in. is a good average. They are found all over Africa south of the Sahara, wherever the country is sufficiently wooded and water is available, while they go as high as 11,000 ft. on the mountains of Kenya.

ROSE-EATERS

Although they are very retiring, they at times do much damage to crops and even flower gardens, roses being specially attractive to them. They are rarely seen in the open, though they will feed outside patches of bush in the early morning and about sunset, when they may be stalked. When wounded, they are dangerous to both men and dogs.

The nyala and Mountain nyala are closely allied to the bushbucks, but are much bigger. The Mountain nyala (*Tragelaphus buxtoni*) is nearly 5 ft. at the shoulder and lives in the mountains of southern Abyssinia. Its horns may be over 40 in. long, and have one complete turn of a deep spiral with the tips pointing outward. It has a coarse dark-brown coat, a white face-chevron and two white gorget patches, and may have other white body markings.

Its relative, the nyala (*T. angasi*), is a native of south-eastern Africa, but is now practically confined to a Zululand game reserve. It has a coarse, slaty coat and stands a foot less than the Mountain nyala: its horns, moreover, have not such a deep spiral as those of the mountain species. The females are chestnut-red with white stripes. They live mostly in bush, whereas the Mountain nyala is found on open heathery moors.

The horns of the situtunga (*Limnotragus spekei*) run to 36 in. and strongly resemble those of the nyala. The habits of the two animals are, however, very different. Situtunga live at all times in swamps or very close to water, in which they sink themselves to the eyes for concealment, and their hoofs are elongated and much splayed to support them on the spongy soil and weeds of their haunts. They are greyish-brown and 4 ft. high, the females rufous and smaller. The islands of Lake Victoria are one of their chief strongholds. They are almost always shot swimming, after being driven from cover across open channels, for hunting them on

foot in reeds and mud is most exhausting, with little chance of success and much of meeting crocodiles or hippopotamuses.

They are found in any wide expanse of reeds from the Sudan to the Zambezi, and may exist in a swamp for years without being discovered, so retiring are they. Most of the Uganda swamps hold situtunga, and they are also found in a few places in West Africa.

The Greater kudu (*Strepsiceros strepsiceros*) is one of the finest of antelopes, with long spiral horns, up to 70 in., handsome coat of white stripes on warm grey and a proud carriage.

Its range extends from Lake Chad to Eritrea and southward to the Cape.

RIVAL WATERBUCKS FIGHTING FOR A MATE

These two male waterbucks of Rhodesia are about to fight for possession of the hornless female seen standing apart on the right. The white ring on the haunches is characteristic of these animals. Wildebeests and zebras are also seen in this picture.

THE GRACEFUL IMPALA OF EAST AFRICA

The impala, which ranges from Kenya to the Transvaal, is notable for its splendid chestnut-red coat and elegant lyre-shaped horns, nearly a yard in length. These antelopes form small herds of twenty or more, with a young adult male in charge.

Kudu are lovers of bush and, in the northern part of their habitat, of steep, rocky hills. Striking features of both sexes are the large and thick throat-fringe. An old bull measures about 60 in. at the shoulder; cows are about 4 in. shorter.

The Lesser kudu (*S. imberbis*), about 41 in. high, is more restricted in its range than its larger relative. It is found from the Sudan to Tanganyika, always on flat ground. It sticks to bush, and, when suddenly encountered, will make amazing leaps over big clumps of bush. It has been known to clear clumps 35 ft. across and 6 ft. high, and although it cannot know where it is going to land, it always seems to come out safely on the other side.

The bongo (*Boöcercus eurycerus*), a large and magnificent bushbuck found in Equatorial Africa, lives on low ground in rain-forest in the western part of its range, but in East Africa rarely comes below 8,000 ft. The old males, standing 4 ft. at the shoulder and massively built, are a deep mahogany colour with white vertical stripes on their sides, a white face-chevron and a gorget patch. The females and young males are bright chestnut-red, with the same white markings.

The smooth horns of the old bull make one spiral turn with wide divergence, are thick all the way up and tipped for 3 in. with white, like ivory. Those of the females are thinner, narrower and measure little over 30 in., whereas the record for the old bull is over 40 in. Such trophies are rare in collections, for bongos live in remote and difficult country for sportsmen.

The remaining antelopes, and the largest of them all, consist of the elands—the Common eland (*Taurotragus oryx*) and Lord Derby's eland (*T. derbianus*). The former, once plentiful in South Africa, has been almost exterminated for its meat and hide. It is tawny, with thin vertical white flank-stripes and sometimes a white chevron on the forehead, a thick tuft of black or brown hair on the forehead and dark-brown or chestnut cheeks. The tail is long and tufted, and the bulls have a large dewlap.

A big bull will stand 70 in. at the shoulder and weigh as much as 1,200 lb., but in spite of their great size elands are very active and can make amazing jumps over bushes and across wide, deep gullies. Their horns are the same shape in both sexes, with two turns of a shallow spiral in a maximum length of 37 in. They are still plentiful in Tanganyika and southern Kenya and also in the Kalahari. In East Africa they may still be seen in herds of up to a hundred strong.

Lord Derby's eland is the same size in body, but has much larger horns, with a wider divergence and a straighter spiral, running to over 40 in. in bulls. It is distinguished from the Common eland by a more rufous coat and a dark-brown face. Further, the dewlap of the bulls begins at the chin instead of on the throat. There is a dark collar, white-edged below, and in many old bulls the neck is covered with long

THE HANDSOME INDIAN BLACKBUCK

Formerly widespread and plentiful in India, the blackbuck has been so severely hunted that it is now practically restricted to the deserts of the western Punjab and Rajputana, where it is protected by law. With its magnificent head and splendid coat—glossy black above, pure white below—it is one of the handsomest of Indian animals.

black hairs and the ears are considerably larger than in the Common eland. Strictly preserved in the Sudan, Lord Derby's eland shows no signs of diminishing in numbers.

The Giraffidae include two species of giraffe and the okapi. All have a pair of frontal, skin-covered horns, but those of the okapi are capped with bone.

The finest and handsomest giraffe is the Somali or Reticulated (*Giraffa reticulata*), so named because of the sharply defined network of white stripes on a rich rufous or liver-coloured ground. Old bulls are magnificent animals, sometimes reaching 19 ft. in height. The species is found only in North Kenya and South Somaliland. They are low-country animals, seldom going above 3,500 ft., whereas the Common giraffe (*G. camelopardalis*) is found up to 7,000 ft. on the high plateaux of East Africa. The Common giraffe has a dull light-yellow ground-colour on which are dark-rufous blotches of irregular shape and distribution. The species is found in open bush country from the Sudan to the Cape, and is, on an average, about a foot smaller than the Reticulated giraffe.

Both species feed mainly on table-topped acacias, bending their long necks over gracefully to get at fresh growth. They may be found in herds up to fifty strong in Kenya, though smaller herds of five to a dozen are more common. Where they are not shot they become very tame; near Isiolo, in the Northern Frontier district of Kenya, they frequently obstruct the roads, gazing superciliously at a car while standing in the middle of the highway, or even endangering their safety by playing "last across." In wilder country, however, they are very wary, for at one time they were much shot for their meat and hides.

Their great height enables them to see over bush and spot a hunter from afar; then they sway away and break

THOMSON'S GAZELLE ON ATHI PLAINS, KENYA

The beautiful Thomson's gazelle is found all over East Africa. Its parti-coloured coat and the bold, dark bars that mark its flanks make it easily recognizable at a distance.

A PARTY OF MALE GRANT'S GAZELLES IN KENYA

Grant's gazelle, standing nearly 3 ft. high at the shoulder, is one of the largest and most impressive of its tribe. It is one of the most conspicuous animals of the Kenya and Tanganyika plains, frequently associating with the smaller Thomson's gazelle.

into a gallop, both legs of a side working together, and so give warning to every other wild animal within a mile's radius.

They fight by banging their long necks against each other, until one is knocked silly; but their usual defence against other enemies is by kicking, either with a cow-kick from the hind legs, or a stabbing motion of the fore-feet.

The giraffe's sole enemy in the natural state is the lion, which may occasionally kill a young one.

The okapi is a much smaller animal than the giraffe; it measures up to 5½ ft. at the shoulder, and has a proportionately shorter neck and legs. It is a curiously ungainly creature, living in dense rain-forest in the eastern half of the Congo. Its body is a purplish brown merging into a warm buff on the neck and face. The underparts are white, as are the thighs, which have several transverse black bars.

Okapis live in such dense forest that they are rarely seen, but they are much commoner than used to be thought, as is proved by the ease with which Africans of the local tribes (such as the Ituri) kill them with bows and arrows for the meat and hide.

They do surprisingly well in captivity, even in England, where the climate would seem to be all against their survival.

The pronghorn (*Antilocapra americana*) resembles an antelope in general build and habits, but is placed in a separate family, the Antilocapridae. Its horns are forked halfway up and the outer sheath is shed annually, the new sheath growing on the horn-core beneath and pushing off the old growth. The horns may be up to 15 in. long. The buck stands 36 in. at the shoulders, and is chestnut-coloured, with a white rump patch.

Pronghorns, which are found from south-western Canada right down to western Mexico, were at one time threatened with extinction. Upon being strictly preserved, they recovered rapidly, and by 1947 there were 181,000 of them in the U.S.A.

Deer (Cervidae) are remarkable in

that many of them produce and shed annually very large antlers, with numerous points or "tines," the growth of which must absorb much of the stag's energy and, consequently, demand a large quantity of nourishing food. Only the stags have them, except in the closely allied reindeer and caribou. These antlers rise from bony pedicles on the skull, just behind the eyes.

Each year, about a month after shedding the antlers of the previous year, bony knobs, covered with soft hairy skin called "velvet," form on top of the pedicles and steadily increase in size to their normal length. The "velvet" continues to cover and protect the antlers, which it also nourishes through minute blood-cells, until full length is reached. The velvet then dries on the horn, becomes brittle and is scraped off against bushes and trees.

THE MUSK DEER

The chief exception to this antler-production is seen in the Musk deer (*Moschus moschiferus*), which is distributed over the mountains of Asia from the Himalayas to China and Mongolia. The buck of this species has long canine teeth in the upper jaw, and he uses them very effectively when fighting. Musk deer are 22 in. high, have a bristly, pithy grey coat, which turns golden-brown in summer, and live much in snow from 7,000 to 12,000 ft. Their feet are loosely splayed out, forming a sort of snowshoe which carries them easily over loose, soft snow in which their pursuers, wolves or

BULL NYALA WITH FEMALES
The male and female of the nyala, a large antelope of South-east Africa, are markedly different; the females bear conspicuous white stripes and lack the superb lyrate horns of the mature bull.

leopards, flounder hopelessly. They are much hunted by man for their abdominal gland, the contents of which form the basis for many oriental scents. Their hindquarters are considerably higher than their shoulders so that, when fleeing downhill on steep ground, they zigzag from side to side with tremendous thrusts of their hind legs, which take them round corners and out of sight with great speed.

The muntjacs, or Rib-faced deer, so called because the long horn pedicles continue down either side of the face to eye-level, also have long canine teeth which can cause much damage to an enemy. They are 22–24 in. high, stockily built and usually bright rufous in colour. Their horns, exclusive of the long, hairy pedicle, may be as much as 9 in. long. In India and eastern Asia muntjacs are known as Barking deer, as

their alarm call is very like the bark of a big dog. There are several species distributed over southern and eastern Asia. There is a black form, *Muntiacus feae*, found in eastern Burma and Siam.

They browse on low bushes and have very long tongues, which they wrap around the end of a twig, denuding it by pulling the leaves into the mouth. It is easy to see where they have fed, as this way of stripping leaves is unique.

Native hunters call them by blowing on the edge of a leaf held between the sides of the thumbs; a squeaky bleat results which is like the doe's call to her mate.

The Fallow deer of Europe have dappled chestnut coats which add beauty to English parks and forests. They were once found over most of southern Europe and part of North

A SOLITARY BEISA ORYX CROSSES THE SCRUB

In the oryx, as in the related gemsbok, the horns are only slightly curved and are very formidable weapons, even to large, fierce animals. The beisa inhabits North-east Africa. Like all the members of the oryx group, it prefers barren, desert country.

A GIANT AMONG ANTELOPES—THE GREATER KUDU

This stately antelope stands 5 ft. at the shoulder, with long corkscrew horns and a heavy fringe along the throat. The old bulls become very wary; when followed, one will sometimes turn a younger bull out of its hiding-place in order to divert pursuit from itself.

Africa, but are now extinct in the latter area, though probably holding their own within a few areas of southern Europe. They were introduced into New Zealand, where they increased so fast that they have had to be kept down by shooting.

The rusine group of southern Asiatic deer includes the sambar, chital, Hog deer, Swamp deer, thamin and Schomburgk's deer. Their horns are all basically of the same pattern, having three main points, the brow tine and the beam forked near the top. This is seen at its simplest in the biggest of them, the sambar, which is 52–54 in.

high, with horns up to 50 in. long, and in the little Hog deer of the swamps, half the sambar's size, with horns up to 25 in.

In the Swamp deer (*C. duvauceli*) the beam forks lower down, and the outer tine throws up three or four points, until a total of five (in addition to the brow tine) is reached.

In Schomburgk's deer of central Siam, believed to be recently extinct, the horns are still more elaborate; the fork occurs low on the beam and as many as twelve points occur on each side.

All these deer have coarse brown

BULL GIRAFFE AT A WATER-HOLE

A well-grown giraffe reaches a height of over 18 ft. and weighs about a ton. Owing to the great length of its neck, it is obliged to straddle its forelegs widely and bend its knees when drinking. It feeds on the high foliage of the acacia tree, which its elongated neck and long, prehensile tongue enable it to reach with ease.

coats, except the chital, which has a smoother chestnut coat, heavily spotted with white, and horns sometimes as long as its height at the shoulder. A herd of chital in a bamboo forest with the sun streaming through on to their spotted coats is one of the most beautiful sights in nature.

Chital and sambar are found together in flat country all over central and southern India, but sambar also go well up into the hills, to 8,000 ft. or more. The breeding or rutting season of the chital occurs in March and April, when the curious braying of the bucks can be heard a long way.

Swamp deer have an erratic distribution. They are found in the swamps of the United Provinces, where they live in grass up to 15 ft. high, and on the same sort of ground in Assam. In central India, however, they are found on dry ground, and the rutting seasons differ in each area of their habitat.

The stags have a loud droning bray which rises and falls like the drone of Scottish bagpipes. They are very pugnacious, often breaking their 40-in. horns in fighting, the click and rattle of their antlers being heard at almost any time of the day or moonlit night, while it is not uncommon to find a 3-in. fragment of antler broken off in the neck or shoulder of a shot stag.

SWAMP DEER AND THAMIN

Swamp deer are mainly hunted from elephants; the curious paddling noises of a herd moving away in front and the lightly swaying surface of the grass guide the hunter to his prey.

Thamin, whose horns make one continuous curve from the tip of the long brow tine, live in swampy country in Assam and Manipur. In this area the ground is spongy, and the feet of the thamin are splayed and pasterns naked.

With Swamp deer, which at first seem to live in similar ground, the feet are normal. The explanation of this difference is that the bottom of the swamp-deer marshes is hard sand, while it is mud within the northern habitat of the thamin. Farther south, in Burma, thamin live on hard ground, and their feet are there quite normal.

SIGHTLESS STAGS

Thamin used to be plentiful, even thirty years ago, but are now rare and have vanished in many districts. They stand about 48 in. (a little bigger than Swamp deer) and have very coarse coats. They are fond of wallowing, and consequently their coats are usually covered with mud. Like Swamp deer they are very pugnacious, and the forward and upward curve of the brow tine frequently causes the loss of an eye and sometimes complete blindness. Totally blind stags seem to get along quite well as long as they keep with a herd, their hearing informing them of the herd's movements; but once they lose the herd they soon fall victims to man or tiger.

The Malayan sambar, which is rather smaller than the Indian species, is found throughout Assam and Burma, Siam, Malaya and in the larger islands of southern Asia as far east as Formosa. Its horns are smaller than those of the Indian species, 35 in. being a good measurement. Sambar are the prey of tigers wherever they are found, yet, even in western Siam, where tigers are very numerous in the hill forests, they maintain their numbers. Like the Indian sambar, they almost invariably have a naked ring round the neck and a sore spot on the throat, caused by a parasite.

The sikas, or Japanese deer, are distributed over most of eastern Asia north of Formosa, but have been killed

A SMALL HERD OF GIRAFFES IN THE

Giraffes prefer open country, where they browse on trees and shrubs. The vertical lines of their great necks and limbs and the characteristic blotched pattern of their coats blend with the broken shadows and make them almost indistinguishable when standing still among the acacia trees which provide their usual food. Owing to their size, vigilance

TRANSVAAL SURPRISED WHILE FEEDING

and great speed (30 or more miles an hour), they have few enemies, apart from man;
their usual manner of self-defence is by delivering tremendous kicks. The giraffe lacks
true vocal cords, but when excited it sometimes makes a curious hissing sound.
Giraffes usually go about in small herds of from half a dozen to as many as fifty.

HIGHLAND RED STAG IN "VELVET"

The lordly Red deer is found in most European countries, as well as in Asia Minor, Persia and the Himalayas. In Britain it is particularly associated with the Scottish Highlands. The branching antlers are renewed annually. During the period of fresh growth they are encased in soft, hairy skin—the "velvet"—which dries and peels away when the new antlers have attained their full size.

148

off in many parts of their country. They are small deer, 33 in. high, with slender four-tined horns. Nowadays they are commoner in the British Isles than in Asia, having been introduced into many deer parks, and having later escaped into isolated woods.

DEER IN BRITAIN

Roe deer (*Capreolus*) are spread over nearly all Europe and northern Asia, wherever there are hills and forest, and, being very retiring in their ways, sometimes continue to exist without the knowledge of their human neighbours. Though at times they do some damage by eating the bark of young trees, they are pleasing additions to the rides of an English wood. The British species is only 26 in. high, with a dark-brown coat, flecked with grey in winter, and a white rump patch. In summer the coat is strongly rufous and the rump patch almost disappears. The Continental European races are a little larger, and the Asiatic larger still (up to 34 in. high, with 17-in. horns).

The largest of all deer, the elk or moose, inhabits a belt of the northern hemisphere, and is to be found in North America, northern Europe, the Altai Mountains and Siberia. They are huge animals, up to 6½ ft. high and 1,600 lb. in weight, clumsy and ungainly in build; yet their mere size makes them impressive, while the queer droop of the muzzle and wide shovel-like horns complete an impression of prehistoric weirdness.

In Scandinavia, where they have been hunted for centuries, dogs held on leash are used to trail them, and have given rise to an established breed of elkhound. In Alaska and Canada the moose is often called with birch-bark horns, which produce an imitation of the challenge of the rutting stags. They live much in marshes and beside water, feeding on lilies, mosses and marsh grasses, and are fine swimmers. Through strict preservation they are still plentiful in Canada, and the U.S.A. census of 1947 assessed their number in the States at nearly 18,000. It is in Alaska that they have been most intensively shot down.

Overlapping the northern half of the moose's habitat are the reindeer of Europe, or caribou of America, in which both sexes have horns, those of the males of great length and complexity, running to 60 in. and forty points. The average height of the stags is 55 in., and the body colour varies from dark cinnamon-brown to coffee and grey.

In Lapland they are used for domestic purposes, mainly transport and meat, but in northern Scandinavia there are still large herds which are truly wild. In northern Canada the big herds migrate in masses and are often wantonly shot down for their meat.

AMERICAN DEER

American deer include the White-tailed deer, the Black-tailed deer, and the Mule deer. The White-tailed, the smallest of these three (it is only 3 ft. at the shoulder), have the widest distribution, being found as far south as Peru. Their name is derived from the white patch on the buttocks and the white tail, which rise and fall conspicuously as they make off, jumping fallen trees as they go. The horns, up to 28 in., curve forward over the face. They are much the most numerous of American big-game animals, over five million being counted in 1947, and more than 116,000 shot in one State—Wisconsin.

Mule deer come next in numbers, with one and a half million. They are more sought after than the White-tailed,

RARE INHABITANT OF THE AFRICAN FOREST

The rare okapi is a smaller relative of the giraffe. It is peculiar in having transverse white stripes across the thighs and haunches. Living in the dense Ituri Forest of the eastern Congo, it was not seen by white men until 1909, although occasional rumours of its existence had reached Europe for some years before.

for they carry bigger antlers and stand 4 in. higher at the shoulder. The antlers subdivide to several points.

Rather smaller than the Mule deer, and under half a million strong, the Black-tailed deer is found in thicker forests and in mountainous country from Alaska to California. These facts make its pursuit an arduous business and, consequently, it is not so easily shot as the other deer. The horns have not so strong a forward curve as in the Mule deer, and are usually of simpler form with fewer tines.

There are several species of little-known deer in South America, of which the largest, about the size of a Scottish Red deer, is the Marsh deer, distributed from Brazil to the Argentine forests.

Rufous in summer and brown in winter, it has horns with several points rising from either side of the fork.

Found in open country over the same area and into Patagonia is the Pampas deer, a small species with three-tined horns similar to but smaller than those of the Indian Hog deer. Only 30 in. at the shoulder, they are dwellers in long grass rather than in forest.

The mountain deer of South America are very small. The Peruvian and Chilian guemals are little over 3 ft. high and have three-tined horns no more than a foot long. Even smaller are the brockets, of which several species are found in the northern half of South America. Only 19 in. high, they almost correspond to the sunis of Africa, their horns being simple spikes under 6 in. long.

The finest deer of all is the magnificent wapiti (*Cervus canadensis*) of North America, which the Americans call the elk. Nearly 5½ ft. at the shoulder, the wapiti carries horns almost as long as its height in very fine specimens, the record being 64½ in. The horns carry a maximum of eight points a side.

In autumn the stags begin to roar, their high " bugling" sending a challenge over long distances; the sound is imitated by hunters to draw a stag nearer. The wapiti call differs from that of Red deer by being higher in tone and not so prolonged.

There are still many in Canada and the United States, 194,600 being counted in the 1947 census of the latter country, but the Asiatic races are steadily disappearing under the pressure of the Chinese demand for the horns in velvet, out of which they make medicines, mainly aphrodisiacs. These Asiatic races are found sparsely from the Tien Shan Mountains to Manchuria.

Red deer were once spread over Europe, North Africa, Asia Minor, Persia and the northern Himalayas, and while they seem to have vanished from North Africa they are still, owing to preservation, found in most European countries.

The size of Red deer varies considerably in different countries, from the 46 in. of the typical British Red deer (*Cervus elaphus*) to the 52 in. of the Kashmir species. They also vary in colour, most of them being reddish-

MUNTJAC OF THE LOWER SALWEEN

In the strange muntjac the pedicles of the hook-like horns are prolonged down the face, giving the animal its popular name of " Rib-faced deer." From its alarm call, resembling the bark of a dog, it is also called the " Barking deer." It bears long and formidable canine teeth. When feeding, it strips off leaves with its long, prehensile tongue.

UNDISPUTED LORD OF THE CANADIAN WILD

The elk, or moose, is the largest of all deer, the fully grown animal standing as high as a carthorse. It is entirely confined to a narrow belt of the northern hemisphere, from Alaska eastwards to Siberia. An imitation on a birch-bark trumpet of the moose stag's deep, challenging call is used as a lure by hunting American Indians. The strangely shaped muzzle and mobile lips are adapted for browsing upon foliage.

FALLOW DEER IN AN ENGLISH PARK
*The graceful fallow deer retains throughout its life the spotted coat which charac-
terizes most young deer. Its lofty, spreading antlers are palmated.*

brown in summer, but in winter they may be grey, yellowish-brown or dark liver-colour.

The antlers have five points a side in the adult stag, and in some species and races the number of points may increase to over twenty. When past their prime the whole antler becomes shorter and thinner every year.

Most Red deer are forest animals, though in Scotland they live (probably as the result of deforestation) on open mountains, which still retain the name of deer "forests." In other countries they choose forest, growing to their greatest bodily size and antler-development where mountains and trees are found together.

In summer, when their antlers are in velvet, the stags go up into more open country to avoid injuring them against trees, and in the Himalayas they spend this time on open moors above the tree-line. In September, when the antlers have hardened, they return to rub off the velvet against the birch twigs.

As the main rut begins they come lower, calling as they roam the hills looking for hinds, and challenging other stags to battle for possession of a harem. These battles are fought mainly by pushing and heaving with antlers locked and heads down; as a rule, little damage is done. A stag in his prime has a prolonged call, "Aunghr-r-r-ree-oh," which rings from mountain to mountain across torrent-filled valleys and, on a moonlight night, is answered by other lovelorn stags.

The fawns, which are heavily spotted with white, are born in the late spring, the mother retiring into cover to drop her calf, hiding the infirm youngster for forty-eight hours until it is able to follow her. They have few enemies in Great Britain.

In England Red deer still flourish in the West Country, and Exmoor stags carry the finest wild heads of any British deer. Scotland, however, remains the one country where Red deer seem likely to survive for many years to come.

MOST PRIMITIVE OF THE MONKEYS

Marmosets belong to the Callithricidae *family of South American monkeys. They are about the size of a squirrel, live in trees, and feed mainly on fruit, grubs and insects. They are the only species of Primate in which the male acts as a nursemaid to the young, carrying them about upon its back and only handing them to the mother for feeding.*

Monkeys and
the great Apes

SIMILARITIES in structure and behaviour between man, the apes and monkeys have been recognized for countless generations. When, in 1758, Linnaeus embarked on his classification of the animal kingdom, there was, therefore, no doubt in his mind that monkeys, apes and man formed a group distinct from other mammals. The name he gave to them was Primates, and he placed the order at the head of all others, because it included man himself. In every subsequent revision of Linnaeus's classification, Primates have remained the "supreme" order. Cuvier is quoted as saying that if a horse had had the task of arranging a classification of mammals we would no doubt have found the horses leading the field.

There have been various revisions of the list of common characteristics which relate monkeys, apes and man. They include nails or claws on the fingers and toes; a collar-bone; eye-sockets completely enclosed by bone; three kinds of teeth (incisors, canines and molars); a posterior lobe to the brain; opposable thumbs or big toes; and mammary glands on the chest. When taken singly, none of these characters, or other common ones which have not been mentioned, is restricted to the order Primates. Together they constitute a distinctive pattern of primitive mammalian attributes. The complex of these characteristics is not, moreover, restricted to the monkeys and anthropoids. They are also found in the group of animals called lemurs; in the animal known as the Spectral tarsier, and, according to most recent authorities, the tree-shrews as well. These used to be classified as insectivores, but they are now included with the lemurs and tarsiers.

Until recently it was also customary to subdivide the order of Primates into three sub-orders: Lemuroidea, containing the lemurs of Madagascar and the lorises of Africa and Asia; the Tarsioidea, containing a single species —the Spectral tarsier, which is found in the East Indies and the Philippines; and the Pithecoidea, containing the New World monkeys of South America and the Old World monkeys and apes of Africa and Asia, as well as the family in which man is classified. In the most recent classification, however, the order is subdivided into two main sections: the first, the Prosimii, contains the tree-shrews, lemurs and tarsiers, all of them small mammals and none having any obvious resemblances to man; the second division, the Anthropoidea, includes the Old and New World monkeys, the anthropoid apes, and ourselves. Monkeys differ from apes in a

155

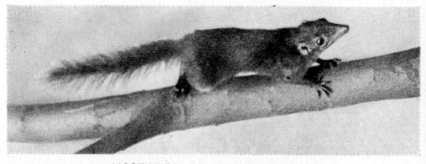

ANCESTOR OF THE PRIMATES

The tree-shrew of South-east Asia is a small arboreal animal not unlike a squirrel in appearance. Probably the earliest Primates were related to animals of this type.

number of characteristics, of which the most obvious is that all but a few species have tails, whereas no apes do. There are only four existing apes: the gorilla, chimpanzee, orang-utan and gibbon, of which the first three are far bigger than any monkey.

The existing tree-shrews are widely distributed in South-east Asia, and are small, tree-living, squirrel-like animals. It is believed that the earliest Primates were related to animals of this type. Their fingers and toes can be effectively used for grasping, but unlike most other Primates, which have flattened nails, they all possess sharp claws.

Tree-shrews feed predominantly on insects, and live in small family parties. They are known to breed for at least eight months of the year. There are indications that in these creatures, as in the rest of the Primates, the sense of vision is becoming more important than in lower mammals, and that of smell correspondingly less so.

True lemurs are now confined to the island of Madagascar, the closely related loris to southern India and Malaya, and the galago to Africa. Some of these are as small as a rat; others as big as a fair-sized dog. Some types live in trees, and others in small troops in rocky country. The lemur's snout is elongated and extends practically in line with the base of the skull, rather than at an angle to it, as in the monkeys. The nose is surrounded by an area of moist, naked skin, which again contrasts with the condition in higher Primates. The face is practically expressionless, owing to its undeveloped musculature, and when petting a lemur it is difficult to know whether the animal is pleased or about to bite. The lower incisor teeth slope forward to form a comb or scraper, which is used, with the help of the single claw on each hind foot, to clean the fur. Sometimes one lemur grooms another's coat in this way.

Lemurs are mixed feeders, and they drink by lapping rather than sucking. The eyes are set on the sides of the head, and there is little overlap of the fields of vision. Most have a breeding season which is restricted to a few months, but the loris breeds throughout the year. One offspring is usually produced at a birth, but twins are not uncommon. The young are usually carried horizontally across the mother's abdomen, sometimes supported by her tail. Little is known about the intelligence of lemurs, but the few tests that have been made do not suggest that it is great.

The Spectral tarsier is the only other modern representative of the Prosimii which we shall consider. It is very important in the story of human evolution, and has been the subject of much learned discussion. The experts regard it as a very primitive and relatively unspecialized Primate, and as a "living fossil" which represents a phase of evolution directly ancestral to the monkeys, apes and man.

The animal is not more than 6 in. in length, and its fur is reddish-brown to grey. Among its more outstanding peculiarities are enormous eyes which are set well to the front of the head. In spite of this, however, the tarsier does not appear to have stereoscopic vision. Its nostrils are ringed by naked skin, but there is no moist glandular muzzle as in the lemurs. The tarsier does show some facial expressions, the most frequent one being to draw up its lips to expose the teeth. In spite of its free upper lip, however, it drinks by lapping rather than by sucking. As far as is known, it feeds predominantly on insects. Both hands and feet have opposable first digits and can be used for grasping, while as an adaptation for hopping the ankles are greatly elongated. The tarsier has true nails rather than claws, and each digit has an expanded disk-like pad on its under-surface. The animal grooms its fur by biting and by scratching with two digits of its hind foot. It breeds continuously throughout the year, and one offspring is produced at a birth, the young being carried clinging to the fur of its mother's belly.

The sub-order Anthropoidea is divided into three "super-families":

LEMUR AND YOUNG

Lemurs have a breeding season which is restricted to a few months of the year. The young are sometimes carried across the mother's abdomen, sometimes on her back.

SPECTRAL TARSIERS

The tarsiers are important in the story of human evolution, being regarded by many
as representing a phase of evolution ancestral to monkeys, apes and man.

the Ceboidea, which comprise the New World monkeys; the Cercopithecoidea, the monkeys of the Old World; and the Hominoidea, the apes and man.

The New World monkeys are restricted to South and Central America, and differ in several characters from those of the Old World. For example, they have three premolar (bi-cuspid) teeth, as opposed to two in the Old World monkeys, apes and man. Their nostrils, instead of pointing forwards, are comma-shaped openings set diagonally on the snout. Some New World monkeys have tails by which they can swing, a feat which no Old World monkey can emulate.

There are two families of South American monkeys, the first of which, the Callithricidae, contains the marmosets, which are either the most primitive or the most degenerate of all the monkeys. The best-known representatives of the second family, the Cebidae, are the Howler monkeys, the Capuchins and the Spider monkeys.

The marmosets range throughout Brazil, Colombia and Bolivia. The animal is about the size of a squirrel. It lives in the trees and is clumsy on the ground. The fur is in general reddish-brown or grey, with patches of white or black in some species. The ears are large and flap-like and on the face are several groups of tactile hairs. The tail is long, but is not prehensile, that is to say, it cannot be used for hanging on or for grasping. All the fingers and toes have hooked claws, except the great toe, which has a true nail, and there are little pads on the palm and on the fingers and toes. Although the big toe is normally held at right-angles to the rest of the foot, its grasping power is weak. The surface of the marmoset's brain is not folded; but, relative to the body weight, it has more brain than almost any other species of sub-human Primate.

The marmoset's food normally consists of fruit, worms and insects, but it will also eat flesh. Its hands are used to grasp food, but strangely enough they are not as a rule used to convey it to the mouth—instead the animal brings its head down to its food.

Marmosets breed at all times of the year, and they often have twins. The young are carried on the father's back, the mother receiving them only for feeding. In no other species of Primate does the male, so far as is known, act as nurse. Marmosets live well in captivity and often make agreeable pets.

The Howler monkey ranges from the forests of Central America to those of Bolivia, and is the largest of the New World Primates, weighing from 16 to 20lb. Its thick-set body is covered with black to reddish-brown fur, and its black face has a longish beard. It owes its name to the hideous noises which it is able to make, because part of its vocal-box or larynx is arranged like a large resonating chamber.

Howlers normally move on all-fours, but as they cannot oppose their thumbs to grasp objects, the thumb and index finger go on one side and the remaining fingers on the other when they walk along branches. The tail is used as an anchor when they rest or sleep, and they can hang by it upside down, helped by

THE INTELLIGENT CAPUCHIN

The capuchin is a small monkey, and is so called because of the resemblance of the hair of its head to a monk's cowl. Despite its small brain, it is very intelligent.

A JUNGLE ACROBAT

The Spider monkey gets its name from the slenderness of its limbs. Its tail is more fully developed as a grasping organ than is that of any other monkey.

their feet, and use their hands to eat.

Their diet consists of a wide range of shoots, leaves, fruits and nuts. They drink by licking water either directly from the foliage or from their fingers. Howlers, unlike most monkeys, are able to swim.

They breed at all times and usually have only one young. At first the infant clings to the fur on its mother's belly, but it soon learns to ride on her back, where it anchors itself by coiling its tail around hers.

Howler communities consist of clans numbering from four to thirty-five individuals of all ages. The average is about twenty. Each group contains more adult females than males. The females are promiscuous, and when in heat may associate with one or more of the males in the clan, for the adult males do not seem to be as aggressively pos-

sessive as are most Old World monkeys.

Each clan seems to keep to its own area of forest, and, when two clans happen to meet, the males engage in vocal "battles," proper fights being rare. Isolated bachelor males sometimes mate with the females of a family party, and sometimes succeed in attaching themselves permanently to a clan.

The Capuchin monkey, so known because of the resemblance of the hair of its head to a cowl, is a small animal weighing between 2 and 4 lb., with a voice as gently cooing as the howler's is loud and raucous. Coat colour varies from species to species, and in some is beautifully variegated. Their natural habitat ranges from the forests of Colombia to those of Panama. Their tails are partly prehensile, and can be used for grasping. Capuchin monkeys make charming pets and they fre-

A "SPIDER" GOES FISHING

Spider monkeys eat fruit, which they can pick whilst hanging upside down by their tails. Nevertheless, they are not averse to a change of diet, as the photograph shows.

quently serve as organ-grinders' monkeys and circus animals. They have even been trained to act as jockeys in dog-races!

Little is known about the social and sexual habits of this monkey in its natural surroundings, but a considerable number of experimental psychological tests have been made on it in the laboratory. It has been found able to distinguish between some colours, but is colour-blind to red. It concentrates very well, and can be taught to distinguish between different weights, and between rectangles of different size, at least as quickly as Old World monkeys. Capuchins quickly learn to use sticks and other objects as tools to obtain food, and in these tests they seem to be every bit as clever as some chimpanzees. This is a remarkable fact, since the brain of a Capuchin does not weigh more than one-sixth of the weight of that of a chimpanzee.

The Spider monkey, which lives in the forests of Brazil and Mexico, derives its name from the slenderness of its limbs. Its most outstanding characteristic is its long tail, which is better developed as a grasping organ than that of any other monkey. By it the animal can hang upside down, with its hands and feet free to pick fruit. In its body proportions and method of locomotion, moreover, the Spider monkey is the nearest approach to an ape in the New World, and it is probably the cause of repeated rumours of the existence of such a beast in South America.

Spider monkeys normally travel along branches on all-fours. They move from branch to branch by swinging with their arms. Their thumbs are almost non-existent, and their hands are, in consequence, of little use as grasping organs.

As with the howler, the social unit of the Spider monkey is the clan. This may contain as many as forty individuals, and adult females outnumber the males. During the daytime the clans break up into smaller groups which normally keep within calling distance of each other, but there is no obvious centralized control, and temporary leadership may fall either on males or females. The adults are sad-looking creatures, but the young are playful.

Spider monkeys have been trained in the laboratory to distinguish between different weights, but they learn less quickly than do some Old World monkeys, and show little aptitude for using objects as tools.

THE CERCOPITHECOIDEA

The Old World monkeys, which form the second super-family of the Anthropoidea, have a wide distribution throughout Africa and South-east Asia. The smallest of them is the Talapoin monkey, which is about as large as a squirrel, and the largest are the baboons, which may be as big as an Alsatian dog. The Cercopithecoidea are subdivided into two sub-families. The first of these, the Cercopithecinae, contains the macaques, baboons, mangabeys and guenons. The second, the Colobinae, includes the Indian langurs, the Proboscis monkey of Borneo and the Colobus monkeys of equatorial Africa.

The nostrils of the Old World monkeys open at the end of the snout, and point forwards rather than sideways. They have the same kind of teeth as we —two incisors, one canine, two premolars and three molars—but, unlike ours, the cusps of their molar teeth are arranged in pairs joined by transverse ridges. All female Old World monkeys have a regularly recurring menstrual cycle. Both the males and females have horny sitting-pads on their buttocks, while many female African and Asiatic monkeys also show either periodic swellings or coloration of the bare skin of the hinder region of their bodies, or both. The maximum swelling coincides approximately with the midpoint of each cycle. Monkeys may mate at all times, but females are more receptive to sexual advances about the middle of their cycles. Normally only one offspring is produced at a birth. From the start the young monkey clings to the fur of its mother's belly.

The Cercopithecinae have cheek-pouches into which food can be stuffed. The Colobinae have no such pouches, but their stomachs are compartmented, the first pocket being supposed to replace the cheek-pouches as a storehouse.

All the Old World monkeys which have been tested have been shown to have colour vision. They are very inquisitive and are always investigating everything in their immediate neighbourhood. They also regularly pick over either their own or a neighbour's fur with their fingers, tongue and lips, in search of loose particles of skin and bits of dirt. The usual belief is that they groom each other in search of vermin, but this is not so, for lice are rarely found in the fur of healthy monkeys. As they pick they usually make a low, not unpleasing chattering noise with their lips and tongue.

SOCIAL BEHAVIOUR

In most Old World monkeys the social unit is a polygamous family, consisting of a male overlord, one or more females and young, and sometimes other attached males. The social behaviour of these animals is usually based on a scale of dominance, the most dominant animals, the overlords, maintaining

BLACK MACAQUES

The macaque group of Old World monkeys comprises a large number of species, ranging from the rhesus monkey to the tailless Barbary "ape." There is a definite scale of dominance among the males, shown in the differing degrees of frequency with which they have sexual contact with the females. Sometimes females subordinate males.

tyrannical control over the rest. In addition, individual and group behaviour is conditioned by the phases of the sexual cycle of the females. A characteristic gesture of all Old World monkeys of both sexes and of all ages and degrees of dominance is to turn their hind-quarters, and sometimes to assume a crouching position, to a fellow animal or to a human observer. This behaviour is called "presenting." It usually indicates submission, and fundamentally has a sexual significance.

Old World monkeys do not seem to be very clear about their social inter-relationships, for these are all governed by the dominance-submission scale. For example, incestuous and homosexual relations are common, although they very clearly do not have the social significance which they do in human society. The animals also do not appreciate the difference between living and dead. Thus macaques and baboons which have given birth to dead babies may carry the corpse about and nurse it for weeks until it is completely decomposed. They may even do the same with a dead rat. This behaviour towards furry objects, which is evidenced from the earliest stages of the monkey's life when it clings to its mother, is a basic social response.

THE MACAQUES

This group of Old World monkeys is widely spread throughout India, Tibet, North China and Japan. In addition, one species, the Barbary "ape"—not a true ape, but one of the few tailless monkeys—is found in Morocco and Algeria, and a few specimens live wild on the Rock of Gibraltar. There is an old saying that when the last monkeys leave the Rock, the British will leave.

The best known of the numerous species and races of the macaque is the rhesus, whose natural habitat extends from northern India into southern China. It is the monkey most usually carried about by the few organ-grinders who still ply their trade. It has also been more extensively used in experimental work than any other monkey, and consequently something is known about almost all aspects of its structure, behaviour and social life. Adults weigh between 10 and 20 lb., and their fur is brown with a tinge of grey. The buttocks are naked and bright-red for some distance around the sitting-pads.

BIRTH AND GROWTH

Macaques can breed at all times, but usually only one young is produced at a birth. In the wild, however, more young are believed to be born in the summer than at other times of the year. Pregnancy lasts about 170 days, which is about 100 days less than in man. The new-born rhesus weighs about 1 lb. and, relative to its adult weight, is therefore heavier than the human infant. The brain-weight of a newly-born macaque is approximately half that of the adult, while in the human infant it is about a quarter. Macaques grow for about seven years, less than half the period of growth in man.

Although the new-born macaque is capable of supporting itself by clinging to its mother, its movements are not co-ordinated. However, it soon begins to explore its mother's fur, and at about the age of a month it begins to leave her body and to move about unaided. About this time the young monkey also begins to take an interest in neighbouring objects and animals. Sexual interests are manifested very early.

Dominance is a marked characteristic of the social relations of the macaque. A dominant animal usually takes all of a

YOUNG RHESUS MONKEY

The best-known member of the macaque group is the rhesus, which is used more exten-
sively for experimental work than any other monkey. Adults have brown fur, tinged
with grey, weigh between 10 and 20 lb., and have bright-red sitting-pads. The rhesus
is familiar to Europeans as the typical "organ-grinder's monkey."

limited supply of food; it does most of the bullying observed in a pair, initiates most fights, and shows a tendency to be groomed rather than to groom. A dominant female may even assume the masculine role in her sexual relations. An animal's degree of dominance does not depend only on its absolute size or fighting ability, but is a complex of the social attitudes which make up personality, the most important of which seem to be aggressiveness and self-confidence. Thus females are sometimes superior to males in the hierarchy of dominance, and a small disadvantage in an animal's body size may easily be offset by unusual aggressiveness. In general, the expression of dominance in macaques, as in most other Old World monkeys, is brutal in the extreme. The subordinate is cowed by the dominant animal and is likely to be set upon by him. Subordinate animals are also in danger of starving if the food supply is limited. But subordinate females in "heat" may obtain some of a limited supply of food from the overlord.

SOCIAL HABITS

Groups of wild macaques have been observed ranging in size from a single pair to a troop of 150 individuals. The most extensive study of their social habits has been made on a colony of 409 macaques which were released on a small island of about 37 acres off Puerto Rico. Many had been tattooed to assist in identification, and after semi-domestication by hand feeding it was possible for a human observer to approach without disturbing their normal behaviour. This colony organized itself into six groups, the smallest of which consisted of three individuals and the largest 147. The average was about 70, and each contained more adult females than males. There is a definite scale of dominance among the males—shown mainly in the degrees of frequency with which they have sexual contacts with females. When in "heat" the females are irritable and restless, and they often solicit the males, with rapid lip and arm movements, and by "presenting." During such an advance the female may be set upon by the male whom she is enticing, but when successful she may wander from the group with her escort, and if he happens to be the dominant overlord the whole group may follow and travel considerably farther than usual. After one male is satiated, the female may in some cases move on to another in her group.

Females in "heat" occasionally make sexual advances towards the males of other groups and are sometimes accepted. A quiescent female attempting to transfer group affiliation in this way would in all probability be attacked by all the monkeys of the clan she attempted to join—and possibly by the males of her own group.

Young males usually leave their parent group when they become independent of their mothers. As a rule they live in bachelor bands. They may join one of the bisexual groups when mature.

Numerous experiments show that macaques can distinguish between different forms and shapes, for example, a triangle and a square; between weights; between sounds of different pitch and quality; between colours; and between degrees of brightness. Their visual acuity, however, seems less than our own. There is no conclusive evidence to show whether the macaques are right- or left-handed, and in spite of much laboratory investigation no definite conclusions have been reached as to whether the macaque is more intelligent or less so than New World monkeys in general and the capuchin in particular.

MEMORY TESTS

Some research-workers have concluded that it is superior in tests which involve memory and discrimination between objects nearly alike, but others claim that the capuchin learns more quickly. Capuchins can learn to use a stick to pull in a piece of food that is out of reach, or to stack one box on top of another to help them get a piece of fruit that is hanging above their heads. Macaques have not shown themselves capable of doing this. They can, however, use objects as simple tools. One investigator describes how a macaque was taught to drive in nails with a hammer, and to saw wood by rubbing it over the teeth of a saw which was held between his feet. He refused to learn the "human" method of sawing. Macaques have also shown some aptitude in solv-

COLOURFUL MANDRILL

A member of the baboon family, the mandrill is remarkable for its bright and conspicuous coloration. Its nose is red, with a scarlet tip, flanked by ridges of slate-blue; its beard is orange-yellow, and its hind-quarters scarlet, with violet sitting-pads.

ing problems requiring a sense of optical continuity. For example, they can pick out, and pull in, that one of several crossed strings to which is tied a piece of food.

A few other species of macaque are worth mention. The first is the Barbary "ape" of Algeria, Morocco, and the Rock of Gibraltar. The upper part of the body of this animal and the outer surfaces of its limbs are yellow-brown in colour, and its tail is rudimentary. The animal was first described by Galen, famous Greek physician of the second century and the "Father of Medicine," and was used by him as a basis for his descriptions of human anatomy. No one knows whether the Gibraltar monkeys are a remnant of a species of macaque which once lived wild in Europe, or whether they were originally imported from across the Straits. Their numbers vary from year to year, and sometimes they become a considerable nuisance and raid gardens and crops. They are then thinned out by shooting. Once the colony was reduced to three individuals, but further animals were imported from Africa. Today it is small, but flourishing.

The Bonnet monkey is a macaque which is closely related to the rhesus. It differs in the radial arrangement of the hair on the crown of its head. The Crab-eating monkey is also similar to the rhesus, but its coat, instead of being brown, is predominantly grey in colour.

CHACMA BABOON OF SOUTH AFRICA

Chacma baboons are about the size of a mastiff. They feed mainly on fruit, and in fruit-growing districts do considerable damage to orchards. At times they have become such a pest that bounties have been offered for destroying them. However, they are still numerous, having, apart from man, few predatory enemies in their present haunts.

The Pigtailed macaque has a small twirly tail, and is probably the most tractable of the Old World monkeys. Some individuals have been trained to collect, under supervision, fruits and botanical specimens. It makes a delightful pet. The Japanese macaque is the model for most common ornaments in which monkeys figure.

THE BABOONS

These are the largest of the Old World monkeys, and are found in many parts of Africa and also in Arabia. All are ground-living animals, and they move on all-fours, the thumbs and big toes being well developed. The baboon carries its tail, which varies in size from species to species, in a curve, the first part going up from the body. Baboons have long snouts, and in the males the upper canine or eye-teeth may reach a length of $1\frac{1}{2}$ or 2 in. Baboons can discriminate between different colours. All have cheek-pouches, and large callous sitting-pads on the haunches. The hinder region in the female forms a "sexual skin," which swells during the middle of each menstrual cycle, and in some species may form an area about 1 ft. in diameter and 4 in. deep.

One type of baboon, the mandrill, is of interest because of its bright and conspicuous coloration. The lips are bright red. The top of the muzzle is red, the tip scarlet, and the ridges flanking it bright blue. The red is due to suffusion with blood. The sitting-pads are violet, and the central area of the hind-quarters scarlet. On the top of the head is a crest of dark, backwardly pointing hair, and an orange-yellow-coloured beard grows on the chin. The tail is reduced to a mere stump.

The Hamadryas baboon is found on both the African and Arabian sides of the Red Sea. It was venerated in Ancient Egypt, being regarded as sacred to and a representation of Thoth, the Lord of Letters. It is a common figure in Ancient Egyptian sculptures and ornaments.

Prenatal life in Hamadryas baboons averages about 170 days—a period similar to that for the Pigtailed macaque—and the baby suckles for about five months. During its early days it nurses and rides clinging to the fur of its mother's belly, but later the infants ride on their mothers' backs. They begin to walk about the sixth month, receiving little or no maternal tuition. The infant soon attains a fair degree of independence, and begins to pay attention to other animals. Sexual activities also begin about this time, and by the time the milk molar teeth are in place many manifestations of adult sexual behaviour are apparent. Immature individuals also engage in a variety of ill-defined play activities amongst themselves, consisting of chasing, tumbling and fighting.

CHACMA BABOONS

The Chacma baboon is found in hilly parts of South Africa, south of the Limpopo. It is just about the size of a mastiff, but is brownish-black in colour. It feeds mainly on fruits, such as the prickly pear, and on roots. It is also reputed to eat scorpions and lizards. Chacmas plunder orchards, and in the sheep districts do considerable damage by breaking down the jackal-proof fences. They are reputed to spread the prickly pear by carrying the seeds in their droppings.

The Chacma has at times become such a pest that bounties have been offered for each one killed. In spite of this, however, their numbers have not appreciably diminished, and they can still be found near Cape Town, even after three hundred years of European settlement. This may be due to the fact that the leopard and other carnivores which are their natural enemies have been practically exterminated in this region. Baboons are not actively hunted in many districts, and every new cultivation offers them a potential feeding-ground. Each female reproduces about once a year, and as far as is known there are no epidemics which reduce the population. Famine and drought probably help to keep the numbers down, and many young and adult individuals are doubtless destroyed in sexual fights.

A rich folk-lore has grown up around Chacma baboons. They are supposed to tear open lambs' stomachs in order to obtain the curdled milk. They are reputed to hurl stones and other missiles at human observers, and when pillaging orchards and plantations they are said to obey the orders of a leader, and post sentinels to give warning of approaching danger. However, such tales have not been confirmed by objective scientific observation of the behaviour of either wild or captive baboons.

THE FAMILY UNIT

Packs of Chacma baboons may number as many as five hundred, but as a rule a troop is made up of less than a hundred, among whom there are many more adult females than males. Each pack consists of one or more polygamous family parties and each usually keeps to its own restricted area. It is not known whether packs ever unite to form bigger hordes, but, when hunted, a pack may split up into its separate family parties.

A wild group of about twenty-five baboons, half of them immature, was once observed consistently for nine days. There were three fully adult males in the troop, the largest of which was accompanied by four females. The

animals spent each night in the neighbourhood of a prominent rocky face, which they left shortly after dawn, to make their way to a small ravine rich in prickly pears some three miles away, where they stayed for a considerable time. The pack later moved on to the crest of a neighbouring hill above the ravine and spent hours rooting about.

DAILY ROUTINE

Their daily routine was remarkably regular, but there were no obvious signs of leadership in the troop. When disturbed, individuals would move off uttering a series of barks, apparently designed to attract the attention of their fellow pack-members. There were no signs of the directional cries so frequently mentioned in the anecdotal literature. No baboons were seen to throw stones or other objects, and, although close to the human observer, they did not attack. It was possible to stumble suddenly upon a pack of baboons after crossing a ridge—an observation which scarcely accords with the tales of sentinels posted to give warnings of approaching danger. Baboons were also seen playing amongst a flock of sheep—again a fact which is scarcely consistent with tales of their tearing open lambs' stomachs to obtain the curdled milk. Stories about human children being abducted and reared by baboons also require corroboration before they can be accepted. They are almost certainly fables.

Wild baboons spend much time grooming their own and each other's fur. Usually the members of the grooming-pairs change frequently, but sometimes two baboons may stay together for an hour or more.

Much has been learned about the social life of the Hamadryas baboon from observations made on a large

WHITE-COLLARED MANGABEY

The mangabeys are a small group of monkeys which inhabit the tropical forest area of Africa. They are about two feet in length, have long tails, and are extremely active, but they are possessed of a gentle disposition and make excellent pets. They spend most of their time in the tree-tops, in large colonies.

SACRED MONKEYS

The Hamadryas baboon is found on both the African and Arabian sides of the Red Sea. It was venerated by the Ancient Egyptians, who regarded it as being sacred to the god Thoth. The animal is easily recognized by its bright-pink face and by the

OF ANCIENT EGYPT

*greyish colour of its fur, which in the male forms a thick cape over its shoulders.
Prolonged observation of colonies of Hamadryas baboons has revealed many details of
their social organization and habits and the activities centring around reproduction.*

colony which lived on Monkey Hill in the London Zoological Gardens. In this colony the supply of mature females was limited, and family parties consisted of a dominant male overlord who acquired as many females as he could hold, consistent with his position in the scale of dominance. The other males were left unmated, but sometimes a bachelor would attach himself to a family group. The groups kept apart except when the colony was fed, but fights broke out which involved most of the colony. These were no doubt intensified by the fact that confinement to a relatively small area prevented dispersal, and by the scarcity of females.

MATING

When moving about, the overlord usually leads his family, but sometimes a female showing full swelling of her sexual skin may, after repeated presentations, induce the overlord to follow her. The chief female in the harem at any time is the one with maximum sexual-skin swelling. She receives most attention from the overlord, and engages more frequently in grooming activities with him than do the other females. Sometimes he may even permit her to share a limited quantity of food, a thing he would be most unlikely to do, unless he were satiated, if she were not in that condition. The overlord usually responds to a female's presentation, but if already satisfied he may attack her. Mating does not usually occur during pregnancy, lactation, or during the phases when the sexual skin is quiescent. Females rarely seek sexual relationships with males other than their overlord, but in his absence they sometimes elope temporarily with the bachelors.

There was fierce competition between males for possession of the available females on Monkey Hill. Fights were frequent. They often began as squabbles over food, or by one animal protecting another which was being attacked by a more dominant individual. Sometimes they started merely as displays of dominance. The fights rarely lasted long, nor did they have any serious consequences, for normally the bachelors accepted the overlord's dominance and made no attempt to abduct his wives. Occasionally, however, the atmosphere changed, and an unmated male attempted to secure a female. The result was invariably a deadly and protracted sexual fight. Sometimes these were ushered in by signs of a decline in the overlord's dominance, as shown by his avoidance of contact with his fellow overlords and the bachelors. The last of these sexual fights seen on Monkey Hill started when a bachelor, who was previously attached to a bigamous family party, seized one of the two females of his overlord. This was the signal for a concerted attack on this family group by all the adult animals in the colony. The prized female was at first covered by the bachelor who had abducted her, but she changed hands several times during the course of the protracted fight. During this period she remained entirely passive, was unable to obtain any food and suffered considerable physical injury. Females over whom such fights raged were almost invariably killed in the general struggle. The males, however, still continued to use the body of a female killed in this fashion as a prized object.

OTHER OLD WORLD MONKEYS

Fewer studies have been made of the intelligence of the baboon than of the macaque and chimpanzee. However, such results as are available show that they are at least as intelligent as the rest of the monkeys of the Old World.

THE SACRED LANGUR

Langurs are found throughout India and Ceylon, and are mainly arboreal. Entellus langurs are held sacred by many sections of the Hindu community, who seldom molest them despite the fact that they are a considerable nuisance.

The guenons or Cercopithequé monkeys are distributed through the forests of most of Africa. They comprise some twenty different types. Few are larger than a fox-terrier, and many have highly-coloured and patterned coats. The smallest member of this group is the Talapoin monkey. It is little bigger than a squirrel. The Cercopitheque monkeys feed on greens and fruit, and live either in small family parties or in larger troops. A colony of Green monkeys was introduced into St. Kitts in the West Indies some three hundred years ago, and is now a considerable nuisance because of the damage it does to plantations.

The mangabeys are a small group of monkeys found in the tropical forest area of Africa. They are long-tailed arboreal monkeys, and their upper eyelids are white. They lack the brilliant coloration of the guenons. Mangabeys are lively and gentle in disposition, and make excellent pets.

Representatives of the second subfamily of Old World monkeys, the Colobinae, are found not only in Africa but also in India and South-east Asia. The genus *Colobus* comprises several species. All are large animals with long tails. Coat colour varies from red to black, and the black varieties have a fringe of white hair on their sides. Their thumbs are vestigial. Little is known about their social life.

The langurs are found throughout India and Ceylon. These monkeys are

SIAMANG GIBBON

The siamang is found in Sumatra. It has black fur and is about twice as heavy as, and somewhat taller than, other species of gibbon. It is also distinguished by a large laryngeal air-sac which is not present in the other gibbons.

mainly arboreal, but move easily and rapidly on the ground. Some types live at high altitudes and apparently do not mind the snow. The body of a big langur may be up to 2 ft. long, and its coat varies from ashy-grey, through red, to dirty yellow in colour. The face and hands are black. Langurs live in polygamous family parties, which may temporarily herd together to form larger bands. The Entellus langur is held sacred by many sections of the Hindu population, and in some places is not molested even when it proves a considerable nuisance—for example, when it pilfers food from stores.

The Proboscis monkey of Borneo is a large animal measuring about 2 ft. 6 in. from crown to rump. It is remarkable for its nose, which is large and distensible and which in males reaches below the chin. In young individuals it is short and upturned, but it grows quickly as the animals age.

The third super-family into which the Anthropoidea are subdivided is the Hominoidea. It is in turn split into two families: the Pongidae or anthropoid apes, which include the gibbon, the orang-utan, the chimpanzee and gorilla, the last three being known as the great apes; and the Hominidae, in which are placed all types of living and fossil men.

Gibbons, smallest of the apes, are found in South-east Asia, where they range from the forests of Assam into those of Burma, Siam, Indo-China, and the Malay Peninsula. They are also found in the East Indies. Within these regions gibbons are found anywhere between the sea-level and 7,000 ft., but they are restricted to forests containing certain food trees. Their skin is black, and they have the densest fur of all the Old World Primates. Hair colour varies from black to brown, through grey to white, and many species are parti-coloured. The Siamang gibbon, which is found in Sumatra, has black fur. Adults of the main genus *Hylobates* seldom weigh more than a stone, or stand more than 3 ft. high. The Siamang gibbon is, however, about twice as heavy and somewhat taller, and has a large laryngeal air-sac which is not found in other species of gibbon.

Relative to the size of the body, the hind limbs of gibbons are longer than in any Primate other than man, and the fore limbs are longer than in all. Unlike all other Primates, including ourselves, the further half of the metacarpal bone of the thumb is not embedded in the palm, and forms part of the free, and as a result relatively long, thumb.

METHOD OF PROGRESSION

The gibbon's fingers and toes are adapted for moving through the trees, but not for grasping objects. It usually moves by swinging by means of its arms, and so jumping from branch to branch. A distance of about 10 ft. is covered in one swing, and up to 50 ft. in a jump. The animal lands with perfect co-ordination at the end of a jump, and then continues its course by arm-swinging and more jumping. In this way gibbons can cover half a mile through the trees at a pace equal to that of a man running fast. When on the ground they usually move on all-fours, but for short distances they may walk awkwardly, knees bent and arms out-stretched as balancers. They cannot swim. Gibbons can hang from a branch by either one hand or one foot, and they usually gather food when suspended by one arm. Their diet consists chiefly of wild fruits, leaves, flowers, eggs and insects. They drink by licking water from the fur on the backs of their hands.

Ischial callosities, or sitting-pads, are present in gibbons. The animals do not have a demarcated breeding-season, and normally only one young is pro-duced at a birth. It is nursed and carried on its mother's belly. The infant begins to walk at about six months, and usually receives little maternal tuition. A female gibbon has, however, been seen to bridge a gap between two branches with her body so that an infant can cross. Young gibbons, like most Primates, are very playful.

THE FAMILY GROUP

Male gibbons appear to be more aggressive than females. The social unit of the community is the family party, which, in contrast to other Old World Primates, is apparently monogamous—although supernumerary adult males have occasionally been seen attached to the family units. A scale of dominance runs through all their social relations, although it is not so marked as in the baboon and macaque. Families are apparently restricted to their own region of a forest. They keep to well-used pathways through the trees, and often keep to particular food and sleep-ing trees. Territorial boundaries are, however, not clearly defined, and bor-derland territories may be contested. A group which intrudes on another's territory is usually repelled.

Gibbons are very noisy, and their most characteristic calls are crescendos of rising notes which end suddenly and without warning. Nine different types of call have been recognized, each with

THE ORANG-UTAN

The orang-utan is a member of the ape family that is restricted to the tropical forests of Borneo and Sumatra. Adult males weigh about 170 lb. and stand from 4 to 5 ft. in height; females are about the same height, but are considerably lighter. Orangs are probably as intelligent as chimpanzees and gorillas, but are not so co-operative in tests, so that little is known about their intellectual capacity.

a different social significance. The animals begin to give voice between 5.30 and 7 a.m., and this is usually an indication that the group concerned is likely to move in less than an hour. The first signs of activity are shown by the youngsters, and in this period there is some sporadic gathering of food and sleepy play. Distinctive calls follow for an hour or more, and then the family sets off to find a feeding place, following a leader. Feeding begins at about 8.30 a.m., and continues for two hours or so. As each animal becomes satiated, feeding gradually ceases, and finally the members of the group move off to some protected place where they spend about three hours resting and grooming their fur. Later more feeding occurs, and towards sundown the group moves off to some trees, usually those with dense tops, and settles down for the night.

It is possible that brothers mate with their sisters, but usually the young males are driven from the family group as soon as they approach sexual maturity. It has been suggested that the mating bonds between male and female gibbons gradually become fixed. But this is by no means sure.

There does not seem to be any clear-cut gap between the intelligence of the gibbon and that of the monkeys. Experiment shows that the gibbon can distinguish between objects of different sizes and colour, and that it is capable of solving problems such as the opening of catches in order to obtain food.

THE ORANG-UTAN

The orang-utan is restricted to the forests of Borneo and Sumatra. It is covered with reddish or yellowish-brown long hair, and is much shaggier than either the chimpanzee or gorilla. Its skin is brownish, and darkens with

increasing age. Adult males weigh about 170 lb. and are from 4 to 5 ft. in height. Females average about 85 lb. in weight, but are only slightly shorter than the males. In both sexes the face is unusually flat, pink, or brownish, and devoid of hair, but adult males frequently have a long, red beard.

PHYSICAL CHARACTERISTICS

The adult male is distinguished by a facial "surround" of conspicuous blue-black pads which vary in size, and consist of fatty fibrous tissue. Both sexes have redundant skin like a dewlap around the lower part of the face. Under this dewlap is a large air-sac of unknown function, which opens into the windpipe above the larynx, and which extends over the shoulder-blades and into the armpits. The eyes are brown and set close together, and the animal has the smallest ear, relative to its size, of all the apes. The thumb is very short, but the big toe is long and opposable. In the adult female the nipples are situated high up and to the sides of the chest. The animal's legs are relatively shorter than in the other anthropoid apes, but its arms and feet are longer than in the gorilla and chimpanzee. A few orang-utans have horny sitting-pads on their haunches.

Little is known about the diet of the wild orang-utan, but it is generally assumed to be a fruit- and shoot-eater. Its movements are very slow and deliberate, and it moves in the trees by slowly swinging with its arms, but not by jumping. Sometimes it descends tree trunks in a series of somersaults. On the ground it moves awkwardly on all-fours. Captive specimens, especially young ones, sometimes walk erect. So far as is known, the orang cannot swim.

At night orang-utans build sleeping nests in the trees, sometimes at heights

of 25 to 40 ft. above the ground, and sometimes in the tree-tops themselves. These nests are from 2 to 3 ft. in diameter, and are built of interwoven twigs and branches.

Very little is known about the social life of the wild orang-utan. It is not a gregarious animal, and it is reported that males live alone except during the mating season. It is unlikely, however, that this is true, as the female is capable of breeding at all times. Pregnancy lasts for nine months. The infant nurses and rides clinging to its mother's abdomen. A baby orang-utan which was separated from its mother was first observed to walk at the age of six months. Growth lasts from ten to twelve years. Two or three females with infants and young have sometimes been seen together.

The orang is not a highly vocal animal, but it grunts, chuckles, and sometimes screams. In captivity orangs look very superior and supercilious, and are little moved by the attentions of spectators. Because of this indifference and because of their general appearance they have often been likened to impassive Mongols.

Some mature individuals are gentle and tractable, but others are irritable and dangerous to handle. The young captive orang is quite different, and is usually playful, energetic and restless. They can be readily trained to mimic human activities, although they are not so apt or demonstrative as young chimpanzees. One young orang is said to have been trained to greet its owner

GORILLA FAMILY

The gorilla is the largest of the apes. An adult male may stand as high as 6 ft. and weigh about 600 lb. Although it can stand and walk erect for a few paces, it normally proceeds on all-fours.

as "Papa." There is reason to think that orangs are as well developed from the cerebral point of view as are chimpanzees and gorillas, but as they are not so co-operative in psychological tests in laboratories very little is known about their capacities. They can certainly distinguish the spatial relationships of different things, and are able to use objects as simple tools. They have also stacked boxes in order to climb to obtain a piece of food which was previously out of reach.

THE GORILLA

The gorilla is the biggest of the anthropoid apes. Two types are recognized: a lowland variety which lives in the Cameroons and Gaboon in West Africa, and a mountain gorilla which is found to the west of Lake Kivu and Lake Edward in East Africa. The lowland variety lives in primeval forest with thick and almost impenetrable undergrowth.

The bigger mountain variety lives in volcanic country, some of which is overgrown with primeval forest. The mountain type differs in structural details. Adult males stand from 5 to 6 ft. tall, and weigh up to 600 lb. Their arm-span may be as much as 8 ft. The skin is black, and the hair long, thick and black. Old mountain gorillas have a grey or white area across the back, the chest and face usually being hairless.

The gorilla is supposed to be the animal mentioned in the *Periplus* of Hanno, the Carthaginian navigator who visited tropical West Africa about 350 B.C. The animal was not known definitely until 1847, when an American missionary sent a skull of a gorilla to Professor Wyman, of Boston.

The gorilla is an exceptionally powerful animal. Its skull has promi-

nent crests to which are attached the muscles which balance the head on the spine, and the muscles which operate its massive jaws. Above the eyes is a heavy transverse bar of bone. Its brain-weight seldom exceeds about half the minimum size usually regarded as consistent with rational behaviour in man. The eyes are dark and the ears small. The lips are thin and moulded over the projecting muzzle. The canine teeth are tusk-like. The hand is broad and relatively short, but the thumb is not so atrophied as in the other apes, and can be opposed to the other fingers. The big toe is also opposable. The gorilla walks on all-fours, the soles of the feet and the knuckles of the hands resting on the ground. It can also stand and walk erect for a few paces. Due probably to its size, it is less aboreal than either the chimpanzee or orang-utan. It sleeps in the trees, building crude nests for the night.

THE DOMINANT MALE

The gorilla's life is believed to be ruled by the principle of dominance, and shot wild males often show the scars of fierce fights. Its family unit is polygamous. It is a vegetarian and in the wild feeds largely on berries, leaves and other vegetable matter. Its calls are usually restricted to a series of low-pitched grunts. Like all Old World Primates, gorillas groom their fur.

Only a few laboratory investigations have been made of the intelligence of the gorilla. It can use sticks as simple tools with which to obtain food, but in general seems to be inferior to the chimpanzee in tests requiring mechanical ability—although it seems to have just as good a memory. A gorilla has built a four-box pyramid on which to climb to obtain food. Young gorillas are less destructive than are other young

CHIMPANZEE WITH YOUNG

The chimpanzee is the best known and most widely distributed of the anthropoid apes. Adult males average about 110 lb. in weight and some 5 ft. in height. Females are about 20 lb. lighter and 1 ft. shorter. Youngsters are playful and easily tamed, but become suspicious and untrustworthy as they grow older.

PLAYFUL YOUNG "CHIMPS"

Pregnancy in chimpanzees lasts about eight months, and usually only one young is produced at a birth. The babies, which are lively, playful and intelligent, receive considerable maternal tuition in walking and climbing. The life-span of the chimpanzee in its natural forest environment is thought to be about fifty years.

apes and monkeys, and are not good imitators. Gorillas display a variety of emotions, but are on the whole less demonstrative than the chimpanzees.

THE CHIMPANZEE

This is the best known of the anthropoid apes, and it has been extensively studied in zoological gardens and laboratories in Great Britain and America. Some information has also been obtained about its social life in the wild. It is a native of western and central Equatorial Africa, including the areas drained by the Congo and the Niger, and it ranges northwards as far as Gambia. It thus has a wider distribution than any other living ape. There are two types of chimpanzee, the usual variety seen in Zoological Gardens and a pygmy variety which is found south of the big bend of the Congo. Adult males of the commoner breed average about 110 lb. in weight and some 5 ft. in height. Adult females weigh about 20 lb. less and are about 4 ft. tall. When standing unsupported, the chimpanzee can pull rather more strongly than man. When braced its pull is as much as five times as strong. Skin colour varies from a coffee colour to almost black. The fur is normally black, but patches of brown, reddish-brown, and grey hairs may appear on various parts of the body. The skin of the face is black or puce-coloured, but both hairiness and face colour vary with age and environment. The typical chimpanzee has keen, brown eyes, a small nose without any fleshy tip, a large mouth with protruding and expressive lips, heavy brow ridges and ears of variable size. The head hangs down on the chest, and there are no cheek-pouches. Bony crests of the type which characterize male gorillas and orang-utans are not as a rule present on the skull of the chimpanzee.

The chimpanzee's trunk is long and narrow, and some individuals have horny sitting-pads on their buttocks. When the arms are hanging by the sides the fingers reach as far as, or below, the knees, the arm-span being about one and a half times the height of the animal. The thumb is short, but the big toe is well developed and opposable. Chimpanzees generally move on all-fours on the ground, but they can stand and walk erect for a few paces. In the trees they move by swinging by their arms. They climb down tree-trunks either feet or head first.

The brain of the chimpanzee rarely exceeds about one-third the size of the human brain, but in its essential structure it is humanoid. The animal's life span is unknown, but captive animals have lived up to about thirty years of age, and the potential span is estimated to be fifty years. Wild chimpanzees feed largely on fruit, stalks and leaves. They are wasteful and messy feeders, and drink by sucking water into their mouths rather than by lapping it.

GROWTH OF THE YOUNG

Pregnancy lasts about eight months, and usually only one young is produced at a birth, but twins have been born in captivity. Baby chimpanzees can feed on solid food by the age of six months, but if left with their mother will continue to nurse for two or three years, although in the latter part of this period they are independent of her milk supply. For a time the baby can only cling to its mother's fur and undertake limited excursions over her body, but by about the third month it begins to exercise. It usually receives considerable maternal tuition in walking and climbing. The young chimpanzee has a full set of milk teeth by the fifteenth or sixteenth month, and the full permanent dentition is in place by the eleventh year, by which time the animal is adult. During growth the head becomes relatively smaller and the body more slender. The general pattern of growth of the chimpanzee is roughly similar to that of man, but it unfolds more rapidly.

So far as is known, the normal family group of wild chimpanzees is the polygamous unit, to which more than one adult male may be attached. Family groups, which occasionally intermingle, vary in size from four to fourteen individuals. They move about in random fashion, and do not seem to stay within the limits of a set territory as do gibbons and Howler monkeys. The animals build sleeping-nests by interlacing branches at heights varying from 10 ft. to over 100 ft. above the ground, and as a rule each chimpanzee builds a new nest every night. With the exception of mothers with dependent young, only one animal sleeps in a nest. In the dry season the animals get up before sunrise. Much of the day is spent foraging, but the animals avoid the direct sun and spend the hottest part of the day resting. They make lots of noise in the forest, both by slapping and banging with the hands and feet on hollow logs, and with their loud cries. Like most other Primates, the principle of dominance rules their social lives. The position of a female in the scale of dominance tends to rise during the period when she is in "heat."

EMOTIONAL REACTIONS

Chimpanzees display a variety of emotional reactions. Youngsters are restless, playful and generally good-natured, and can easily be trained to clown such human activities as eating at table or riding a bicycle. They make excellent circus animals. As adolescence approaches they become more serious and morose, and the adult is usually suspicious and untrustworthy as a pet.

Chimpanzees have stereoscopic vision and thus appreciate their world in three dimensions. They distinguish between different sizes, geometrical shapes, colours and weights. Of thirty chimpanzees which were tested, about twenty-five had a marked preference to use one hand, but left- and right-handedness was about equally distributed among the animals studied.

INTELLIGENCE TESTS

Many tests of the chimpanzee's intelligence have been made in the laboratory. The animals can use objects as simple tools, and without initial training have stacked boxes and climbed on to them in order to obtain food which was previously out of reach. Pairs of chimpanzees have been trained to co-operate in solving some problems. They have been trained to work for poker chips as a reward, and after amassing a number to use them to get pieces of fruit out of a slot machine. Although they have no language, it would seem therefore that they can symbolize to some extent, for the chips in these experiments correspond to money in our lives.

In many experiments chimpanzees have been seen to arrive at the correct solution smoothly and rapidly without recourse to the more usual method of "trial and error" learning. Such behaviour has also been shown by a variety of other animals, including monkeys, and the supposed mental superiority of the chimpanzee over the monkeys is by no means established. Nevertheless, it is probable that the cerebral cortex is more important in the chimpanzee than it is in the lower Primates, and as the animal is more ready to concentrate on experimental problems it is easier to teach.

Land animals gone back to water

MAMMALS, although many of them are recognized to be fine swimmers, are generally regarded as land animals; nevertheless, they include three groups which live in the water: seals, sea-cows and whales. The last two groups are truly aquatic, but the first group is more properly described as amphibious because, although seals are more active and at home in the water, part of their life is spent on land.

Mammals are warm-blooded, air-breathing creatures, often covered with hair and having two pairs of limbs which support the weight of the body. The young are incubated within the maternal body and at first require considerable parental care, being suckled by the mother for a varying period of time after birth.

These characteristics would seem peculiarly unsuited to any mode of life other than a terrestrial one, but it will be seen that these basic mammalian characters have been preserved and at the same time modified in the aquatic groups, so as to render them perfectly adapted to their environment.

Sea-lions (*Otaria*), fur-seals or sea-bears, walruses (*Odobaenus rosmarus*) and True seals (*Phocidae*) belong to a sub-order of the Carnivora, the Pinnipedia, that is to say, the "fin-footed."

The Pinnipedia form a connecting link between purely terrestrial and purely aquatic forms. Generally marine, they are widely distributed throughout the temperate and colder coastal waters of both hemispheres. Occasionally they swim up the larger rivers and some inhabit the larger inland seas and lakes.

The term "fin-footed" describes the most striking modification in structure which has occurred in this group: both pairs of limbs or flippers are fully webbed and are long and fin-like in shape, the greater part of the limb being encased within the skin of the body. The body itself is streamlined and covered with hair, and has a thick layer of blubber under the skin. The tail is very short and plays no part in locomotion. The teeth have become modified for holding and biting, and the large carnassial teeth so characteristic of many terrestrial carnivores are absent.

It is interesting that the True seals show these modifications to a more marked degree than do the other members of the sub-order. The hind flippers are so closely bound up with the tail that they are useless for locomotion on land, and the ankle joint has developed into almost a ball-and-socket for greater mobility in swimming. When on land True seals shuffle along by contractions of the body muscles and with a sculling movement of the front flippers, the tail and hind flippers raised up out of the way. Sea-lions, fur-seals and walruses, on the other hand, can raise themselves on both pairs of limbs, the hind flippers being turned forwards, and can walk or gallop in an ungainly fashion, even at considerable speed for short distances.

In True seals and walruses no external ear-lobes are visible, whereas are similar. All seals swim and dive with the greatest of ease and indulge in astonishing antics in the water, sometimes leaping clear out of the water in pure sport. The grace of these movements is, of course, dependent upon elegance of form, the smaller, more streamlined True seals exhibiting finer, cleaner action than the larger sea-lions and the huge walruses. When swimming slowly only the front flippers are used,

WEDDELL SEAL WITH TWO PUPS

The Weddell seal was at one time very plentiful on the island of South Georgia, in the South Atlantic, where this photograph was taken, but has become much rarer. The pups grow at an astonishing rate, gaining as much as 7 lb. in a single day.

these are visible in sea-lions and fur-seals. The nasal openings in the skull of the True seals are placed dorsally, whereas in walruses, sea-lions and fur-seals they are in the usual position at the end of the snout. All these differences have led naturalists to place the True seals, walruses and fur-seals, together with the sea-lions, in three different families. The habits of these families but when speed is required the hind flippers are also brought into action. Seals are strong and fearless in heavy surf and have been seen to show selective powers in choosing suitable landing-places in rough weather.

Owing to the dorsal position of the nostrils, the True seals do not have to raise the head much above the surface of the water when they need to breathe;

the other members of the Pinnipedia, however, raise the head well out of the water. Inspiration and expiration are accompanied by a whistling sound. The nostrils have strong muscles for closing them tightly when the animal is submerged.

HUNTING AT GREAT DEPTHS

The depth to which seals dive and the time of the dive's duration are points on which more information is needed. A northern fur-seal was recently captured with a fishing-net at a depth of 240 ft., and there is also recent evidence to show that fur-seals feed on a deep-water species of fish, thus diving farther down than has been hitherto recognized. An Elephant seal (*Mirounga byronia*) was timed in a dive lasting twelve minutes, but it is probable that longer periods of submergence are general, perhaps as long as eighteen minutes or more.

A seal under observation in an experimental tank was repeatedly seen to breathe out more forcibly than usual on submerging, the dive being thus accomplished with very little air in the lungs. Marked slowing of the heart-beats—to as little as one-fifteenth of the normal rate—has also been found to occur immediately before diving. This results in decreased circulation of blood through the tissues, and consequently the amount of oxygen consumed will be reduced. In a Grey seal (*Halichoerus grypus*) which was kept under observation, this dropped from 20 per cent to 2 per cent during submergence. In the Elephant seal, which has a normal oxygen capacity of 40 per cent, the time of duration of a dive may be twice as long as in the Grey seal. In other words, there is probably a direct relation between the oxygen capacity of the blood and the time of submergence.

This latter is in turn probably governed also by the degree of activity during the dive, for it is then that seals exert themselves most strenuously in swimming and hunting for food, all of which is caught in the water. Another interesting fact which emerged from these experiments is that during a dive the blood-supply to the skin and the underlying layer of blubber is very much reduced. This prevents excessive loss of body heat peripherally and may cause a rise of temperature in the internal organs. When the animal surfaces, the increased circulation distributes the heat uniformly once more.

Although movement on land is an arduous business, all seals frequently haul out on beaches, rocks and ice-floes to rest or bask in the sun. They have been found half a mile inshore, out of sight of the sea, having travelled slowly and laboriously over what must be for them a considerable distance. Nevertheless, they can on occasion move with speed for short periods. A man must run to keep up with an Elephant seal when it gallops.

SORROWFUL EXPRESSION

Seals have large, sensitive eyes over which there is a continuous flow of tears when the animal is on land. As there are no ducts to carry the tears away, large wet patches form below the eyes, giving the seal a sorrowful look which has engendered a feeling of pity in many observers. The tears prevent irritation by dust and heat to the surface of the eyes, and it has been noted that seals have become blind during the exertions of a circus tour.

The other senses are also well developed, the degree of intelligence is high, and on the whole their nature is inoffensive and docile. Young sea-lions are easily trained to do a number of

A YOUNG ELEPHANT SEAL DEFIES THE CAMERA

Sea-elephants, or Elephant seals, are the giants of their tribe, a full-grown male reaching a total length of 22 ft. and a weight of about 2 tons. The females, however, like the one shown above, are much smaller. Their blubber yields a valuable oil.

tricks. Seals are inquisitive animals. I have seen a Grey seal swimming under water off the coast of Lundy Island to surface ten feet or so away from an unsuspecting bather. They allow observers to approach quietly quite close, although a sudden movement or noise will cause them all to make off in panic to the sea. Only during the breeding season do they exhibit much pugnacity or ferocity.

The breeding habits of seals vary considerably and more information is needed on some species. Almost without exception seals are gregarious; they generally band together in small groups, but during the breeding season vast herds may be seen. Thus circumstances allow them to be either promiscuous or polygamous.

As far as is known, fur-seals mate either on the land or on the ice-floes, and this may very well allow considerable freedom in their sexual relationships. During the autumn and winter months the seals remain at sea, and those frequenting polar regions, like the Harp seal (*Phoca groenlandica*) and the Weddell seal (*Leptonychates weddelli*), have a continual struggle to keep open the breathing-holes in the pack-ice. In the spring and early summer they haul out for the breeding season.

The female Leopard seals (*Hydrurga leptonyx*) appear singly on the pack-ice to give birth to the pup, but in other genera the females are more often found in groups, sometimes in large herds, which are later joined by the males. The pup is large and well developed, sometimes nearly half as long as the mother, and covered with a thick woolly coat, which is shed for the first hairy coat during the suckling period before the pup takes to the water.

Suckling lasts from four to six weeks, during which time the pup grows at a great rate. A Weddell seal pup has been found to gain as much as 7 lb. in a day. It is interesting that in some seals milk teeth appear and disappear during foetal life and that shortly after birth the adult teeth are functional, so that at an early age the pup is able to fend for itself.

The Common seal (*Phoca vitulina*), which is found in small colonies around the British coasts, quite often gives birth to its young on a sandbank, which may be covered at the next tide. The pup must, therefore, take to the water within a few hours; and so the woolly coat is shed before birth and the coarse hair coat developed. Lactation in this species is said to last only a few days, but more evidence on this point is needed. The Common seal frequents sandy bays and estuaries. On the other hand, the Grey seal, which is also found around the British coasts, favours rocky coasts, and the pup is often born in a cave above the tide-level, since it is not ready to take to the water as early as the Common seal.

Seal pups are born singly (although there are reports of twins having been seen, these need substantiating); consequently, when the mother is away, there is no other pup to snuggle against for warmth. Seals born on ice-floes have been seen shivering with cold when left alone, because at first they have no thick layer of blubber under the skin for their protection.

Courtship and mating-play have been observed among Harp seals (so called because the adults have a harp-shaped mark on the back). These seals frequent pack-ice in the Arctic seas to breed, and the adults arrive on the floes in

DUEL BETWEEN ELEPHANT SEALS

Bull Elephant seals are extremely pugnacious during the mating season. Their fighting technique consists in rearing up and slashing at one another with their huge canine teeth. Sometimes they seek to pin each other down, while a fearful wound is inflicted.

vast numbers in January. The females retreat far into the pack and there, toward the end of February, the pups are born, covered at first with thick white wool. The males generally remain apart from the females, although sometimes a male is seen in company with a mother and pup; but about two weeks after parturition mating again takes place. The males swim up and down in the open leads between the masses of ice, raising themselves out of the water and diving up and down in a sort of rhythmic dance, and frequently turning somersaults. They may engage in fights for possession of the females, and often get bitten sharply by the females themselves if their approach is not welcome. Mating takes place sometimes in the water and sometimes on the floe.

About April the rest of the herd arrives, yearlings, two-year-olds and the young adults which are just sexually mature. By this time the pups have got their hair coat and are ready to learn to swim. They are pushed into the water by their mothers, who swim with them and help them if need be. In the early weeks of life two serious dangers may threaten the pups. The ice-floes may break up and drift away, so that the mother may not be able to find her pup again, or rough weather may pile the floes on one another, crushing the pups to death.

STRONGLY GUARDED HAREMS

Among the True seals, the Elephant seal was until recently thought to be the only polygamous kind; recent research has shown, however, that the Grey seal is also polygamous.

The female Elephant seals are herded into groups, each group or harem being jealously guarded by a single male. These enormous, ungainly animals are the largest of all the seals. The male,

when fully grown and with hind flippers outstretched, measures 20–22 ft. and weighs about 2 tons. It carries on its snout a curious inflatable proboscis, slightly reminiscent of the trunk of an elephant—hence its name. The females are much smaller and measure only 9–10 ft. Beneath the skin, which is covered with greyish-brown hair, is a very thick layer of blubber, which makes the whole body "tremble like a bag of jelly" when the animal moves on land.

ELEPHANT SEALS

Elephant seals are found in large numbers on the sub-Antarctic islands, South Georgia, Kerguelen, Heard and Macquarie. They remain at sea during the winter months, but in South Georgia, where their breeding habits have been studied, the females come ashore in herds towards the end of August and the pups are born shortly afterwards. There is one pup to a family. About a week later the males or bulls join the females and pairing takes place. The bulls are very pugnacious and continual fighting goes on over the possession of the cows, accompanied by loud bellowings and with inflated proboscis. The bulls rear up on the hinder third of the body and slash each other with their canine teeth. If one bull topples over after an unsuccessful lunge, the other comes down on top of him with all his weight and bites his neck or back, sometimes tearing out a lump of skin or blubber nearly a foot square. This finishes the fight! One bull stands guard over a harem of twelve to twenty cows.

There is a considerable number of bachelors in the herd and they try to poach the females away from the harem, so the old bulls are kept busy fighting these intruders. The females snap and

GREY SEAL OFF SOUTHERN IRELAND

The Grey seal haunts the rocky eastern shores of the North Atlantic, being the largest species (8–10 ft.) commonly found in British waters. The young are often born in caves above tide-level, where they remain until strong enough to go to sea.

quarrel among themselves and roar and rear up if approached too closely or annoyed.

About the end of October the virgin females arrive on the beaches and pair, and then in December the harems break up and all the seals go to sea. They have starved during the breeding season, so now they feed actively and return to the islands again in January or February to change their coats. They go to sea once more in March and April and remain away until August comes round again.

Walruses, which are the sole members of the second family of the Pinnipedia, are exceeded in size only by the Elephant seals. They are gentle creatures, unless attacked, when they will band together and fight fiercely.

Both sexes have an enormous pair of tusks in the upper jaw, which measure up to 20 in. or more and which can inflict fearful wounds. A fully grown male walrus reaches a length of 11 ft. and over; the females are rather smaller. The walrus is believed to be monogamous. The young are born in late spring or early summer and occasionally two occur in a family. They are found only in the coastal waters of the Arctic regions, on beaches and ice-floes, moving slowly from one feeding-ground to another in small colonies, but showing no regular migration.

There remains the family which includes the sea-lions and fur-seals. These animals are also polygamous, and the habits of those herds which have been closely studied are very similar to

BABY SEALS OF THE BRITISH ISLES

The Common seal is native to the North Atlantic and North Pacific, and is the kind most frequently seen around the British Isles. It often enters the estuary of the Thames and other rivers. These pups were encountered on the Norfolk coast.

WALRUS HERD IN THE ARCTIC

In spite of its long, pointed tusks and air of ferocity, the walrus is an inoffensive creature. But when molested, as it often is by Polar bears, it can prove a dangerous antagonist. The enormous tusks are used for digging up mussels and other shellfish, and as grappling-hooks for clambering about upon the slippery ice.

those of the Elephant seal. One very large colony of southern sea-lions is found in the Falkland Islands and has been under observation for a number of years. The size of the harem is probably about nine to ten cows to one bull, but varies considerably, and there is a herd of bachelors and idle bulls. The pups are suckled for a variable period, sometimes until the next one is born, although they begin to eat solid food by the time they are six weeks old.

The only extensive breeding-ground of the fur-seal is on the Pribiloff Islands, off the coast of Alaska. Here in May or June the males arrive in great numbers and engage in tremendous battles for favoured parts of the beach. After about three weeks the females

arrive and give birth to the pups a few days later. These weigh 10-12 lb. at birth.

As in the other polygamous species of seal, there is a great difference in size between the males and the females. An adult male fur-seal varies between 7 ft. and 8 ft. in length and weighs about 500 lb., whereas the adult female is about 4 ft. long and weighs only about 90 lb. The males can begin to breed when they are four years old, but are not physically mature until they are seven. As the males fight for positions on the breeding-grounds, it is possible that the four-year-olds are precluded from parenthood by sheer lack of body weight. The females can begin to breed at two years of age and bear the first pup when they are three years old.

Shortly after parturition, pairing takes place, one bull serving perhaps eighty or even a hundred cows in his harem. The sexes are present in approximately equal numbers, and so the idle bulls and young bachelors congregate in separate communities near the breeding-grounds and spend their time playing, eating and sleeping throughout the summer.

As in Elephant seals, the old bulls guard the harem continuously, never going to sea to feed throughout June and July. The females, however, are allowed to do this, recognizing their pups without difficulty on their return. The pups are suckled for about six weeks and at the end of this period they are taught to swim.

The old bulls go to sea about the end of July and about this time the virgin females come ashore and pair with the bachelors. With the approach of winter the beaches are completely vacated and the journey south begins; it may extend as far as southern California, perhaps the longest migration undertaken by any mammal.

With regard to the life-span of seals, we have information on only a few genera. The Common seal and Grey seal have been known to live seventeen to eighteen years in captivity. The sea-lion and the fur-seal live for twelve to fourteen years, and the Harp seal for at least eight years and probably rather longer. Among their natural enemies are the Killer whale, which preys on seals, and the Polar bear, which attacks the walrus.

Seals eat fish, small crustacea, cuttle-

SEA-LION SWIMMING AT SPEED

Sea-lions, together with the fur-seals, are distinguished from other members of their order by the presence of small external ears. Expert swimmers and divers, they are also remarkably agile on land, owing to the strength and flexibility of their hind flippers.

BULL FUR-SEAL WITH HIS WIVES AND FAMILY

The fur-seal has been all but exterminated in the Antarctic, but in the Northern Hemisphere, owing to legal protection, there are still many flourishing colonies. The herd seen here is on St. Paul Island, Alaska. The old bull in the foreground, conspicuous by his luxuriant fur cape, is jealously guarding his harem.

fish and sea-birds, the diet varying with the animal, its age and the seasonal abundance of the food. When the young Harp seal begins to feed independently it first takes small crustacea, which swarm in the sea and are easy to catch. The yearlings of the same species feed on small fish as well as crustaceans, and the adults take fish and cuttle-fish besides crustaceans, if no other food is available.

Elephant seals are known to feed largely on cuttle-fish, as do the southern sea-lions. The Grey seal and the Common seal of the British coasts take herring, which makes them unpopular with fishermen. The Crab-eater seal of the Antarctic, as its name implies, likes "lobster krill," small crabs which are very plentiful in the cold waters of the higher latitudes. Walruses live on shell-fish, such as mussels, which they scrape off rocks and dig up with their long tusks. Sand and stones are found in

considerable quantity in the stomachs of many seals. Chewing food caught under water is impossible; the prey must be swallowed whole, and probably the sand and stones help to shred up the food when it reaches the stomach.

Some seals catch penguins, and the Leopard seal has been seen skinning the birds by ripping up the abdomen and then shaking the carcase until it is free of the skin. It also preys on other seals which it drags off the ice-floes, and frequently tears lumps from the floating carcases of whales.

Seals vary in colour from dark blackish-brown and grey to pale grey and yellowish-white, with a sprinkling of dark spots and streaks. The males of sea-lions and walruses have a thick mane on the neck and shoulders, with a reddish-brown tinge. The woolly coat of the pups can be white, grey or brown. This appears to be correlated with the environment at birth—white and pale-

DINNER-TIME FOR DOLPHINS, MARINE STUDIOS, FLORIDA

*Though at first sight easily mistaken for gigantic fish, the dolphins are true mammals
and are classed among the smaller relatives of the whales. They display great agility
and gracefulness in the water, and can leap high into the air with ease in order to
seize their food, snatching fish in their many-toothed jaws with wonderful skill.*

grey pups being found in genera frequenting ice-floes, and darker pups in those breeding on beaches.

Seals were more widely distributed in the past and more abundant than they are today. Certain species have been virtually exterminated by man, and their occurrence in their old haunts is now regarded as a great rarity. They have been hunted in different parts of the world from very early times for food, oil and skins, records existing even from the Stone Age of north-western Europe. But it was not until the eighteenth and nineteenth centuries that some kinds were made the object of intensive exploitation, following upon reports from various explorers of their extraordinary abundance. It is significant that all the species were gregarious seals, congregated in vast herds for breeding.

RUTHLESS SLAUGHTER

Fur-seals, whose beautiful thick undercoat is so valuable to furriers, were once found on all the Antarctic and sub-Antarctic islands, but were practically wiped out by ruthless slaughter in the early part of the nineteenth century. Immense numbers were taken annually. Two seasons alone, when 320,000 animals were killed, reduced the herds on the South Shetland Islands beyond the possibility of recovery. Exploitation of all the breeding-grounds has been so pitiless that today, outside one small island off the Falklands where a colony exists under rigorous Government protection, fur-seals occurring in the Antarctic are something of a zoological phenomenon.

If the United States, as owners of the Pribiloff Islands, had not in 1912 prohibited sealing for a period of five years, a similar fate would have overtaken the stock of northern fur-seals.

During this close period careful observations were made of the colony which remained and as a result "farming" of the herds was instituted, on lines approaching as closely to the farming of domestic animals as is possible where a wild community is concerned. Under American control, the number of seals killed each season is carefully estimated to allow sufficient breeding-stock to remain intact. As far as possible only bachelors (and three-year-olds at that) are taken. As the bachelor herd is found on separate beaches, selection is a simple matter, the inoffensive nature of the seals and the difficulty with which they move on land making them easy to catch.

The walrus was formerly plentiful as far south as the southern coast of Nova Scotia, but today it is confined to the Arctic regions, where for the present it is adequately protected by the difficult terrain. It was intensively hunted for oil, hide (used in saddlery) and tusks. Of the True seals the two genera victimized were the Harp seal and the Elephant seal. Today they are protected by Government agreements. They are hunted (under regulation) for oil. The Elephant seal was once as widely distributed in the Antarctic as was the fur-seal, but ruthless exploitation has exterminated it, except for the herds previously mentioned, in which stocks appear to be sufficiently well established to support a regulated industry.

THE SEA-COWS

Sea-cows belong to a separate order, the Sirenia, which are thought to be distantly related to the forerunners of the elephants. They are purely aquatic and show marked adaptation to this mode of life. The body is spindle-shaped, with a flattened head and a blunt muzzle. The front flippers are

SOUTHERN FUR-SEAL WITH HER NEWBORN PUP

This photograph of a female fur-seal assiduously licking her newborn pup was taken in the islands of Algoa Bay, Cape Colony, South Africa. The pups are suckled for six weeks and are then taught to swim. When the female fur-seals go to sea to feed, they leave their pups behind on the ice, but recognize them without difficulty on their return.

shaped like oars and the greater part of the limb is encased within the skin. The hind limb has completely disappeared and the hip-girdle is represented only by a pair of small rod-like bones. On the other hand, the tail is strongly developed for swimming and ends in a pair of lateral flukes. The nostrils are placed dorsally on the muzzle, the eyes are small and there are no external ears. The skin is dark grey in colour and beneath it is a thick layer of blubber.

Sea-cows are herbivorous, feeding on seaweeds. It is thought probable that the ancestors of the sea-cow adapted themselves to an aquatic existence by taking to the waters of rivers and lakes the banks of which were covered with lush vegetation, finally being lured to the edge of the sea where seaweed

could be found in abundance. Mastication is impossible for these animals feeding under the water, so that sea-cows crush the plants against the hard roof of the mouth and then swallow the mouthful whole. The upper and lower jaws are covered with a hard skin, and the teeth, except the upper tusks, either gradually disappear or else drop out and are continually being replaced by a new series from behind.

As would be expected from their feeding habits, sea-cows frequent shallow coastal waters. They are found in tropical and sub-tropical regions along the shores of the Atlantic, the Indian and the Pacific Oceans, and in the estuaries of large rivers. They are very susceptible to sudden change of temperature. For instance, in January,

1940, when the air temperature off the coast of Florida was as low as 19 deg. F. and the water temperature in Charlotte Harbour dropped suddenly from 68 deg. F. to 46 deg. F., five dead manatees were found in the neighbourhood.

They are slow, lazy, gentle animals, quite fearless and unsuspicious, and show affection towards each other. They generally move about in small groups of nine or ten together, though as many as fifty have been reported, concentrated into a loose herd during the day and scattered at night, when the animals feed and are most active. Not much is known of the breeding habits, but they are believed to mate in shallow water and after a gestation period of about a year usually give birth to a single pup, though occasionally two are seen in a family. They would appear to be monogamous. The nipples are placed rather far forward on the underside of the female, and this, together with the habit which the pup has of sheltering under the mother's flipper, points to the origin of the old mariners' stories and legends of "mermaids."

Sea-cows have been hunted from earliest times and, because of their habits, are easily caught, the adults being harpooned from open boats or caught with the young in nets and fish-traps. The flesh is esteemed as a great delicacy, some writers comparing it with veal, others with pork and also recommending it smoked, when it compares well with bacon. The blubber yields a large quantity of oil which is used for burning, as a lubricant for dressing leather or medicinally. The hide makes strong leather when tanned, the tusks good ivory knife-handles and the bones yield charcoal for sugar-refining. Many superstitions centre around sea-cows, and charms and amulets are made from their bones and teeth.

Protective measures and control of hunting should have been instituted and enforced years ago. Of the three kinds of Sirenia, one has become extinct within historic times. Steller's sea-cow (*Hydrodamalis stelleri*), the largest member of the order, measuring up to 24 ft., was formerly abundant in the

CAST ASHORE IN NORTHERN AUSTRALIA—A DUGONG

With the exception of the manatee, the dugong is the only surviving sea-cow; 10 ft. in length, slow and of a harmless disposition, it is being steadily exterminated. Its broad, horizontal tail forms a powerful swimming organ.

North Pacific, off the east coast of Kamchatka. In 1741 its haunts were discovered by Bering and the naturalist Steller. When traders followed the explorers, the sea-cows provided such an accessible food supply that a quarter of a century later they were exterminated by those hunters who would have succeeded in wiping out the fur-seals as well had not legislation prevented this second catastrophe.

Records of the abundance of the other kinds, the dugong (*Dugong dugon*) and the manatee (*Trichechus manatus*), show that numbers have declined to such an extent that possibly before another quarter of a century has passed they too will be extinct.

The dugong occurs in the Indian and Pacific Oceans, from the East African coast to the Philippines, Formosa and the east coast of Australia. It reaches a length of 10 ft. Everywhere in its range it is hunted by local fishermen and its distribution is becoming increasingly restricted. Each decade brings fresh reports of its non-appearance in former haunts, and nowhere are there any protective measures.

The manatee is an inhabitant of the Atlantic coast-lines. It is found in the estuaries and lower reaches of the West African rivers and coastal lagoons from Senegal to Angola, in the West Indies, the Gulf of Mexico, northwards to the coast of Florida and southwards to the Orinoco and the Amazon. It grows to a length of about 12–15 ft. and

SCHOOL OF PILOT WHALES

Many kinds of cetaceans show a tendency to congregate in large numbers. When such "schools" are driven into shallow water by adverse weather or by hunters, large losses usually ensue. The Pilot whale, about 28 ft. long, inhabits the North Atlantic.

has been kept alive in zoological gardens.

In West Africa it is protected by law, but the law appears to be ineffectively enforced, since the special nets used for its capture are not prohibited. Consequently, the numbers are slowly but certainly diminishing.

By contrast, on the coast of Florida, where netting is prohibited, the manatees are now fairly plentiful, showing clearly how control assists the stock to recover. In the western Atlantic generally it would appear that the manatees are not in grave danger of extermination, yet the facts that "their range is limited, that they are inoffensive, and that they are much sought after by man for food" cannot allow one to be sanguine about their future.

Unfortunately there is not enough accurate information on the breeding habits of Sirenia for efficient regulations to be formulated. If this were available it would be possible to restrict hunting by close seasons and to prohibit indiscriminate killing, while at the same time ensuring a useful and permanent supply of meat to the local populations.

CETACEANS

The last order of aquatic mammals to be considered is the Cetacea, which includes the whales, porpoises and dolphins. Of the three orders this is the most highly specialized of all. Cetacea live mostly in the high seas and exhibit great diversity of size. The great Blue whale can measure as much as 93 ft., while the Common porpoise is never more than 6 ft. They are sharply divided by the presence or absence of teeth in the adult into two sub-orders, Toothed whales (Odontoceti) and Baleen whales (Mystacoceti).

In the Toothed whales the teeth are simple, undifferentiated pegs, designed for grasping and holding the food and not for mastication. The difficulty of chewing food under the water has already been pointed out.

Although teeth are present during foetal life in Baleen whales, they disappear by the time the young whale is born, and are replaced by two rows of horny plates which hang down from the roof of the mouth. These plates, or baleen, are placed transversely and are fringed on the inner surface with bristly fibres, forming a sieve to strain the small crustacea and fish on which these whales feed.

STREAMLINED BODIES

Whales have streamlined bodies and broad, flattened heads, paddle-like front flippers, no hind flippers and a tremendously powerful tail with large laterally-expanded flukes. The body skeleton is not extended into the caudal flukes, which are formed of skin and muscle only. As in Sirenia, all that remains of the hip-girdle is a pair of small bones beneath the flesh. The front flippers are movable only at the shoulder-joint, the rest of the limb forming a rigid, oar-like process used for balancing and steering, while the great tail is the chief organ of propulsion. Whales cannot move their necks at all; they are unique among mammals in this.

In the Baleen whales the paired nostrils are placed right on top of the head, close in front of the brain-case. They are furnished with a set of spiral folds, which are forced into one another by the pressure of the water when the animal submerges. The single nostril of Toothed whales is also on the top of the head, the exception being the Sperm whale, in which it is placed towards the end of the snout. It has a series of valves, covered by an external flap of cartilage and controlled by muscles which contract to close them when the whale dives. There is no gullet as in other mammals. The nasal passages are directly connected with the windpipe, so that when the whale swims with open mouth, catching its food, no water can find its way into the lungs.

STRUCTURE OF WHALES

The eyes are small, set rather low on the side of the head in very thick bony sockets, and are specially adapted for focusing under water. Most whales are short-sighted when viewing objects above the surface, because the eye-lens has no power of accommodation. The outer covering of the eye is thickened as a protection against the variations in water-pressure. The tear-gland secretes a greasy substance to counteract the irritant effect of the salts dissolved in sea-water.

There is no external ear-lobe and the opening of the auditory tube is very small; in some porpoises it is too narrow to admit the passage of the lead of a pencil. It is sometimes concealed by a flap of skin. Nevertheless, the auditory region of the brain is extremely well developed; consequently the ear must be efficient in transmitting water-borne sound vibrations. The ear-bones and the surrounding region of the skull are very thick and heavy. The sense of smell is believed to be lacking in whales.

It has already been mentioned that the Baleen whales eat small fish and crustaceans. These are taken into the mouth with a large volume of water, which is pushed out with the help of the large muscular tongue and the long muscle bands in the floor of the mouth, the baleen plates acting meanwhile as a sieve to retain the animals. Catching this type of food is an easy matter, because it exists in vast shoals in certain parts of the ocean, and the whales browse on these shoals at their leisure.

Toothed whales live on larger fish, squids and octopuses, the pursuit of which is a more strenuous business, but again quantities of sea-water must be swallowed with the prey. The mechanism which prevents whales "dying of thirst" is as yet not understood. There is a complicated series of compartments in the stomach, which are more sharply divided from one another in Toothed whales than in Baleen whales, and are clearly designed so that the food will pass through several stages of gastric digestion. Whales are voracious feeders and the stomach can hold enormous quantities of food; the mass of crustacea, called "krill" by whalers, taken from one Blue whale weighed more than a ton.

Water conducts heat twenty-seven times more quickly than air, so that there must be some mechanism to protect the whales from too great a loss of body-heat through constant immersion. The skin is bare, with no sweat-glands and below it is a thick layer of blubber which is richly supplied with blood-vessels. The body temperature, which is about 95 deg. F. to 96 deg. F. (it has been measured in a few species), is always higher than that of the surrounding water, even in tropical regions.

THE BLUBBER

It has been generally supposed that blubber acts as an insulating layer in all aquatic mammals, thus conserving the body-heat. Recent experiment has, on the contrary, shown that blubber is a good heat-conductor, and by reason of its extensive blood-supply the *outward*, as well as the inward, passage of heat can be controlled and the internal body temperature maintained constant. If the animal is swimming rapidly and therefore producing more heat, in-

TWO-DAY-OLD DOLPHIN WITH ITS MOTHER

This underwater photograph, taken at the Marine Studios, Florida, illustrates the proverbial gracefulness with which the dolphin speeds through the water and which, together with its elegant form and playful disposition, made it a subject dear to ancient artists. The female dolphin bears a single offspring at a time and tends it devotedly.

creased circulation through the blubber will accelerate the loss of heat to the water all around. Conversely, if the animal is moving slowly or in colder water, the blood-supply will decrease, either by diminished heart rhythm due to less exertion, or by constriction of the superficial blood-vessels by the cold, and consequently less heat will be lost. It is considered unlikely that a similar mechanism is present in the Sirenia, or they would not be fatally affected by sudden changes in water temperature.

Whales do not remain at the surface, breathing with their nostrils above the water, but come up and empty the lungs by "blowing," refill the lungs and then submerge again. Therefore, the breath is held for a varying length of time, depending on the depth of the dive. The "blow" is visible, partly by the water vapour in the expired air condensing in contact with the colder atmosphere, and partly because expiration often begins just before the whale breaks surface. The whistling sound of the blow can be heard at some distance on a still day. Whales are generally believed to be mute, though some porpoises make a lowing sound when harpooned.

There is evidence that the larger whales dive to considerable depths, where the pressure of the water is great. The problem of how they are enabled to withstand the hydrostatic conditions is very puzzling and complex. In those whales which only make shallow dives, surfacing frequently, adaptation to submergence need not be so elaborate as in those genera which "sound" deeply and for longer periods.

The vertical distribution of food is clearly a controlling factor. The whales which feed on crustacea and small fish probably frequent the upper 100 metres (330 ft.) of the ocean, since it is in this layer that the shoals occur. A Humpback whale has been drawn up from a depth of 110 metres (363 ft.), entangled in a submarine cable. The body of the whale must have been under a pressure of about 182 lb. per square inch. The

Toothed whales, which eat larger fish and cuttle-fish, must dive deeper still to catch their food, since these animals live on the sea-floor. A cable-ship hoisted up a Sperm whale from 3,240 ft., where the pressure must have been as much as 1,400 lb. per square inch of body surface.

The tough, thick blubber, the special structure of the nose and throat, and the eyes and ears encased in the heavy, bony skull are all clearly adapted to withstand pressure. The lungs are also reinforced by elastic tissue, muscles and additional cartilage and have very large air-spaces or alveoli, but the mechanism by which exchange of gases takes place

COMMON PORPOISE LEAPS FROM THE SEA

The wide, blunt jaw of the Common porpoise distinguishes this mammal from the dolphin, with which it is often confused. The porpoise frequents the North Atlantic, Baltic and Black Sea; like the dolphin, it feeds on fish. Shoals of porpoises commit such serious depredations in fishing-grounds that this otherwise inoffensive animal is regarded by fishermen as a nuisance. Its fat yields oil, used by watchmakers.

(in spite of increased pressure) between the blood and air in the lungs and between the blood and the tissues has been the subject of much speculation. One theory holds that the whale ventilates its lungs thoroughly by a series of short breaths, then dives with the lungs filled to capacity and remains submerged until the oxygen contained in them is practically exhausted. This may well be the case in whales making frequent shallow dives, but in those species which sound for as long as three-quarters of an hour the existence of additional reserves of oxygen has been postulated. These reserves would be built up in the tissues between soundings while the whales remain at the surface for five or six minutes, blowing perhaps twenty to forty times. The complex vascular networks found at the base of the skull and along the vertebral column were regarded as being among these storage depots, but recent work indicates that during a deep dive they may act as a "shunting system" to accommodate the blood pressed out of the peripheral vessels. Diminished heart rhythm, which occurs in the Pinnipedia, has so far not been noticed in whales under experimental conditions (porpoises have been kept under observation in a tank), and this shunting mechanism may have been developed instead.

DIVING DISEASE

The question arises in connexion with deep diving: how do whales escape caisson sickness (diving disease) when they surface again? Caisson sickness is a serious danger to human divers. According to Dalton's Law, the amount of nitrogen in the blood increases in proportion to the pressure. If return to the surface is too rapid, there is not time for all the nitrogen to diffuse out of the blood again and bubbles of gas may remain in the vessels and cause embolism. Great care must, therefore, be taken to draw the divers up slowly.

WHALES AND HUMAN DIVERS

The great difference between human diving operations and the soundings of whales is the fact that the diver is supplied continuously with air and therefore with nitrogen, whereas the whale dives on a sustained breath. Hence the amount of nitrogen taken down in this initial supply is not great enough to cause saturation of the blood during compression. Moreover, as the whale comes out of its dive and rises to the surface, the great elasticity of the lungs will cause them to expand again slowly and regularly as the pressure decreases, allowing the blood-gases to escape into the air-spaces of the lungs before the moment for expiration occurs; the lungs can thus be emptied in the minimum of time. There is also the possibility that when the whale seeks the surface the circulation speeds up owing to the lack of oxygen; in fact, the whale emerges "bursting for air." These two factors will speedily bring about the return of the blood-gases to normal.

Young cetaceans are larger at birth than the young of any other mammals. They are very highly developed and need to be so, for they are born in the water and must be immediately able to swim and escape drowning. The mammary glands of whales open into large reservoirs where the milk collects. When the calf is suckled, these reservoirs are emptied by contractions of adjoining muscles in the matter of a few moments.

Whales migrate to temperate regions to breed, even at the expense of being without food for three or four months;

during this time they will draw on the reserve food stored in the blubber. In the large Baleen whales the gestation period is about ten to eleven months (a single calf is the general rule at birth) and the suckling period lasts for about six to eight months. These whales are probably monogamous, moving about the feeding-grounds in small groups. The young whales become sexually mature at two years, but are not physically mature until they reach the age of five or six years.

THE SPERM WHALE

The Sperm whale (*Physeter catodon*) is the only one which shows marked disparity of size between the sexes, the males measuring up to 60 ft., the females only about 33 ft. This difference in size is correlated, as it is in the Pinnipedia, with the polygamous habit. Sperm whales are found during the breeding season in two herds, one containing the bulls with their harems and the calves, the other the bachelors and idle bulls. The gestation period lasts for just under a year and the young are born in subtropical and temperate waters, where pairing also takes place, after which there is a tendency for the bulls to move off to colder regions during the polar summer months. Normally the females and young whales migrate to the tropics for the winter, where they are joined by the returning bulls.

Much work remains to be done on the life-history and anatomy of the Sperm whale—notably the function of the great spermaceti organ, which gives the head its curious characteristic blunt shape and large size, needs to be investigated. The formation of ambergris is still a matter of speculation. Lumps of varying size are found in the intestines or floating in the sea, and are much valued by the perfumery trade as a fixative for essential oils. Fragments of cuttle-beaks are found embedded in the ambergris, cuttlefish as well as large fish forming the main food of Sperm whales. Although not the largest of whales (it is exceeded by the Baleen whales, the Blue and the Fin), it is in many ways the most impressive and fantastic of the Cetacea, and has stirred the imagination of writers and poets from Old Testament times to the present.

Cetaceans are found in all the oceans and seas of the world and in all latitudes. Some of the smaller porpoises and dolphins are common around the British coasts and are occasionally reported as being seen up rivers. A few Cetacea live in fresh water, notably the dolphins which are found in the Ganges, the Yangtse, the Amazon and the Plate. Colour in Cetacea ranges from bluish-black through grey to yellowish-white and white. The belly is lighter than the back. They are—with the exception of the Killer whale (*Orcinus orca*), which preys on smaller whales and seals among other animals—gentle, inoffensive creatures which show great care for their young. The reported ferocity of the Sperm whale is probably due to the pain inflicted by harpooning.

WHALING BECOMES AN INDUSTRY

Whaling was originally practised in coastal waters, but when it developed as an industry the Arctic Ocean was the chief scene of operations, the principal quarry being the Greenland Right whale (*Balaena mysticetus*). This is the least streamlined of all the large Baleen whales (it grows to a length of 60 ft.), and its slow turn of speed made it an easy victim for the old method of whaling from open boats with hand harpoons.

By the beginning of this century the

FIN WHALE "BLOWING" AS THE HARPOON STRIKES

The Fin whale is one of the greatest of all creatures, being surpassed in size only by the giant Blue whale. The senseless depredations of large-scale mechanized whaling, which originated with the introduction of the Sven Foyn harpoon gun in 1865, have reduced the stock of whales throughout the world to a dangerously low level.

scene of the whale-hunts had shifted from the Arctic to the Antarctic, the old whaling-grounds being no longer profitable. For a time the swifter Blue whale (*Balaenoptera musculus*) and Fin whale (*Balaenoptera physalus*) had eluded capture, but only until faster ships were built. The Fin whale is found in the colder waters of both hemispheres, but the great Blue whale, largest living mammal, lives mainly in the Antarctic. With the development of "pelagic" whaling (that is, with factory-ships, not shore factories) the total number of whales killed annually in the Southern Ocean rose steadily until it reached a peak in the season 1930-1, when over forty thousand whales were killed there by the whaling fleets.

By this time the work of the *Discovery* Committee, backed by the Colonial Office and initiated by scientists concerned by the need for conservation, had advanced sufficiently for definite recommendations to be made for the regulation of the industry. In the summer of 1931 these were formulated by an International Convention and later became law, which has been implemented by mutual agreement between the countries concerned ever since. Unfortunately, although the activities of the whaling companies were curtailed, nothing was done to prevent their expansion!

Before 1939 the southern stocks of Blue and Fin whales showed signs of depletion, and although of necessity

"STRAINER" IN THE MOUTH OF A FIN WHALE

Despite their vast bulk and strength, all the whalebone whales feed entirely upon plankton—the minute organisms and small fishes floating near the surface of the sea. The "whalebone," comprising three to four hundred horny plates on each side of the mouth, forms a sieve with which the plankton is strained from the sea-water.

END OF THE HUNT—A BLUE WHALE HAULED ASHORE

With a length of nearly 100 ft., the Blue whale is the largest of known creatures, living or extinct. It is one of the most sought-after victims of the whaler. Modern whaling has become a highly organized industry, employing specially designed vessels, air reconnaissance and both floating and shore factories.

during the war years 1939-45 very little whaling took place, it is doubtful whether the rest period was long enough for such slow-breeding animals to recover. The whaling returns for the last three seasons show that the average length of the whales caught is decreasing, and the statement has also been made that fewer pregnant females are being taken. These facts, coupled with the additional fact that the minimum length at which whales may be killed has been fixed below the average length at which they become sexually mature, lead to the conclusion that those whales now being caught have had at most one calf, or even none at all. In these circumstances the recruitment of the already depleted stock cannot be sufficient to maintain adequate breeding.

Blue and Fin whales are not the only ones fished in the Southern Ocean; Sei whales (*Balaenoptera borealis*) and Humpback whales (*Megaptera nodosa*) are also taken and must be regarded as being also in a similarly dangerous position.

Whale-oil is used for the manufacture of soap, margarine and glycerine. Formerly the meat and bones were only made into cattle-cake and fertilizers, but at the present time the critical world food situation has centred interest also on the canning and refrigeration of whale-meat for human consumption.

The need for conservation on an international scale is very great if aquatic mammals are to survive as living inhabitants of the seas, and not as dead, stuffed specimens in museums.

FRUIT-BAT, OR FLYING-FOX

Flying-foxes are really enormous bats, some of which have a wing-span of as much as 5 ft. Some species roost by day in caves; others, like that seen above, hang by their hind feet from the branches of trees, with their wings wrapped round their bodies. A large "camp" of flying-foxes may contain millions of bats, clustering close together.

Mammals which
fly and glide

ANIMALS of many different kinds
have conquered the air during the
course of evolution, and none
more successfully than some of the
mammals. True flight in animals calls
for the development of two basic things,
planes to act as aerofoils supporting the
body while it travels through the air,
and powerful muscles to provide the
necessary forward thrust by moving
them. Many animals have developed the
first without the second and are therefore able only to glide, for they must
derive their thrust either from a push at
take-off or from gravity. If the latter,
they must start their flight from an
elevated place and lose height throughout its course. No animal has achieved
either of man's most successful solu-
tions of the problem of flight, the
rotating propeller and jet-propulsion;
nor has man been able, in spite of many
experiments, to construct a machine to
fly by wing-beats.

The animals which have successfully
acquired the power of true self-sus-
tained flight are the insects, the extinct
pterodactyls amongst the reptiles, the
birds, and in the mammals the bats.
Many others have got as far as gliding,
but no farther; animals such as the
flying-fish, the flying-lizards (*Draco*) of
the Orient, the flying-phalangers and
flying-squirrels. In all of these the power

of flight has been evolved quite independently; again and again have earth-
bound animals tried to cut their bonds
and sail into the air.

This is well shown even among the
mammals that can only glide. These are
the caguan or "flying-lemur" of the
Far East, the flying-phalangers or
opossums of Australasia, and the flying-
squirrels which inhabit all the con-
tinents except Australia. None of these
groups is closely related, and the flying-
phalangers, being marsupials or
pouched mammals, are far removed
indeed from the others. Yet within this
group alone the ability to glide has been
separately evolved at least three times:
by the Great flying-phalangers, by the
Lesser flying-opossums, and by the
feathertail (Pygmy flying-opossum).
Similarly with the flying-squirrels;
those belonging to the family Petauristidae, which occur in Europe, Asia and
North America, are very distant cousins
of the African family Anomaluridae,
and the structures making gliding
possible have certainly been evolved
quite independently in the two families.
Thus, though different mammals have
reached different stages in the evolution
of flight, they do not show us different
stages of a single evolutionary line.

All the gliding mammals are arboreal,
and it is, of course, among mammals

BAT EMITTING ECHO-LOCATING SQUEAKS

During the Second World War a group of American scientists discovered that bats employed a system of echo-location similar to radar. Their tests revealed the fact that bats emit a series of ultrasonic squeaks which, reflected back from surrounding objects, enable the animals to locate their position whilst flying in the dark. The above photographs show a bat in flight; signals are being sent out through the open mouth while their reflections are immediately detected by the super-sensitive ears.

which live in trees that one would expect to find the origin of flight. With the gliders the process seems obviously an extension of the habit of leaping from branch to branch, gliding merely making the range of the normal jump very much greater. But the origin of the bats, with their unrestricted flight, is very much more difficult to guess. The glider's planes are no more than extensions of the skin of the body between the limbs, and become more efficient as they become more elaborate, the animal's ordinary movements being unhampered by their presence. In the bats, on the other hand, the whole structure is so modified and specialized for flight that stages in its evolutionary history are hard to imagine. No doubt the evolution was a gradual process, as the fossils show it was in birds, but what sort of beast could a half-evolved bat be? The fossil record does not help us, for the earliest known remains are those of perfect bats, very little different from their living descendants, although separated from them in time by the fifty million years which have elapsed since the early Eocene period.

MODIFICATIONS FOR FLYING

Animals which have taken to aviation find that they can travel at speeds much higher than those they have been used to on the ground. This at once sets them a new problem, both of observation and control, for their wits must now be sharpened so that they may take in their surroundings at a glance, and their reactions in response must be equally rapid if they are to avoid an early and fatal crash. The more efficiently they fly the greater will be their speed, and the greater the need for this heightened perception and activity.

It is, therefore, in the most efficient fliers, the bats, that we find the most extraordinary modifications in this direction, the recently discovered faculty of echo-location providing a striking example. Echo-location has been studied in only one or two species of American insect-eating bats, and nothing is known of the extent to which it may occur in all the thousands of other species throughout the world, or whether it is used by the large fruit-eating bats, which, being very different in habits, are unlikely to have it. We must not assume, therefore, that it is a universal attribute of all bats, or that it is used all the time even in those species which have it.

AVOIDANCE OF OBSTACLES

Most of the insect-eating bats are night-fliers, and many of them hunt their prey beneath the gloom of trees, yet their eyes are very small and unlikely to help them much under such conditions. Further, it has been found that bats can fly without colliding with surrounding objects even in complete darkness, or after they have been blindfolded. These facts have long been known, and much speculation has been made on how bats are able to achieve the seemingly impossible. One theory was that the wing membrane of bats is very sensitive to pressure changes in the air, so that the animals can, in effect, feel objects at a distance without actually touching them. Another suggested that a similar function is performed by the peculiar glandular pads and leaf-shaped skin-flaps that occur on the snouts of many species, but there was little evidence to support these theories.

Nearly a quarter of a century ago a British scientist suggested that perhaps bats become aware of nearby objects by means of reflected sounds. He was quite correct, but he did not follow up his observations with experiments to give a full proof, so that it was left to two American physiologists of Harvard University to make the crucial tests only a few years ago, during the Second World War. Their fascinating researches revealed the whole story.

BATS' ECHO-LOCATION

The echo-location of bats is a most astounding parallel to man's radar (or should we put it the other way round?), except that, unlike man's invention, it employs sound-waves instead of electro-magnetic ones. The basic principle of radar is simple: if a signal is sent out and reflected from an object, and if the rate at which the signal travels through space is known, then it is easy to calculate the distance of the object by noting the time taken for the echo to return to the sender. If, in addition, the signal is sent out in a narrow beam, measurement of its horizontal and vertical angles gives, together with the known distance, the exact position in space of the object observed.

And this is just what bats do, emitting short bursts of very high-pitched sound as the signal. The sound-waves are ultrasonic, ranging in frequency from thirty to seventy thousand vibrations a second, being most commonly about fifty thousand a second. Sounds of this pitch are quite inaudible to human ears, whose upper limit is in the neighbourhood of twenty thousand a second, but the ear of the bat is able to perceive them. In order to be useful the signal must be short and frequently repeated; the bat must send out a series of ultrasonic squeaks. Each signal lasts about five-thousandths of a second, and thus will contain, at a frequency of fifty thousand a second, about two hundred and fifty cycles of vibration.

Successive squeaks must be emitted so that there is sufficient time between them for the echo of the first to come back before the second is sent out, otherwise there would be no knowing which echo belonged to which squeak. The nearer a bat is to an object the shorter this interval need be, for the echoes will be quicker in returning. And this is exactly what happens; when the bat is at rest preparatory to flying, the signal is repeated five to ten times a second, and in normal flight the repetition rate is from twenty to thirty a second. But when the bat approaches an object the rate rapidly increases to fifty or sixty a second, and then drops away again as the obstacle is left behind. It is believed that bats use their echo-location not only in avoiding obstacles but also in finding their insect prey.

PECULIARITIES OF BATS

In correlation with the possession of echo-location there are several peculiar structures in the anatomy of bats. The larynx and vocal cords are very massive and strong for such small animals, so that the necessary power can be given to the signals. In the ear the minute muscles acting on the drum, and the chain of microscopic bones which transmit sounds from the drum to the inner-ear, are so arranged that they can prevent such transmission. When a bat gives an ultrasonic squeak the power is so great that it would probably deafen the ear for a moment and prevent the echo being properly heard. The action of the ear-muscles is to put the ear out of action for a fraction of a second so that this shall not happen. In an exactly similar way man finds it necessary to have a suppressor in his radar sets to prevent their being "paralysed" by the outgoing signal and, therefore, unable to receive the echo.

The ear-flaps of many bats are peculiar, for in addition to the main flap there is a smaller one standing up in front of the ear-hole. This extra flap is called the "tragus," and the suggestion has been made that the function of the tragus is in some way to help in determining the exact direction of the received echo. Many bats have a leaf-like appendage of skin on the nose—the Horseshoe bats take their name from its presence—and in those species which

recognize its own voice, and thus avoid confusion when a number of bats are flying close to each other. The risk of confusion is also decreased by the fact that ultrasonic sounds do not travel far, just as audible sounds die away in the distance, the range of a bat's squeak being only a matter of feet. This naturally requires that the reaction time of a bat on receipt of information by the

BAT IN FLIGHT

Many bats have a secondary ear-flap (the tragus) which stands out in front of the ear-hole. The function of this organ is not definitely known, but it is possibly to help the bat in determining the exact position of an object returning an echo.

possess it there is usually no tragus in the ear. It is possible that the nose-leaf helps to focus the emitted signal into a narrow beam, for it is known that the echo-locating squeaks can be sent out through the nostrils as well as through the mouth.

No two bats are likely to make a squeak of exactly the same pitch and consequently each is probably able to

echo-location system must be very, very short: the flight of many kinds of bats is thus characterized by quick turns and sudden twists.

The echo-locating ultrasonic squeaks of bats are quite different from the ordinary voice which is used when the animals are excited in any way. A captured bat will give out very audible squeaks and chattering if frightened,

GREATER FLYING-PHALANGER

The Greater flying-phalanger is found in the forests of eastern Australia, where it lives on the leaves and buds of the eucalyptus tree. It has a web-like expanse of skin which extends from elbow to ankle and enables it to execute long glides from tree to tree. This flying-web is tucked up out of the way when not in use.

and there is often a lot of squeaking, very noticeable to a human listener, from a crowded bat-roost when the animals are awakening before the evening flight. The normal voice is, however, high-pitched, and some people find that they cannot hear it. There is a peculiar side effect of the echo-locating squeak; the rapid succession of inaudible sounds itself makes a note whose pitch is that of the repetition frequency, and can sometimes be heard as a buzzing sound.

GLIDING MAMMALS

Echo-location, or something giving similar results, is obviously essential to the bats which fly about swiftly in the dark. But although many of the gliding mammals are also nocturnal, nothing of the sort is known in them. Nor should we expect to find it, for their gliding flight is very much less specialized and is used only at considerable intervals, most of the animals' time being spent in climbing about the branches of trees. In all the gliders the whole body is turned into a plane by the skin of the sides extending down the limbs towards the hands and feet, and joining them together by a web which can be spread out as a flat sheet when the limbs are extended. The web of skin is large in some species, smaller in others, and in some it also reaches from the arms to the sides of the neck, and from the legs to the tail.

The marsupials are a division of the mammals which differs from the others in that the young are born at a very early stage of development and are carried about for a long time after birth attached to the teats of the mother, in many species protected by a pouch, as is well known to everyone in the kangaroo. This and other anatomical characters separate the marsupials widely from all the other mammals, so that they form a well-defined group. They are nearly all confined to Australia and New Guinea, excepting the opossums and a few others living in America. Evolution has produced a great diversity of forms among the marsupials, parallel to its production of superficially similar forms in the other mammals. Thus there are the marsupial "mole," the marsupial "wolf," and many others in which both form and habits resemble those of animals in the other group.

Though there are no "marsupial bats," there are several sorts, both large and small, of "flying" marsupials which can glide. Like many marsupials they are all clothed in beautifully soft, silky fur, which extends on to the flying web. Much is known of their anatomy and of their geographical distribution, but all too little of their life histories and habits when alive, in spite of the fact that they are all easily tamed and make delightful pets.

PYGMY FLYING-OPOSSUM

The smallest species, the feathertail or Pygmy flying-opossum (*Acrobates pygmaeus*), is a tiny creature only 2½ in. long, not as big as a large mouse, with a tail of about the same length. There is a very narrow fold of skin along the sides between the arm and leg which is effectively made much wider by a fringe of hairs growing from its edge. The tail looks like a feather, for a long fringe of hair grows on each side of it, giving an additional area to act as a plane during gliding. The skin from which the fringe springs at each side of the tail is also produced into a small flattened ridge. The feathertail shows the most rudimentary form of gliding web; its nearest relative, the Pen-tailed phalanger of New Guinea, has a similar tail but no body-web, and so cannot fly.

The feathertail is common in the

TINY AUSTRALIAN GLIDER

The feathertail is the smallest gliding mammal. Its flying-web is very rudimentary, merely a small fold of skin, fringed by hairs, which stretches between arm and leg.

eucalyptus forests of eastern Australia, where it is often found in small family parties. It makes a nest of shredded leaves and bark in a cranny of a hollow tree, from which it comes forth to feed at night; it is said to be insectivorous.

LESSER FLYING-PHALANGERS

There are several species of Lesser flying-phalangers (*Petaurus*), or flying-squirrels as they are often called in Australia, a name to confuse the unwary. They are small to medium-sized animals, clothed in silky fur of soft greys and fawns, with a darker stripe along the back. They are nocturnal and arboreal, making a nest in a hollow branch and coming out by night, gliding from tree to tree by means of the flying-web, which is wide and stretches from the edge of the fifth finger to the ankle. After the young one has been kept in the pouch for about two months, it is carried clinging to the back of the parent for some time longer.

According to Gould, the "flying-squirrels" feed on the flowers of the various kinds of gum-tree, but he adds that they show great activity at night "while running over the small, leafy branches, frequently even to their very extremities, in search of insects, and the honey of the newly-opened blossoms."

Although the Greater flying-phalanger (*Petauroides*) is superficially much like a large edition of the last, it is by no means a close relation and has evolved the flying-web and gliding habit quite independently. It is about the size of a rabbit and has a very long tail, much longer than the body, and the flying-web extends from the elbow to the ankle. Like the "flying-squirrels," it can make very long glides from the top of one tree to the base of another, rising a little at the end of the glide to check its speed for landing. Le Soeuf and Burrell record a measured glide between trees eighty yards apart, and another of fifty-five feet which occupied one and a half seconds. They tell us that these phalangers, though numerous in the eastern Australian forests, are difficult to find (they are strictly nocturnal), and that the "surest indication of their presence is to see an animal gliding swiftly from the top of one tree to the foot of another, and to hear the *clop* as the creature lands on the bark." Their food consists of leaves and buds, chiefly of eucalyptus trees.

A surprising thing about all these gliders is the manner in which the flying-web tucks up out of the way

AMERICAN FLYING-SQUIRREL

Flying-squirrels are found in Asia, eastern Europe and America. In addition to being able to glide, they are as agile in trees as ordinary squirrels, which they resemble.

when not in use; the animals are entirely unhampered by its presence while climbing about, and it is so inconspicuous that it could be easily overlooked. The very opposite is true of the caguan or "flying-lemur" (*Cynocephalus*, formerly *Galeopithecus*), whose flying-web is larger than that of any of the other gliders, and so voluminous that the resting animal, as big as a cat, looks as though dressed in a large, ill-fitting fur gown. The web starts at the side of the neck, extends to the hand, thence to the foot, and thence to the end of the tail; like the rest of the body, it is covered with short, soft fur, dark brown in colour mottled with whitish flecks.

CAGUAN'S ANATOMY

The anatomy of the caguan differs so much from that of other mammals that it is placed by itself in a separate order. It has no close relatives, and its affinities are unknown. The edges of the lower front teeth, which are flat and project forwards, are cut up into numerous points like a comb, and, indeed, it has been suggested that it is as a comb that they are used in dressing the fur, just as are the similarly procumbent, but otherwise very different, teeth of the true lemurs. There are two species of

caguan, one living in the forests of Malaya, the other in those of the Philippines; they are nocturnal and spend the day asleep, clinging to the trunk of a tree (not head downwards like a bat) or suspended by all-fours from a branch. They hold on with their sharp claws like a cat, and move about in a series of jumps interrupted by long pauses, as though the exercise tired them greatly. They pass from tree to tree by gliding, and, unless by accident, probably never descend to the ground, on which their movements are very clumsy.

Wallace says that he saw one of these animals "run up a tree in a rather open space, and then glide obliquely through the air to another tree on which it alighted near its base, and immediately began to ascend." He found the distance between the trees was seventy yards, and the descent not more than thirty-five to forty feet. The food consists entirely of leaves, buds and fruits, with occasionally, perhaps, an insect. The single young one is blind and naked at birth, and clings to the fur on the breast of the mother, who carries it about with her and glides from tree to tree with it in this position. Very little is known about these animals.

SHORT-HEADED FLYING-PHALANGER

The Short-headed flying-phalanger of Australia is one of the species of Lesser flying-phalangers—sometimes referred to by Australians as "flying-squirrels." It is about the size of a rat, is very sturdily built, and lives on flowers, honey and insects.

The only other placental mammals that are adapted for gliding are some of the rodents; two families in this order are gliders, but they are very distantly related and have certainly evolved their flying abilities quite independently of each other, though superficially they show many points of resemblance.

The Petauristidae are the true flying-squirrels and are quite closely related to the ordinary squirrels; like them they tend to be bright-coloured or to be marked with conspicuous patterns, often of chestnut, black, yellow, and white. The headquarters of the family is Asia, and many species are found throughout the continent; they are classified into about a dozen genera, of which one

extends into eastern Europe and another is confined to North America. In all species the flying-web extends along the sides between the arms and legs; in the larger Asiatic species (genus *Petaurista*) the web is further supported by a gristly rod arising from the wrist, and extensions of the web run from the arm to the cheek, and from the legs to the basal part of the bushy tail. In the smaller flying-squirrels of the genus *Sciuropterus* the web does not extend from the legs to tail, but the latter is flattened, and the hair is arranged as a fringe along each side, acting as an additional plane, in a way reminiscent of that in the feathertail. Though flying-squirrels have often been seen active by day, they are much more nocturnal in their habits than the ordinary squirrels. They make their nests, lined with chewed-up bark, in the hollows of trees and spend most of the day sleeping curled up there. They are very lively animals at night, and their agility in trees is quite unhampered by the flying-web; and indeed they are as nimble when on the ground. All the species are in the main herbivorous, though it is said that they will also eat insects and other animal matter when they get the chance.

The gliding of the flying-squirrels is very similar to that of the flying-phalangers—from branch to branch, or from the top of one tree to the base of another if the distance is great. It may here be pointed out that the terms used by many naturalists in discussing the structure of the gliders are very inappropriate. It is quite incorrect to call the flying-web a "parachute," as is often done. None of the animals parachutes, that is, descends from a height more or less vertically and passively; all of them glide in an obliquely horizontal direction, the whole body, with the webs at the sides, acting as a plane. The plane is not necessarily flat, though in many species it is approximately so, for Sanderson records that in one of the larger African flying-squirrels "the whole animal assumes the shape of a small umbrella." Even so, the action is that of gliding, not parachuting. Although unable to sustain their flight by any propulsive effort once they are launched, they are able to change direction by altering the trim of the web, just as a human glider can steer his craft. The flying-web is often not only

UNIQUE CAGUAN

The anatomy of the caguan, or Flying lemur, is different from that of any other mammal, and it has thus been placed in an order by itself. Its flying-web, unlike that of other gliding mammals, hangs about it in voluminous folds when it is at rest. This strange creature is found in the forests of the Malay Peninsula and the Philippines.

223

PLANE ACTION OF AN ORDINARY SQUIRREL

This picture of a European squirrel in mid-air between one tree and another shows clearly how the flying-web may have arisen as an extension of this habit. The squirrel's close relatives, the true flying-squirrels, glide in an oblique horizontal direction.

called the "parachute," but the "parachute membrane," surely an unsuitable term, for it consists of two thicknesses of skin, the upper and under, both covered with hair, with, in some species, a considerable amount of muscular tissue between them.

The so-called African "flying-squirrels" of the family Anomaluridae are peculiar not only in their internal anatomy but also in the support for the web and the character of the tail. As in *Petaurista*, there is a rod of gristle supporting the web, but it arises from the elbow, and extends the edge of the web beyond the profile of the arm. The web also extends from the leg to the base of the tail, which is covered on its underside with a number of large overlapping scales that help the animal to climb up vertical surfaces. Sanderson has made some most interesting observations on these animals in West Africa. He found that the large *Anomalurus*

fraseri prefers to land on the trunks rather than the branches of trees, and that at the end of a glide the head is lower than the tail. Just before landing the arms and head are thrown back and the tail is swept up behind so that the animal is brought into a vertical position for alighting. It instantly clings to the bark and starts ascending, using the fore-feet together, arching the back and drawing up the hind-feet, the action being like that of a looper caterpillar. The scales on the tail and the claws of the hind-feet are dug into the bark as the fore-feet are advanced, and the process is repeated, the animal galloping up a smooth bole at an astonishing speed.

Sanderson found that the smaller species of the genus *Idiurus* are gregarious, flocks of as many as a hundred of two species living together in one tree. "If disturbed during the daytime they seem to be in no way disconcerted by the light, but issue forth from the holes,

GIANT BAT HANGING FROM PERCH

Flying-foxes, found throughout the tropics of the Old World and Australia, are nocturnal and frugivorous; their cheek-teeth have flattened crowns adapted to crushing their pulpy diet. They roost in large colonies during the day, hanging head-downward from their perches, with their wings wrapped around them. The day, however, is not spent peacefully, for they are always jostling one another noisily.

career about the surface of the trunk and branches, faster than mice on a level floor, take to the air in clouds, floating away among the neighbouring trees like bits of soot from a chimney, steering themselves over and around obstacles with the facility of birds, and landing silently hundreds of feet away, without any apparent loss of height."

All these African flying-squirrels are vegetarians, feeding on fruits and flowers. With one exception they are nocturnal, spending the day asleep in the hollow of a tree. The exception, *Anomalurus beecrofti*, lives, not in the hollows, but among dense foliage at the extreme tops of the forest trees, where it is active by day. In correlation with its habit, the colour is bright green above and golden-yellow below, a colour scheme which makes it inconspicuous and protects it from being spotted by predators.

FLYING-FOXES

Similar in their diet, but very different in all their other habits and their structure, are the fruit-bats or flying-foxes. These enormous bats, some of which reach a wing-span of 5 ft., are found throughout the tropics of the Old World. They form one sub-order, the Megachiroptera, of the order Chiroptera (bats); the other, which contains the much smaller insect-eating bats, being the Microchiroptera. The first sub-order, though it contains very many species, is overtopped by the second, which contains over a thousand. The flying-foxes have rather elongated snouts, and this feature, together with the reddish fur of many species, gives them their name. But they are not fox-like in habit, being entirely vegetarian and feeding on flowers and fruit. Some species roost by day in caves, but others hang up, freely exposed to the light, in the branches of trees. Many of the flying-foxes are gregarious and gather at their roosts in enormous numbers. One Queensland roost or "camp," as it is called in Australia, was half a mile wide and four miles long; it contained literally millions of bats which darkened the air as they took to flight about sundown. It is not surprising that the Queensland fruit-farmers regard flying-foxes as their enemies, though actual surveys have shown that the overall damage done is not as great as might be supposed.

QUARRELSOMENESS OF BATS

When roosting, flying-foxes hang freely by their hind-feet from a branch and wrap their wings round their bodies. But a camp during the day is not filled with peacefully sleeping bats; there is continual movement and noise as the bats quarrel and jostle each other for the best perches, those dispossessed flying off to another part of the camp. Camps are used for several days or weeks at a stretch, but sooner or later a move to new quarters is made, for at night the bats have to go where flowers are opening or fruit is ripening. In Australia not only are local movements such as these made, but seasonal migrations also take place; during the summer the bats come down into New South Wales, but retreat to tropical Queensland during the winter.

The cheek-teeth of the flying-foxes differ from those in the other bats, having flattened crowns adapted to crushing up their pulpy food. As in the other bats, the thumb is free and carries a sharp, curved claw; it is used in climbing about the branches, and when the bat is feeding one foot and one thumb are often used for support, the other for manipulating the fruit. Like those of all bats, the wings consist of a

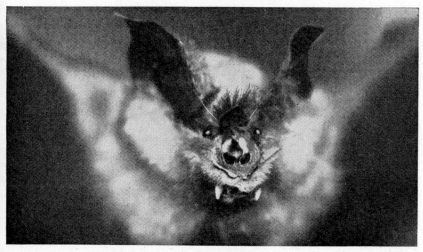

HEAD OF A HORSESHOE BAT

The Horseshoe bat is so named because of the shape of its nose-leaf. The function of the nose-leaf may be to focus into a narrow beam the supersonic signals emitted by the bat.

double layer of skin, more or less bare of hair, extended by the greatly elongated fingers of the hand, and attached to the legs as far as the ankles. The web between the legs is comparatively small in extent, and there is usually no tail, but if one is present it is small. Many of the fruit-bats are distinguished by having a claw on the second digit of the hand, that is, the one in the leading edge of the wing. A single young one is born at a time, and is carried about clinging to the fur of the mother, whose teats are placed far on the sides of the chest, in the armpit under the wing.

Though the flying-foxes are numerous in species and innumerable in individuals, they are as nothing compared with the insectivorous bats, which are by far the most successful group of flying mammals. Though none of the insect-eaters reaches a large size, the number of species is immense and is exceeded only by those of one other order of mammals, the rodents. Once bats had conquered the air they found

no rivals in their new environment, which they have exploited to the full, with the evolution of a vast number of species. This is surely because they have used flight not merely for gaining access to safe hiding-places where predators cannot reach them, but also for the active hunting of their prey in the air. All the other flying and gliding mammals use their power of flight only to reach their feeding-places or to escape from their enemies; it is, in fact, a well-developed form of laziness.

Some of the insect-eating bats belie their name and, as we shall see, have very peculiar feeding habits. But most of them prey upon night-flying insects which they catch upon the wing; many of them, too, devour their food while in full flight. The actual capture of insects appears to be done with the mouth, and it has recently been found that the glands opening on the lips of some species form a sticky secretion to help entangle the prey. But catching a large insect is quite a different matter from

QUAINT ROOSTING "FLITTERMICE"

Here is a small colony of sleeping bats, clustering together in order to keep warm. British bats, like the greater number of species, are insect-eaters; and in winter, owing to the scarcity of insect life, they are obliged to hibernate usually in dark crannies.

eating it, for it must be manoeuvred so that the hard bits are discarded and only the juicy parts consumed. Some species carry the captured prey to a regular perch to do this, and the ground beneath becomes strewn with wings, heads and other hard insect remains. The British Pipistrelle and Whiskered bats often do this, the feeding-perch being a different place from the sleeping-roost. On the other hand, both these species and many others can, and very often do, deal with their catch by bringing the tail forward under the body, so that the web between the legs forms a pouch, into which the insect is thrust and manoeuvred so that it can be eaten without the necessity for alighting.

This operation can only be accomplished by those species which have long tails that help to support the flying-web. There are many species which have no tails, short tails, or even tails which, though long, are not included in the web between the legs but project freely. In some at least of those species which cannot make a temporary tail-pouch a captured insect is tucked into the web under the wing while the bat bites it to pieces. The British Horseshoe bats, which have comparatively short tails, use this method of dealing with their food.

Bats are so completely adapted to flight that they are not, as a rule, very good performers on the ground; nevertheless, many sorts on alighting can scuttle away with surprising agility into the crannies in which they sleep. In flight the legs of a bat are widely spread to extend the flying-webs, and this is made easy because the top of the leg-bone is twisted to such an extent that the whole leg faces backwards, and the knee thus appears to bend the wrong way; the legs of a bat walking on a level surface bend up like those of a grass-hopper. The feet are small, and the toes all about the same length, with sharp, curved claws, while from the ankle a gristly rod, the calcar, extends the edge of the flying-web between the legs and helps to support it.

When they roost, many sorts of bats creep into crevices in hollow trees, under roofs, or in caves, where they cling to the surface, often head downwards. But others, such as the British Horseshoe bats, hang freely suspended by the feet, and wrap the body up in the wings, as do the flying-foxes. Horseshoe bats are very agile at perching in this position; as they alight they turn a somersault in the air, grasp some minute projection with the feet, close the wings, and there they are—instantly transformed into something that looks like a weird insect cocoon hanging from the ceiling.

Bats need a lot of food, and when insects get scarce at the end of summer, bats living in temperate countries can do one of two things to avoid starvation, migrate or hibernate. In North America and on the European continent some species do migrate, flying south to warmer places where insects abound. But in Britain they choose the other alternative and hibernate in some sheltered spot. During hibernation bats become torpid, and their rate of breathing, their temperature, their heart-beat and all other bodily activities are greatly reduced; so close do they approach the border-line between life and death that if disturbed they may take as long as half an hour or more to "come to life" again.

Even during the summer, the daytime sleep of bats often goes a long way towards torpidity, and this, together with limited activity—for many bats fly only for an hour at dusk and dawn—

spins out their lives to comparatively great lengths. A small mammal of comparable size, such as a shrew-mouse, which is continually active, has to eat at least its own weight of food every day, and dies of old age before it is eighteen months old. But a bat, which spends nine-tenths of its time not only asleep, but more than half dead, does not wear out nearly so quickly; an example of our smallest species, the Lesser Horseshoe bat, has been known to reach an age of at least nine years.

Life-spans of this order are essential to bats if they are not to become extinct; they usually produce one, sometimes two, and rarely three, young at a birth once a year. For a species to maintain its numbers each female must leave at least one daughter who survives to breed;

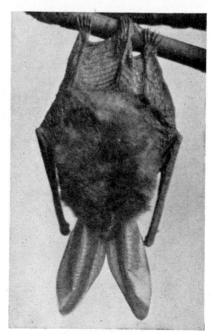

LONG-EARED BAT

In proportion to the size of its body, the Long-eared bat has larger ears than any other creature. Its hearing is keen.

and, allowing for accidents and the production of males, this will mean producing at least three offspring in a lifetime. As far as is known, female bats do not breed until they are two years old, so they must reach an age of at least something over five years in order to fulfil these requirements.

Many bats of temperate parts of the world mate in the autumn before hibernating, but the females do not become pregnant until after awakening the following spring. The sperm received from the male lies dormant inside the female throughout the winter sleep, so that fertilization is delayed, and the embryo does not start to develop until the resumption of activity. It is not known if, or in what way, this peculiar arrangement can be of advantage to bats. When the young is born it is carried about clinging to the fur of the mother, and is suckled at her breasts. In some of the Leaf-nosed bats there is an additional pair of teats near the groin; these "anchoring nipples" do not produce milk, as do the ones on the breast, but serve as hold-fasts which the young bat grasps in its mouth while clinging to its mother.

PREDATORY BATS

Some of the Microchiroptera have given up their diet of insects and taken to very strange foods. In the tropics there is a family of rather large bats, the Megadermidae, which have powerful jaws and large canine teeth. Some of these are the hawks among the bats, and they feed upon the smaller insect-eating species; they are sometimes called Cannibal bats, but that is hardly fair, for we do not call hawks and owls cannibals because they eat other birds. Stranger than these are the Fish-eating bats which have been found in several parts of the world, India, Burma and the tropics of America. In the Caribbean region a species of *Noctilio* leaves the land as dusk falls and flies out over the sea, where it catches small fish, swooping down and snatching them from the surface of the water with the sharp claws of the feet.

VAMPIRE BATS

In tropical America, too, dwell the almost legendary Vampire bats, which live on the blood of other animals. Contrary to popular belief, they are quite tiny species, and some of the larger bats with fierce, ugly-looking faces which have been called "vampires" are not blood-drinkers. There are, in fact, only three such species, forming the family Desmodontidae. Their upper front teeth are flattened, elongated and have excessively sharp edges, like little razors, which are used to shave off a thin layer from the skin of the victim, so that the blood oozes from the minute bloodvessels which are severed. The vampire does not lull its victim by fanning it with the wings; it settles very lightly, and runs on the surface with great nimbleness to select the spot for its bite, supporting itself high on its legs and arms, with the flying-web tucked close up out of the way. When it has cut the skin it does not suck the wound, but laps up the oozing blood with its tongue. A captive vampire fed from a glass of blood lapped at such a speed that "a pulsating ribbon of blood spanned the gap between the surface of the fluid and the creature's lips."

The loss of blood suffered by man or his domestic animals from a vampire's bite is negligible; nevertheless a bite may lead to serious results, for it has been found that the bite of a vampire, like that of a mad dog, can transmit rabies. In the West Indies fatal outbreaks of this terrible disease, both in man and

JAVELIN VAMPIRE

The Javelin is not a true vampire and derives its name from its appearance, not from blood-sucking habits. Contrary to usual belief, vampires are small bats and are more to be dreaded as disease-carriers than as blood-suckers.

animals, have been traced to the attacks of vampires. As far as is known, no other species of microchiropteran bat is inimical to man; indeed, the vast majority are directly beneficial through the enormous number of insects that they destroy.

But bats can serve man in other ways; bat-roosts in caves often contain many thousands of bats, and where such roosts have been in existence for long, perhaps for hundreds of years, the deposit of droppings on the floor may reach a depth of many feet. This layer of guano is a valuable agricultural fertilizer which has been mined with profit in many parts of the world. But the most fantastic use of bats is the bat-bomb, which was invented in America during the Second World War. Small 1-oz. incen-

diary bombs, with delayed-action fuses, were strapped to bats, which were packed in containers holding from one to five thousand; the bats were gathered from a Texas cave whose population was estimated at between twenty and thirty millions, and if kept at a low temperature they needed no food or attention for long periods. The container, attached to a parachute, was thrown from an aeroplane, and arranged to open at a thousand feet to let out the bats, which scattered widely and settled in the target area; in one trial a dummy village was successfully burnt down. However, the long-awaited perfection of atomic weapons made the use of bat-bombs unnecessary. Man's inhumanity to man is matched only by his brutality to brutes.

THE ONLY NATIVE BRITISH SQUIRREL

This handsome, bright-eyed little fellow is a Red squirrel, the only species of the squirrel tribe that is native to the British Isles. During the last half-century it has been outnumbered in many parts of these islands by the larger Grey squirrel, introduced from North America. Squirrels spend most of their lives in the tree-tops, where they build large nests composed of twigs, moss and leaves and known as "dreys."

Gnawing animals

SINCE a rat-catcher has now come to be known as a Rodent Operative, nobody is any longer in doubt that a rat is a rodent. It might even be said that for most of us the rat typifies the rodents as a whole, but, whatever the case, the rat is only one of the 6,400 forms of rodents found throughout the world, and the order Rodentia is the richest in species as well as in numbers of individuals and the most successful in the mammalian world. A measure of the adaptability of rodents is perhaps best seen in the extent to which they have been able to occupy practically every type of habitat. Thus we have the burrowing rodents, climbing rodents, aquatic rodents, desert rodents, gliding rodents, and so on.

What do we mean by adaptability? When we say one animal is more adaptable than another, do we suggest that there is something inherent in the physical or mental make-up of that animal which gives it advantages over others, or is there something in its equipment which enables it successfully to meet changing conditions? The answer in the case of rodents is at least partially seen in the structure of the incisors, which, in the great majority of cases, constitute an efficient pair of chisels serving a variety of purposes; they probably reach their highest efficiency in the beaver or porcupine.

The rodent incisors differ from our own in a number of features. To begin with they are rootless and grow as fast as they are worn away. Secondly, they are deeply set in the bone structure of the skull. Thirdly, the surface is coated with enamel on the front of the tooth only, so that as the tooth of the upper jaw works against its opposite number in the lower jaw the inner edge wears away more rapidly than the front edge and so a constant chisel-edge is maintained. A few examples will be sufficient to show the value of these cutting incisors. We have the familiar action of the beaver in felling trees; the rat gnawing through tins to get at preserved foods or biting through lead pipes, plasterwork, and solid planks; and the habit of the North American porcupines of chewing bottles.

It is usually the way that any marked advantage is apt to be linked with a strong disadvantage, and in this case a prerequisite of the efficient functioning of the rodent incisors is that their cutting edges should meet exactly. If for any reason this does not happen and the teeth get slightly out of place, the edge is not worn away, but the tooth goes on growing from the base, becomes enormously long and curved and hampers the feeding of its possessor. It not infrequently happens that a rat is found in a starving or dying condition because its incisors have grown out in this way.

The order Rodentia is subdivided into three main groups: the Sciuromorpha, or squirrels, marmots and beavers; the Myomorpha, or rats, mice and voles; and the Hystricomorpha, or the porcupines, cavies and agoutis. The distinction between these three groups rests primarily on details of the structure of the skull and limb bones. Normally, however, the squirrels are recognizable as a group because they have for the most part bushy tails, whereas the Myomorpha usually have naked or thinly haired tails. The Hystricomorpha, typified by the spiny porcupines, nevertheless include a number of animals having no obvious features in common except it be their large size.

WORLD-WIDE ANIMALS

Squirrels are world-wide (except for Australia and Madagascar). Wherever there is a wood or a forest there are squirrels, but they do not necessarily need trees, because wherever there is vegetation there are squirrels. Although squirrels may range in size from the Pygmy squirrels of West Africa and Borneo, no larger than a mouse, to the giant Indian squirrels as big as a large domesticated cat, and although they may show a great diversity of colour, they have so many characteristics in common that one is seldom in doubt of their identification as squirrels. There are, for example, the bushy tail, the well-haired body, often tufted ears, sharp claws, and active diurnal habits which contrast strongly with the nocturnal habits of so many other rodents. They are almost entirely vegetarian, except for a few species which are specially adapted for eating insects.

So far as their habit is concerned squirrels may be divided approximately into three groups—flying squirrels (dealt with in the section on "Mammals which Fly and Glide"), ground squirrels and typical squirrels, the last being exemplified by the imported Grey squirrel or the British native Red squirrel.

The ground squirrels include such well-known examples as chipmunks and susliks and a wide variety of other forms distributed mainly in the open country of North America and South and Central Asia. The term "ground squirrel" is not a very apt one in so far as though it indicates squirrels that spend most of their time on the ground, there are those which readily take to trees when danger threatens, as well as those which go to earth; it is perhaps these latter, which remain either on the ground or burrow into it, which may be conveniently regarded as the typical ground squirrels.

Outwardly the ground squirrels differ from the typical Grey squirrels, for example, in having longer and stouter bodies, shorter tails and often longer snouts, so that they resemble to some extent the ground-living marmots which are distantly related to them. In other words, instead of being active, agile tree-dwellers they are sometimes waddling and clumsy ground-dwellers.

STORES FOR THE WINTER

Another noticeable feature is that they are more complete hibernators than the arboreal squirrels. This is almost to be expected, for they inhabit open treeless country, and survival through the severe winters must depend on their avoidance of exposure. Their complete hibernation depends on an ability to store up fat in their tissues, which is supplemented in some species by stores of grain in the burrows, the function of which would appear to be to feed the emaciated animal on its emergence from the winter sleep.

In the Oriental tropical region there are two genera of forest-living ground

PRAIRIE DOGS FEEDING

With their large, powerful digging claws, Prairie dogs are experts at tunnelling. Their burrows form extensive "cities," with sentries to give warning of danger.

squirrels—*Rhinosciurus* and *Hyosciurus*—which have gone a stage further than other ground squirrels in the lengthening of the muzzle, and in addition their incisor teeth have become so reduced in size as to be practically functionless. In fact, these teeth are so thin and small that they cannot be used for gnawing, but can still be used for seizing insects and ants on which they feed.

Rhinosciurus has developed an extremely long extensile tongue with which it gathers in ants together with, apparently, a large amount of grit which produces exceptionally early wear in the cheek teeth, reducing them to mere stumps at a comparatively early age. It is not possible to draw hard-and-fast conclusions from this, but it is at least stimulating to compare the long muzzle, the long tongue, the diet of insects and the reduction of the teeth in other ant-eating forms, such as the scaly ant-eaters and the ant-eaters of South America, which will be dealt with in the section on "Some odd animals."

Squirrels of arboreal habit, which are represented in Britain by the native "Red" and imported "Grey," are all very much alike in build. The majority do not vary much in size, although there is considerable variation in colour. They are found throughout the world, except in Australia and Madagascar, wherever there is wooded country. In general their diet is vegetarian, but they will augment this with insects, birds' eggs or even young birds as, for example, in the case of both the Red and Grey squirrels. It may be worth emphasizing at this point that, contrary to the usual belief, it is not only the Grey squirrel which destroys birds' eggs and young; the Red squirrel is equally culpable.

The general similarity in form and habit of the arboreal squirrels makes it unnecessary in this limited space to particularize many species. It is, however, a suitable opportunity to consider in slightly more detail one species only, and for this purpose we cannot do better than take the Grey squirrel (*Sciurus carolinensis*), a native of the eastern U.S.A., deliberately imported into Britain as a pet in private parks towards the end of the nineteenth century. It has so taken to its new quarters and so increased in numbers that British farmers have to wage incessant warfare to keep its numbers within bounds.

The introduction of the Grey squirrel is merely one example of the many importations or introductions of animals made by man either deliberately or accidentally. Very rarely are these without accompanying evil and the Grey squirrel is no exception to this. It is not true to say that the Grey squirrel is ousting the native Red—rather, it is occupying the territory vacated by a species already diminishing in numbers.

THE GREY SQUIRREL

One interesting aspect of the introduction of the Grey squirrel is the fact that the dates of the introduction are known and it has been possible by means of censuses to study statistically its spread throughout the country. This research is not sufficiently advanced to enable us to draw far-reaching conclusions, but it does shed a little light on one or two typical rodent problems. It has been found, for example, that when the Grey squirrel population in a given locality approaches saturation point one or more pairs of immature squirrels will migrate, but they do not merely leave the area for the nearest suitable locality. Instead, a pair is likely to wander for up to thirty miles from their original home before settling down, passing a number of good feeding-grounds on the way.

IMPULSE TO MIGRATE

An obvious interpretation of this is that once the stimulus to migrate is applied it carries the animals much farther than their physical needs demand, and it suggests a clue to the mass migrations of the lemmings—that familiar story—where the pressure of population sets up a migratory impulse which may in some cases end, after a long trek overland, in a sort of mass suicide in the sea. It is interesting to recall that in America mass migrations of squirrels have also been noted, though the causes and consequences have not yet been fully studied.

Since we have turned our attention to America it is also of interest to note that, whereas the British accuse the Grey squirrel of ousting the Red squirrel, in eastern U.S.A. the native Red squirrel is known to have a positively aggressive behaviour towards the Grey squirrel. It may not be out of place to add to this recital of the anomalies of the Grey squirrel the following observed fact; that whereas the beast becomes a pest in open country, it does not become troublesome in a park, and this has been strikingly brought out in the contrast of its behaviour in the open country with its behaviour in the parks, particularly in Canada.

The marmots (*Marmota*) and Prairie dogs (*Cynomys ludovicianus*) belong to the same family as the squirrels and have

TWO YOUNG BEAVERS ARE TAUGHT DAM-BUILDING

Canadian beavers are among the star engineers of the animal world, and their lodges and dams are marvels of ingenuity and skill. Here two young beavers are being taught by their watchful mother to fell a sapling by biting through the stem. Meanwhile, the father beaver goes for a swim in the lake. Note the mother's broad, flat tail.

the same skull characters, but differ in outward appearance and habits from the typical squirrels. In them the tendencies seen in the ground squirrels have been carried still further. They have round plump bodies, short tails and enlarged digging claws and they are habitually burrowing. There is, moreover, a complete hibernation; this is underlined by the legend associated with the woodchuck (*Marmota monax*). It is said that this animal will emerge from hibernation, but if it sees its own shadow cast by the sun will go back again to sleep. It would appear that modern meteorological research does not entirely disprove this legend.

Marmots are typically found in mountainous country living among the rocks. In North America they are found principally in the Rocky Mountains, in Europe in the Alps, and in Asia in the Himalayas and the Central Asian ranges generally. Their food is mainly grass, roots, tubers and bulbs, and they habitually remain close to the mouths of their burrows into which they dive rapidly at any sign of danger. It seems to be fairly well established that they do rely on the warning from sentries, who raise the alarm with a peculiar high-pitched whistle. The characteristic diet has resulted in one species, the woodchuck, becoming an agricultural pest in North America.

The difficulty in exterminating the woodchuck consists in the animal's extreme wariness, its deep burrow to which it can retire, and the fact that its size—it is as large as a large cat—together with its sharp incisors make it a formidable adversary to a dog.

The Prairie dog is related to the marmot and is of similar build, with fat body and waddling gait. It seldom goes far from its burrow, and is as great a pest in the prairie country as the woodchuck is in the farm lands. The burrows are a danger to horsemen, and prairie dogs, which have been reliably computed to number millions over an area of a few square miles, have been sufficient, with the burrowing habit, to alter the appearance of the land; for their method of burrowing tends to throw the countryside into a series of mounds. It is not unusual for rattlesnakes and burrowing owls to be found in the burrows of the Prairie dogs, and at one time this was thought to be an amicable sharing of the subterranean home. It has now been found, however, that the rattlesnake and the owl are there to feed on the Prairie dogs.

Of the two species of beavers the Canadian beaver (*Castor canadensis*) is probably known to everybody, while the European beaver (*C. fiber*) is almost unknown. The beaver was widespread in Europe until about the Middle Ages, but is now restricted to a few localities in France, Germany and eastern Europe.

ENGINEERING FEATS

The Canadian beaver is $3\frac{1}{2}$ ft. long with a blunt head and a broad, flat, scaly tail. Its front feet are clawed for digging, its hind-feet webbed. It feeds on the bark of saplings and other vegetation, burrows into banks of rivers and builds lodges and dams by felling trees and skilfully placing the trunks in position. In appearance and structure it is virtually impossible to tell the two species of beaver apart, yet the European beaver does not carry out the engineering feats so characteristic of its North American cousin. It is believed, however, that this is only a result of persecu-

tion, that the dams and lodges betray the presence of the beaver with fatal result to it; and recent evidence tends to show that where the European beaver is protected the absence of persecution results in a re-assertion of the habit of damming rivers.

PROTECTED ANIMAL

There are other interesting comparisons to be made between the two species; in Europe the beaver was seriously reduced in numbers for the sake of its fur. In North America the value of the beaver fur was responsible for opening up much of the continent, and at one time the pelts were actually used as currency. In the end, however, the animal became scarce and today we see the beaver protected not only in Europe but in North America, where wise conservation is restoring it to its former position.

The remainder of the Sciuromorpha includes Pocket gophers, Pocket mice, Kangaroo rats, Cape jumping-hares and Scaly-tailed flying squirrels, all of which in spite of their differences are believed to be related through their skull characteristics.

The Pocket gophers (*Thomomys*) are specialized burrowing rodents, mole-like in form, with a highly sensitive tail, and able to move both backwards and forwards in their burrows. Like the moles they have minute eyes and ears; they honeycomb the ground with their burrows and feed on roots and bulbs just below the surface, often doing much damage to crops. With the aid of their external cheek-pouches they are able to carry away more food than can be eaten on the spot.

Pocket mice (*Perognathus*) and Kangaroo rats (*Dipodomys*), of the southern U.S.A., belong to the same group as the gophers, but the Kangaroo rats have long hind-legs and long tails, and they progress kangaroo-like by leaps. They, too, have cheek-pouches and come out at night to feed on seeds. They spend the day in their burrows, blocking the entrances with sand to keep out the heat and the bright light, and possibly also snakes.

The Scaly-tailed flying squirrels, though superficially squirrel-like, have somewhat different skull characters suggesting that they are only distantly related to the true squirrels. They are dealt with in the section "Mammals which Fly and Glide."

Finally, in the group Sciuromorpha we have the Cape jumping-hares (*Pedetes cafer*), which are included here merely as a matter of convenience for their relationships are very doubtful.

Kangaroo-like, they are about the size of a hare, with large eyes and ears, hoof-like claws on each of the four toes of the hind-feet and hairy tails. They live in colonies in burrows made in loose sandy soil in the open plains of East and South Africa.

The sub-order Myomorpha (rats, mice and voles) includes a bewildering number of species, many of which are noted for their large populations. They are the most successful of all mammals if judged by their ability to thrive in all sorts of places and under all sorts of conditions, for practically no part of the world is without its rats and mice.

Where they are not native they have been unwittingly introduced by man, and constitute throughout the world an economic scourge and a frequent

KANGAROO RAT OF SOUTHERN UNITED STATES

The Kangaroo rat is peculiar to North America. It moves by leaps of its long hind-legs, somewhat in the manner of a kangaroo, and stores its food temporarily in cheek-pouches. To avoid heat, light and enemies, it blocks the mouth of its burrow with sand.

CAPE JUMPING-HARE OF SOUTH AFRICA

The Cape jumping-hare somewhat resembles the jerboa, but is about as big as a cat, with relatively enormous hind-legs and undersized fore-paws. It ranges from the Cape to as far north as East Africa, and congregates in colonies.

carrier of disease. Their small size, wary habits, ability to feed on anything edible, their burrowing and gnawing powers, as well as their rapid rate of reproduction, are factors against which man-made controls are virtually impotent. Nevertheless there are some members of this sub-order, such as dormice, jerboas and Mole rats, which, although they fit naturally into the scheme of things, have not become widespread or numerous.

The great bulk of the Myomorpha is contained within the limits of two families: the Cricetidae and the Muridae, and these two families, although remarkably alike in external form, exhibit anatomical differences which not only serve to separate the living members but indicate clearly that they have been produced along two quite independent lines of evolution.

The Cricetidae include rats and mice of the American continent, together with all the voles of the world and the hamsters and lemmings found in Europe and Asia. The Muridae include the rats and mice of the Old World. Since, however, the words "rats and mice" are used for both these families, it will avoid confusion if the members of the Cricetidae are spoken of as "cricetines" and those of the Muridae as "murines." Of the many species of cricetines found in America, mention should be made of the Pack rat, the Banana mouse and the Fishing rats.

The Pack rat (*Neotoma*) builds large

nests of sticks and leaves around cactus bushes. In addition it has a strong instinct to collect bright objects and will, like the magpie, carry away coins, nails, and so on. But it has one peculiarity to distinguish it from the rest of the animal thieves, inasmuch as when it steals something it often leaves behind another object to replace the stolen article—usually a stone.

In the days of large banana imports the Banana mouse (*Nyctomys sumichrasti*) was frequently an involuntary visitor to Britain on the banana boats.

The Fishing rats (*Ichthyomys*) live in the mountain streams of tropical South America, have flattened skulls, hook-like upper incisors and webbed hind-feet for swimming. They probably feed on fish and other small aquatic animals.

The Common hamster (*Cricetus cricetus*) of Europe and Asia is the arch-hoarder. It not only has cheek-pouches for temporary storage of food, but stores up in its complicated burrows bushels of potatoes, carrots and other such crops. Since a female hamster may have anything from six to eighteen young at a birth, the menace to crops can be readily imagined.

The Golden hamster (*Mesocricetus auratus*) probably presents the most striking anomaly of the whole animal kingdom. In its native haunts it is extremely rare, but as a semi-domesticated animal it is remarkably abundant. In 1839 the first Golden hamster was made known to zoologists. It was not

A HAMSTER VISITING HIS "PANTRY"

The Common hamster of Europe and Asia is remarkable for its propensity for hoarding food. Grain and root crops are heavily pillaged by this robust, voracious little creature, which stores up its booty in huge quantities in underground granaries, in preparation for the winter. This rodent is black below, yellow and rufous above.

seen again, however, until 1930, when a female and twelve young were dug out of a hole eight feet deep in Syria, taken to Jerusalem and there kept in captivity. In the following year some of the progeny were brought to England, where the species rapidly became popular as a pet and as a laboratory animal. Such a history would probably have been impossible but for the very high birthrate, a female Golden hamster being capable of producing a litter of from fourteen to twenty-two young in fifteen days, the young being fully grown at eleven weeks.

MIGRATION OF THE LEMMINGS

Related to the Golden hamster and showing something of its extraordinary fecundity is the well-known Norwegian lemming (*Lemmus lemmus*). Although there are other species of lemming, this one will serve as a pattern for the rest. There are probably few natural phenomena about which more has been written than the migration of the lemmings, or about which more misleading ideas are current.

The usual story conveyed by writers on this topic is of vast columns of lemmings moving across country, nose to tail, fording rivers over the dead bodies of their comrades who have preceded them, swarming over the mountains, through the valleys, until they reach the sea, into which they continue their frenzied drive in a sort of mass suicide. Such an idea is often supported by artists' drawings depicting this entirely fictitious scene.

The truth is that it is surprisingly difficult to find anyone who can produce a photograph showing more than one lemming at a time. The basis for this exaggerated story lies in a phenomenon, the cyclic rise and fall of rodent populations, which is a common feature of many species of the order of rodents.

The Norwegian lemmings, small guinea-pig-like animals coloured a vivid black and yellow, live on the mountains. Now and then over a period of years the population starts to build up; locally a "saturation" population develops and many individuals move down from the mountains into the valleys below in search of food. However the increase goes on and as the population continues to rise the movement outwards also continues, and in the course of this there is little doubt that the dead bodies of lemmings can often be seen floating in the fjords in considerable numbers.

While it may be true that the high rate of reproduction coupled with an abundance of food are the primary factors in such a cyclic rise in the population, it would appear that this is linked with some emotional impulse which we cannot appreciate. The fact that some individuals are found drowned suggests that the original stimulus to migrate goes on beyond the bounds dictated by circumstances and assumes the proportions of a kind of hysteria in which all sense of self-preservation is overborne and lost.

END OF THE CYCLE

Conversely, such a periodic rise in numbers is always followed by a fall. This is occasioned by the inroads of predators, the over-grazing of food supplies, outbreaks of disease, and other such recognizable factors. At the same time we may postulate that there is a recession of the emotional stimulus, although we cannot prove this. At all events, the net result is that at the end of the cycle the lemming population has assumed its former proportions and its former range on the high ground.

The last group of the cricetines is

THE LEMMING—HERO OF A LEGEND
The Norwegian lemming, popularly believed to migrate periodically in immense hordes which not even the ocean can turn aside, is a cheeky-looking little creature with a striking black and yellow coat and, by all accounts, an exceedingly bad temper.

the voles, small mouse-like creatures, with short tails, small eyes and loose fur almost hiding the short ears. They are found almost exclusively in the northern ranges of both the Eastern and Western Hemispheres, living in the barren tundras and areas of coarse grass which forms the main part of their diet.

They are all similar in form and appearance, and although there is a large number of genera and species, each one of which presents its own peculiarly interesting features, it is not possible to deal with them here in more than general terms. Like the lemmings, the great majority of voles are subject to periodic fluctuations in numbers, so that it is usual to speak of "good vole years" and "bad vole years." Moreover, since voles form the staple diet of so many predators, such as stoats, weasels,

foxes, owls and hawks, the rise and fall of vole populations is matched with periodic abundance and relative scarcity in the numbers of those animals that prey upon them.

One of the larger of the voles is the water-vole (*Arvicola amphibius*), often wrongly called the "water-rat." It differs from the true rat, however, by its blunt head and its small eyes and ears almost concealed in fur. Perhaps the strangest thing about the water-vole is that, while it feeds very largely on aquatic plants, burrows in river banks and is an active and efficient swimmer and diver, it has no special modifications of the body to this end, except a slight fringe of hair on the sides of the hind-feet which can be detected only by the closest and most careful scrutiny. Over a large part of Europe, the water-vole is replaced by a nearly related

WATER-VOLE ABOUT TO GO FOR A SWIM

The water-vole is often erroneously called the "water-rat," although it is not a true rat at all. It burrows in the banks of streams and spends much of its time in the water, in which it is just as active as it is on land. Anatomically speaking, its sole modification for its largely aquatic existence is a slight fringe of hairs on its hind-feet.

species, which curiously enough is naturally terrestrial and burrows like a mole!

The largest of the voles, the Musk rat (*Ondatra zibethica*) has a particular claim on our attention for two reasons; it is an important fur-bearing animal and, in the effort to exploit it, it was introduced into Europe for breeding on fur-farms, whence it has escaped and become a pest; its large burrows have undermined the banks of rivers and in some places converted whole stretches of the countryside into marshland. At one time in Britain there was the fear that irreparable damage might be caused but a vigorous campaign against the Musk rat averted this. In some parts of the U.S.A. the annual harvest of

millions of skins is carefully adjusted to leave sufficient breeding stocks for the following season. The maintenance of these breeding stocks is possible through the high rate of breeding, which may be summarized as three to five litters of six to eight in each litter in a year.

The family Muridae—the murines according to our earlier definition—is the most successful family of the rodents, not only in numbers but in adaptability. Although closely related to the cricetines it is noticeable that the phenomenon of periodic fluctuation of populations is absent or, at the least, not well marked. On the other hand it does appear that their adaptability enables them to increase in numbers locally in a more steady manner, with an outward migration from centres of increased population which results in permanent extension of their range.

The practical result of this, in general terms, is that rats and mice, following man all over the world, have successfully colonized wherever there is a human settlement. At the same time it is the case that there are spasmodic and rapid increases in the populations, particularly of mice, giving rise to occasional plagues. In order to illustrate, briefly but vividly, the successful spread of murines throughout the world it may be mentioned that the Black rat (*Rattus rattus*) did not reach Britain until the return of the Crusaders and the Brown rat (*R. norvegicus*) has been there little more than two hundred years.

The importance of mice and, particularly, rats as pests of stored foods and as carriers of disease can hardly be over-emphasized. The loss of stored foods —cereals in bags, tinned foods of all kinds—as a result of being eaten or merely fouled by rodents, amounts to several million pounds' worth per year in Britain alone. If, leaving other factors unchanged, we could exterminate all rats and mice, a great part of the world's food problem would be solved.

The effect of the murines as carriers of disease can be illustrated with two examples. The first effect of the introduction of the Black rat to Europe was the Black Death, which in places carried off nine out of every ten of the human population. In more recent years we

BRIGHT-EYED AND MOUSE-LIKE—A BRITISH BANK VOLE

The Bank vole is not a mouse, although it so closely resembles one. The voles belong, however, to the same order as mice, and, like the latter, are guilty of serious depreda-tions, especially among stores of grain, or seed corn in the ground.

have the problem faced by the armies in Burma, where heavy casualties resulted from scrub typhus—a disease carried in a mite living on the rat.

One of the outstanding characters of rodents as a whole is their propensity for storing food. Reference has already been made to this in regard to the voles and it is a familiar feature of the squirrels. Some of the murines are equally addicted to this habit, and a good example is seen in the Bandicoot rat or Indian Mole rat (*Bandicota bengalensis*), which is rather like the Brown rat in appearance and is common in India, where its numerous burrows are marked by heaps of excavated earth. The Bandicoot rat stores grain in its burrows and in times of emergency the villagers raid these stores.

Fortunately, most of the murines are of small size and it is particularly fortunate that the giant rats of New Guinea, which reach a total length of 3 ft., have a comparatively local distribution. Moreover, the giant rats have not yet adopted the habit of sharing human habitations with their owners.

THE ENDEARING DORMOUSE

In contrast to its more troublesome, and to most people repulsive, relatives the dormouse (*Muscardinus avellanarius*) has managed to stake a particular claim in our affections. Its squirrel-like ways, bright eyes, bushy tail, pink feet, engaging habits, and the fact that it keeps to the hedgerows and does not exist in noticeably large numbers, have made it something of a favourite, even to those—which include the majority—who have never even seen it. Above all it is the best-known example in Britain of a hibernating animal. With the onset of autumn it accumulates a store of fat, builds a nest of dry grass and, at the proper moment, retires into the nest,

closing the entrance so securely that it is impossible to see how the animal gets in. There it goes into a deep sleep until the following spring.

The jerboas have specialized in a life in the hot sandy deserts of Africa, Arabia and other parts of Asia. The body is rat-like in size, but the build is more that of a kangaroo, with long hind-legs and long attenuated tail that acts as a third support when at rest. The front limbs are small and are practically never put to the ground, being used almost exclusively for holding food.

"DESERT RATS"

Jerboas are nocturnal, remaining in burrows during the day to escape the heat and the intense sunlight, blocking up the entrance to make this more certain. They appear to be capable of living without water and feed exclusively on the seeds of desert grasses. Being nocturnal, their eyes are large, also their ears, and the toes of the hind-feet are fringed with thick hair-tufts below to enable the jerboas to get a grip on the loose, moving sand. Relatively to their size their powers of leaping are probably greater than those of any other mammal.

The name of the final sub-order of rodents, Hystricomorpha (porcupine-like animals), is apt to be misleading, for it includes not only porcupines but the agoutis, coypus, vizcachas and pacas. Most of these are confined to South America and the rest are represented by the porcupines of Africa and southern Asia. Some are as small as rats, but a fair proportion of them are large. Not all are spiny; indeed, most have a normal hairy coat. All have one character in common, an outward twisting of the bony part of the lower jaw.

The porcupines are divided into two families, the Hystricidae or Old World

CRESTED PORCUPINE WITH ITS BABY

*Porcupines of the Old World—of which the Crested porcupines above are examples—
are ground-living animals, while their American relatives are tree-climbers. Although
it is not true that porcupines can shoot their quills at aggressors, they can nevertheless,
by running backwards with quills erected, inflict painful wounds with them.*

porcupines and the Erethizontidae of
the New World. The former have their
bodies heavily armed with long spines,
are nocturnal and hide up in burrows
during the day. The spines are an
effective defence and, as so often
happens where an animal possesses a
good passive defence, there appears to
be something in the nature of a warning coloration, in this case a black-and-
white pattern. This "hands off" signal
is supplemented by the habit of rattling
the quills of the tail, which is a further
warning to would-be aggressors.

These porcupines, which are vegetarian, feeding on roots, bark, cultivated
crops, fruit, and so on, range in size
from the African brush-tailed porcupine (*Atheroura africana*), about the
size of a rabbit, to the Indian porcupine
(*Hystrix lecura*) up to 3½ ft. long and
weighing up to 40 lb.

It is surprising that porcupines
should be active only at night, since on
all counts they should have little to
fear. Their bodies are thickset, their
feet and claws powerful, and the quills
seem sufficient to discourage even such

JERBOA—LOVER OF THE HOT, SANDY DESERT

Jerboas have become specialized for a life in the desert. They feed upon the seeds of desert grasses and can live for long periods without water. Their hairy toes grip the loose, shifting sand, while their enormously long hind-limbs propel them forward in leaps of impressive and relatively kangaroo-like magnitude.

animals as leopards and tigers. Although it is not unknown for a porcupine to be killed by one of the larger cats, the victor usually retains traces of the event in the form of spines in the face and pads—but there is no truth in the belief that porcupines can shoot their quills at the enemy!

It may, however, be worth mentioning that a porcupine can and will rush backwards at its enemy with the spines erect, and it is in such rushes as these that loose quills often fall out or may be left behind in the attacker's skin.

The New World porcupines, although resembling in many ways those found in Africa and Asia, are not closely related. If they had a common ancestor then the two groups must have diverged a fair way back, speaking geologically, for there are differences in their skulls and in their teeth, and they are mainly tree-climbers with the hind-feet adapted for this. The South American porcupines have long prehensile tails. There is only one species in North America, the Canadian porcupine, which has the body covered with thick hair almost completely concealing the spines. Although the quills are short they have the unpleasant character of being barbed and once this barbed type has entered the skin, it may work its way through the flesh for a considerable distance, if the quill is not quickly removed.

The Canadian porcupine (*Erethizon dorsatum*) measures up to 3½ ft. long and weighs up to 40 lb.; it feeds on bark, buds and leaves, often climbing trees to get them. It remains active throughout even the coldest winter and is often a great nuisance in the vicinity of camps, owing to the habit of gnawing the handles of tools such as axes or picks or gnawing through glass bottles; in many places it has been outlawed.

The South American porcupines are more markedly adapted for tree-climbing, their long prehensile tails often bearing stiff bristles at the root to assist in gripping the smooth trunks and the hind-foot having a fleshy pad which can be opposed to the four toes for grasping.

The remainder of the South American hystricomorphs are without spines, except for some known as the Spiny rats which have short weak spines

mixed with the fur of the back, but these cannot be compared with the quills of the porcupines. All the rest are soft-furred and can be conveniently grouped with cavies and their kin; the most familiar of these are the domesticated guinea-pigs derived from the Brazilian cavy (*Cavia aperea*) and already domesticated by the Incas of Peru when the Europeans first visited that country. Many of the wild cavies live in the long grass or among rocks. The Patagonian cavy (*Dolichotis patagona*) is hare-like and is often called the Patagonian hare. Its long hind-legs bear three toes with hoof-like claws. It is very wary and depends for safety on its speed.

The capybara (*Hydrochoerus hydrochaeris*) is the largest of all rodents,

PLAIN-DWELLERS OF SOUTH AMERICA

The cavies are all South American animals and are very widespread, from grassland to high, rocky country. They include the familiar guinea-pig, or Brazilian cavy. The plain-dwelling Patagonian cavy, illustrated above, somewhat resembles a hare, although it is a burrowing animal. Like the hare, it is fleet of foot.

THE CAPYBARA—LARGEST OF ALL RODENTS

A full-grown capybara weighs well over 100 lb., and hence this animal is by far the biggest of all rodents. It inhabits swamps and the banks of streams in South America and swims with ease, being able to remain under water for several minutes at a time. Only by taking to the water can it escape from its arch-enemy, the jaguar.

about the size of a pig, weighs up to 110 lb., lives in troops in tropical South America and feeds abundantly on greenstuff. For this reason it is not welcome in plantations, but apart from this it is inoffensive. It lives near rivers and lakes and takes to water readily to escape its enemy, the jaguar.

The paca (*Cuniculus paca*), heavily built and about the size of a small pig, is remarkable for the capacious cheek-pouches used for storing food and especially for the way in which the cheek-bones (which in the rodents are normally narrow bridges) are much enlarged to form a shield-like outer protection to the pouches.

The agoutis (*Dasyprocta aguti*) of Mexico to Peru are rabbit-like, with long slender legs and hoof-like claws on the three toes of the hind-feet. They live in thick cover and depend on speed for safety, and it is possible that the early ancestor of the horse had feet very similar to these, and for the same reason. The hind-feet of the agouti and those of the early horse furnish a fine example of convergent evolution, where a similar shape or structure is developed in response to a similar need.

The next animals in order, the chinchillas (*Chinchilla laniger*), are very scarce in the wild state, but their history is worth recounting. They were once numerous in the high mountains of the Andes, when it was discovered that they possessed a very fine fur which could be sold at a high price. As is usual where quick money is the temptation, they were hounded almost to extinction while their furs fed a trade synonymous with luxury and opulence, a cloak of chinchilla fur often fetching as much as £1,000. When their numbers had sunk so low they were not worth hunting, the South American governments stepped in and protected the remainder. Subsequently an enterprising American managed to transport half a dozen of the living animals to California with the object of setting up chinchilla farms. The progeny from these have been sold at high prices as breeding pairs, but it is unlikely that anything in the nature of a flourishing industry will result, because of the poor wearing qualities of the skins. The chinchilla fur is very fine to look at and has a greater number of fibres to the square inch than that of any other mammal, but it is on this account that the hairs are rapidly broken and worn.

MOUNTAIN CHINCHILLAS

The chinchilla is an attractive squirrel-like animal, nearly 1 ft. long, with a bushy tail of about the same length, large eyes, delicate ears and a silver-grey fur. A clear distinction must be drawn between the True chinchilla and the Mountain chinchilla or Mountain vizcacha (*Lagidium*) which is also found in the Andes and their foot-hills from Peru to the Argentine. It is larger than the True chinchilla and, having fur of poor quality, has not been persecuted. Mountain chinchillas live in colonies in rocky places, feeding on grass and herbage. In any case they would be difficult to exterminate, for they seldom venture far from the mouths of their burrows, are extremely watchful for enemies and give a clear warning whistle at any sign of danger. Their general mode of life recalls very strongly that of marmots. One marked peculiarity is the way the bushy tail is carried with the end third curled upwards.

The coypu (*Myocastor coypus*), which lives in the Argentine, is a large rat-like animal 3½ ft. long, including the long naked tail. It is aquatic and lives on a large range of vegetable food. "Nutria" is the name given to its underfur after the guard hairs have been removed, and because of the value of this fur the coypu has been introduced into many parts of the world. In Europe, including Britain, nutria farms have been set up.

AN IMPORTED PEST

In Britain, during the Second World War, the coypu was released or escaped and became established in the Norfolk Broads and similar localities; it is apt to do considerable damage, not only by feeding on the vegetation but by trampling it down. Through the agency of the British Ministry of Agriculture some four hundred coypus were killed during the war years because of the damage they were doing, but there is no danger of their undermining river banks in the same way as the Musk rat.

In the U.S.A., on the other hand, certain marshy areas considered useless for any other purpose are used as natural breeding grounds for the coypu, several hundred thousand furs being harvested from this source each year. The coypu is often seen in fairs under the label "giant sewer-rat"; this is, of course, a deception, but the animal fully merits being shown as a curiosity, for it is unique in the animal kingdom in that the teats of the female are situated high up on the sides of the body so that the young may suckle as the family party swims about.

The tuco-tucos (*Ctenomys*) of the pampas of South America have

SOURCE OF NUTRIA FUR—THE COYPU

The rat-like coypu is a native of the Argentine, but has been introduced into other parts of the world, including Great Britain, for the sake of its valuable fur, known as nutria. The coypu is aquatic, as is evidenced by its curiously webbed hind-paws. It thrives in Britain, and in a wild state tends to become an agricultural pest.

cylindrical bodies, small eyes and ears, large digging claws, small tails and prominent incisors. In other words, they are mole-like and as might be expected make extensive burrows in open country.

The story of the hutias is in many respects a romantic one. Two species are known—*Plagiodontia aedium* being the first made known to us, by the great French naturalist Cuvier in 1836. Then nothing more was heard of it. In 1927 the fossil of a second species, *P. hylaeum*, was discovered. Then in 1948 one more specimen of *P. aedium* was found, and living specimens of the second species, *P. hylaeum*; yet it is clear that both these species must at one time have been numerous, for their remains are found in quantities in caves and kitchen middens in the West Indies. Presumably they were used as food by the natives.

They are terrestrial in habit and keep closely to the scrubland in remote areas and, as a consequence, are likely to escape notice. Nevertheless, it does appear that they are extremely reduced in numbers and fast approaching extermination—a process which the introduction of dog, cat and mongoose to the islands of the West Indies is bound to further hasten.

CANE AND ROCK RATS

Another strange freak is the cause of speculation. In Africa are found the Cane rat (*Thryonomys swinderianus*) and the Rock rat (*Petromys typicus*), both related to the South American hystricomorphs, and one wonders how they can be in the Old World, for they are the only hystricomorphs there apart from the porcupines. The Cane rat, known in West Africa as the grass-cutter, is just over 2 ft. long with a coat of harsh bristly hair. It is found in reeds near water and is an expert swimmer and diver and the sugar-cane crops often suffer from its activities. The Rock rat of South-west Africa, rather like a rat with a bushy tail, is remarkable in having ribs so flexible that it can squeeze through crevices.

TWO OBSCURE GROUPS

Finally we include in the hystrico-morphs two groups of rodents whose relationships are obscure but which seem to have some affinity with the animals that we have been discussing.

The gundis (*Ctenodactylus*) have plump bodies, short legs and stumpy tails and live among rocks in the desert country of North Africa and Abyssinia. They are about the size of guinea-pigs and have a similar shape. Their claws are covered with stiff bristles which probably brush away the sand when digging. The inner toes of the hind-feet have, moreover, stiff bristles and horny combs for cleaning the fur.

The Mole rats (*Spalax*) are all mole-like in shape and habits. Like the moles they excavate long tunnels in which they store large quantities of bulbs and roots. When storing bulbs it is their habit to bite out the green-growing tip so that the bulb will be kept fresh for a long time and act as a reserve against times of scarcity.

Not so long ago any book on natural history would have included rabbits and hares in the section devoted to rodents; they would, it is true, have been separated from the typical rodents on account of the second pair of upper incisor teeth under the name Duplicidentata (double-toothed); but their relationship with the rats, squirrels and porcupines was not seriously questioned.

Now, however, the expert view is that any similarities are purely coincidental,

THE MOLE RAT SHOWS HIS FEARSOME TEETH

Adapted for a burrowing life, the Mole rat has many of the characteristics of moles,
such as very small eyes and the absence of external ears. As though in compensation
for these deficiencies, it can display long and exceedingly formidable incisor teeth.

and the rabbits and hares, together with their dwarf relatives the pikas (or Mouse hares) should be classified as a separate order under the name Lagomorpha. Among the structural features which have led to the separation are the secondary upper incisors and many points in the form of the skull in which it differs widely from that of any true rodent. Another important reason for distinguishing two separate orders lies in their geological history, for no fossils have yet been found intermediate between the two groups or even considered ancestral to both.

In fact the only serious resemblance between lagomorphs and rodents lies in the development of ever-growing, rootless gnawing incisors, but even here there is an important difference. In the lagomorphs the incisors are covered with enamel on all surfaces and never become sharpened into such effective gnawing tools as in the rodents, whose incisors have chisel-like edges, thanks to the soft dentine behind the hard enamel on the front surface. In fact the incisors of a rabbit or hare are used more for cropping grass or browsing on leaves than for true gnawing—the winter gnawing of the soft bark on fallen twigs or the gnawing of turnips and other root crops seems to be the limit of their powers—and it is noteworthy that rabbits and hares do not seem to enjoy the facility exercised by practically all rodents of holding hard objects in the forepaws the better to bring the gnawing teeth to bear.

Another very obvious difference in character between the lagomorphs and rodents lies in the conservatism of the former. One of the most characteristic features of rodent life is adaptability. As already pointed out above, rodents have been able to adapt themselves to almost any mode of life, whether burrowing as in Mole rats and gophers, leaping in biped fashion as in jerboas, swimming and diving as in Musk rats and beavers, or climbing and taking to the air as in squirrels and flying squirrels.

In strong contrast to the catholicity exhibited by rodents the lagomorphs have been very unenterprising; they remain strictly terrestrial, and even those, such as the Common rabbit, which habitually burrow show no special modifications for this purpose. It is true that in Australia rabbits, under the pressure of hunger, have been known to climb trees to reach the foliage, and that in America the Swamp rabbit will swim without hesitation. Both these habits, however, are obviously of recent growth and have led to no structural modifications.

RABBITS IN AUSTRALIA

Yet in spite of these obvious drawbacks it may be said that rabbits and hares have not been unsuccessful in keeping their place in nature. In spite of their palatability to man and to a host of natural predators, many of the numerous forms continue to flourish throughout the world, and even, as in the case of the rabbits, may constitute an economic pest of great magnitude. The experience of Australia illustrates this point—for introduced into a country of limitless space, favourable climate and few natural enemies, the European rabbit quickly became a thorn in the side of the sheep-farmer and agriculturalist, although the returns from the sale of its flesh and fur have saved it from being an entirely unmitigated pest. The high reproductive rate, combined with ability to take advantage of almost any cover, and the ability to live on scanty vegetation, are all factors contributing largely to the successful maintenance of the rabbit and hare population of the world.

FOLLOWERS OF THE ROMANS

Of all the many species in this group, undoubtedly the best known is the Common rabbit (*Oryctolagus cuniculus*). Before the Roman conquest of Europe and Britain it was found only in Spain and Portugal, and perhaps also in North Africa, but soon after the Roman occupation it was found in all the countries under Roman sway. Since then it has continued to be both a first-class pest to the farmer and a boon to the cottager, so that, in spite of all the campaigns against it by farmer and forester, few country people would really be glad to see the last rabbit.

An interesting physiological adaptation in the rabbit (which possibly goes some way to explain its ability to lie up for days at a time in the security of its deep burrow when alarmed by outside disturbances, or hindered from feeding by inclement weather) is its ability to re-ingest its own faeces. This habit has been commonly observed in domestic rabbits, and has also been seen in wild ones; and from examination of stomach contents it has been found to take place in wild rabbits mainly at night. There seems to be here a resemblance in function to cud-chewing, except that in the rabbit the food hurriedly cropped in the open passes half-digested through the digestive tract to be swallowed and re-digested fully at leisure in the security of the burrow, instead of being regurgitated from stomach to mouth as in cattle and sheep.

Of all the lagomorphs, the Common rabbit is the only species which habitually burrows, and it is also distinguished by its gregarious or social nature. All the hares, by contrast, live above ground and, while they may at times gather in family or social groups, they normally live a more solitary life, and their young are born above ground in grass shelters and are soon able to see and run. In contrast, young rabbits, which are born in underground security, are blind and helpless for some time.

True hares, of the widespread genus *Lepus*, are much alike wherever they are found, from California to eastern Asia and over much of Africa. The name "hare" is not applied in the U.S.A. to these animals, but the Californian jack-rabbit (*Lepus californicus*) is in spite of its name a true hare, and is one of the speediest of its race. At times jack-rabbits have become so numerous that organized drives over the plains have resulted in thousands being herded into corrals like sheep, there to be slaughtered.

Farther north in the American continent, as far as the limit of tree growth, the Snowshoe rabbit (*L. americanus*) is ubiquitous. Like the Varying hare (*L. timidus*) of West Europe and northern Asia, a mountain animal, it undergoes a seasonal coat change; in winter the coat matches its snowy surroundings. Its popular name derives from the broad and very hairy hind-foot, spreading the weight of the animal on soft snow. However, its chief interest to zoologists lies in the cyclic fluctuations of its numbers; such cyclic changes have been closely studied and found to be linked with corresponding "waves" in the populations of the more valuable fur animals

NORTH AMERICAN JACK-RABBIT IN ITS FORM

At one time classed as rodents, rabbits and hares are more suitably consigned to the order Lagomorpha, for there are many structural differences between them and true rodents. The American "jack-rabbit," or hare, has at times become so numerous in the U.S.A. as to constitute a real nuisance to farmers.

SNOW-WHITE ARCTIC HARES IN WINTER

All hares undergo seasonal variations in colour, their coats assuming a lighter tint in cold weather. In winter the Arctic hare is snowy white in tint. Its form, a cavity in the snow, often becomes arched over, protecting the animal from the cold wind.

such as fox, wolf, marten and lynx, which all depend very largely on the Snowshoe rabbits for their living. Long series of records of Canadian fur catches have made it possible to pick out the "rabbit years," which seem to come in seven-to-ten-year cycles.

Such little-known species as the fluffy-tailed, red-furred Rock rabbit (*Pronolagus crassicaudatus*) of the South African kopjes, the tortoiseshell-coloured Sumatran hare (*Nesolagus netscheri*) and the tiny Nelson hare (*Romerolagus nelsoni*), hardly bigger than a guinea-pig and confined entirely to the slopes of a Mexican volcano, cannot be fully described here.

Still less known are the tiny pikas or Mouse hares (*Ochotona*). No larger than guinea-pigs, almost tailless and

with short rounded ears, these dun-coloured little animals live among piles of rocks in two regions of the world only—the Rocky Mountains of North America and the great mountain ranges of Central Asia. One species (*O. wollastoni*) spends its whole life at elevations of 17,000 ft. or more in the Himalayas. Unlike some other animals living in such bleak surroundings, they do not hibernate but instead cut and dry grass in the late summer and store it in miniature hayricks under overhanging rocks for winter use; such hay piles often lead to the detection of a pika colony. Another name for these animals is Calling hare or Whistling hare, for they are noted for the ventriloquial bleating note by which they give warning of danger before diving under the rocks.

BABY KANGAROO TAKES A PEEP AT THE WORLD

Kangaroos have only a single offspring at a time. The latter is born in a very immature state and is only partially formed, being little more than an inch in length. It grows to full development inside its mother's pouch, where it remains, secure against the world, for many weeks before becoming sufficiently mature to venture forth.

Some odd animals

THERE are various interpretations to be placed on the word "odd," but here it is used to denote those animals which are out of the ordinary; or, to use the more scientific terminology, those that are more highly specialized or are more primitive than the others, and so are singled out for our attention.

We cannot do better than start with a familiar example, so well known that we are inclined to overlook its claim to be classed as odd, the Common mole. The Common mole (*Talpa europaea*), found throughout temperate Europe and Asia, is one of a fairly compact family that includes several species of True moles, the mole-shrews and the Water moles, the last having webbed feet and long tails and being entirely aquatic. In addition, there are the Star-nosed moles (*Condylura cristata*) of North America, so called because the tip of the nose is decorated with a star-shaped rosette of fleshy, highly sensitive papillae, or feelers. Another family (Chrysochloridae) includes the Golden moles of Central, East and South Africa. All of these belong to the order Insectivora, which also includes the shrews, hedgehogs and related animals in other parts of the world.

There is, however, another kind of mole, in Australia, entirely unrelated to the rest; this is the Marsupial mole, which is of interest in that it is an example of how animals far removed in their relationships can resemble each other in form and habit by a process of convergent evolution.

The Common mole typifies all moles. It is some 6 in. long and is remarkable in living almost entirely underground. It excavates an extensive system of tunnels, throwing the excavated earth on the surface at intervals in what we know as molehills; and everything in its bodily structure is adapted and subordinated to this odd mode of life. We may reasonably say that it swims through the ground and like all good swimmers has a torpedo-shaped body. The tail is almost gone, the limbs are very short and there is no obvious neck, the head being confluent with the body. The chief digging organs are the front limbs, efficient shovels for scraping away the earth. If anyone doubts the wisdom of comparing the movement of a mole to a swimming action, he has only to await the opportunity of seeing a mole moving just under the surface of the ground. The mole can create a furrow almost as fast as a man can walk.

Naturally, there are many things we do not know about an animal living so much underground, but by piecing together the occasional observations of field naturalists, and by studying the results of researches made on the habits of moles in captivity, we can form a reasonable picture of the animal.

If need be, it can swim rivers, using the same action of the front limbs as drives it through the ground. In re-entering the earth, after having come out on to the surface, it digs itself in with an action and a speed that can only be described as diving. We can safely assume, therefore, that when underground it moves moderately rapidly, whether passing along its permanent highways or constructing its temporary runways. Any creature feeding mainly on earthworms must be quick in its actions, for the worms can be speedy and elusive in their natural element.

Such remarks as these present moles as active animals; and this is the truth. Those kept in captivity have been found to be highly nervous, restless and active, feeding voraciously and unable to go more than four hours without food. Furthermore, their habits suggest unusual strength in such small beasts. There is every reason to presume that a mole is descended from an ancestor that was a fairly normal quadruped, but that the bones of its skeleton have all become foreshortened and thickened. This is particularly noticeable in the humerus, radius and ulna of the fore-legs. The rest of the specializations are fairly well known. The eyes and ears are minute and hidden in the fur; the reduction in size and efficiency of both these sense-organs is due to the fact that neither of them is much needed under-ground. As compensation, however, the snout is a highly specialized sense-organ, the function of which is to help the animal to find its way about and to

WANDERER OF BRITISH LANES AND FIELDS

The hedgehog, with its extremely effective defensive armament of prickles, is a familiar sight in the British countryside. It destroys large numbers of harmful insects.

THE SLOTH—BY-WORD FOR INDOLENCE

The sloth's world is an inverted one, and he has become adapted to living upside down,
suspended by his large, hooked claws and powerful limbs from the branches of tall trees.
There his sluggish movements and lichen-infested coat make him practically invisible.

track down its food in perpetual darkness. Finally, the fur being without set, its possessor is enabled to move with equal ease forwards or backwards in the narrow burrows.

Shrews, also insectivores, live a very different life and at first sight do not suggest any close affinity with moles. Indeed, they are usually looked upon as mice, but they have the long tapering snout and the same kind of teeth as the mole. They merit attention here for two reasons. Firstly, like moles, they show a restless, nervous activity, and the snout is highly sensitive. Secondly, they are (again like moles) very susceptible to shock. Another characteristic is the short life—a maximum of fifteen months—linked with a high birth-rate and a high death-rate. Dead shrews are,

therefore, frequent. If a shrew dies in the grass we do not see it. If it dies on a footpath it will be seen. Because dead shrews are fairly commonly seen on footpaths, the legend arose that a shrew could not cross a path made by human feet and live!

One of the queerest of all animals is the Hero shrew (*Scutisorex congicus*), found in a limited area of the Ituri Forest, Belgian Congo. A large shrew, up to 9 in. long, it derives its name from the native belief that its charred remains, worn as a talisman, confer invincibility upon the wearer; the individual thus fortified will enter dangerous elephant hunts or meet other hazards with confidence. This belief in its magical powers is based on its extraordinary strength, which natives delight in demonstrating on a captive animal. A man weighing, say, 160 lb. will balance precariously on the animal's back with one bare foot, taking care not to stand on its head. After various incantations it will be released. Having borne a weight sufficient to kill any normal small animal, the Hero shrew merely shakes its body and moves off quite unperturbed.

The secret of this performance lies in the strength of the shrew's backbone. The vertebrae are very large proportionately to the size of the animal, and are beset with numerous bony spines interlocking each vertebra with its neighbours.

SPINES AND QUILLS

Another member of the Insectivora familiar to everyone, the hedgehog, (*Erinaceus europaeus*) provides another contrast. Although differing from moles and shrews in its bony structure (particularly in the characters of the skull), the general form of the teeth is similar to theirs. Moreover, it has the retiring and unobtrusive habits of the Insectivora. It is outstanding for its coat of defensive spines. There is a similarity here with the porcupines (order Rodentia); this is something of a case of convergent evolution, for the spines of the hedgehog and the quills of the porcupine have many details of resemblance. It is, however, the contrasts which are most striking, for the quills of the porcupines are not only a defensive armament, but can also be a potent offensive weapon, whereas the hedgehog uses its prickly coat in passive defence only. Consequently, we find nothing in the nature of a warning coloration in the hedgehog. Here, then, is another fact that points towards, without necessarily proving, the validity of the warning-coloration principle.

The rest of the Insectivora are mainly rodent-like in outward form, but all have the tapering, sensitive snout and the numerous sharp-pointed teeth related to an insectivorous diet, and it is not necessary to deal more fully with them here. It is, however, of interest to compare the sizes of different groups of mammals. The rodents, for example, constitute a very large order, with numerous species. The Insectivora constitute a comparatively small order, with a fairly high proportion of unusually specialized forms. As a rule, the high degree of specialization goes hand-in-hand with a limited number of forms. So we shall find that our odd animals belong to small or comparatively small orders.

An outstanding example of this is seen in the sloths, of which there are but three species, occupying a restricted territory in Central and South America. The three species are the Three-toed sloth (*Bradypus tridactylus*) and the two species of Two-toed sloth (*Choloepus didactylus* and *C. hoffmanni*), and all three are as closely linked with a life in the trees as the moles are with a subterranean life. Similarly, the whole structure of the body is directed towards and correlated with this unusual mode of existence.

SLOW-MOTION EXPERTS

We are all familiar with their lethargic, slow-motion movements, and with the fact that they spend most of their time hanging head downwards from the branches of trees in a reversal of the usual quadruped position. In point of fact, however, neither of these popular concepts is strictly correct, for the normal resting habit is to cling from branches head upwards, the suspended position being used mainly when they are on the move. Moreover, although during daylight hours their movements are lethargic, they can climb moderately quickly at night-time (when they feed on leaves and the flowers of *Cecropia*), or when alarmed. Nevertheless, the structure of the body reflects the characteristic hanging posture. The limbs are suspensors, the toes being enclosed in skin to form a pad bearing the large, hooked claws. All the strength is in the arms, there being no heavy musculature in the body. Sloths can move over the ground, dragging themselves along by using the hooked claws as grappling irons; and they can swim—on the back, with an overarm stroke of the long front legs.

Where other animals have striven for speed, in defence or attack, the sloths have specialized in "going slow." As if to aid them in this, the hair is grooved and in the grooves lives a microscopic green plant, so that, when bunched against a tree-trunk or a branch, the animal resembles a vegetable growth, or even a bundle of dried grass or an ants' nest. Further, the hair, which in tropical animals functions mainly as a raincoat (set so as to throw the water off the back), is set in the reverse direction in sloths, so as to throw the water off the belly which is habitually directed upwards.

For a long time sloths were grouped with ant-eaters, armadillos, pangolins and aardvarks in a single order, the Edentata, or animals without teeth; for, although they differ widely in structure, appearance and habits, they all agree in having no teeth in the front of the mouth. The order Edentata was, however, somewhat of a zoological

GREAT ANT-EATER, OR ANT-BEAR

The Great ant-eater of South America attains an overall length of 8 ft. It feeds entirely on termites—the so-called "white ants"—which it catches with its long, sticky, worm-like tongue. Its powerful, hooked front-claws can break open the strongest ant-heap. They are so large that the animal must walk on the sides of its feet.

wastepaper-basket, an order into which a number of animals that did not readily fit into the general scheme were thrown. In a taxonomic sense, therefore, all these are very definitely odd animals. Today, we have got as far as restricting the Edentata to the sloths, ant-eaters and armadillos—and even this is a rather mixed bag. The pangolins, on the other hand, are placed in a separate order, the Pholidota, and the aardvarks in the order Tubulidentata.

The ant-eaters, of Central and South America, are truly edentate, that is, entirely without teeth, whereas sloths have peg-like cheek-teeth, although lacking the front teeth. Ant-eaters feed entirely on termites and other soft-bodied insects, being beautifully adapted to this end. The muzzle is long and slender, and the mouth is a tubular opening at the tip. The tongue is long and sticky, for picking up the termites, and the salivary glands are unduly large, serving doubtless to keep the tongue continually moist and providing a means of rapid digestion. Further, the third toe on each front foot bears a large claw for digging out the termites from their tough nests.

The Great ant-eater (*Myrmecophaga jubata*) is 4 ft. long, with a tail the same length, and both the hind part of the body and the tail are covered with a long curtain-like fringe. The eyes are small, the ears short and the muzzle very long and tapering. So specialized for digging are the claws on the front feet that the animal is compelled to tread on the sides of the feet, with the claws turned inwards. The general colour of the body is steel-grey, but a bold black stripe

NATURE'S DESIGN FOR A TANK—THE ARMADILLO

Armadillos inhabit the New World, ranging from South America to as far north as the southern U.S.A. All are heavily armoured on the back and sides with horny plates.

RESEMBLING A BEAST OF MEDIEVAL LEGEND

With its fantastic armament of overlapping scales, like an antique coat of mail, the pangolin presents a strangely unreal appearance. Its large, powerful tail is used in climbing, while the tree-living types use it as a supporting "bracket" when leaning back at an angle from a tree-trunk—their normal resting position.

runs diagonally from the chest to the root of the tail, forming a disruptive pattern which breaks up the outline of the body and thus tends to conceal the ant-eater from its enemies.

The tamandua (*Tamandua tetradactyla*), of Central and South America and Trinidad, is half the size of the Great ant-eater, and lives in trees though it has a diet of soft insects. Its muzzle is shorter, the digging claws less strongly developed and the tail is prehensile. The single young is carried pick-a-back by the mother.

Most curious of the three is, however, the Little or Two-toed ant-eater (*Cyclopes didactylus*), the size of a rat, with glossy, golden-buff fur. It, too, lives in trees, has feet adapted for climbing and a strongly prehensile tail. The front feet have only two toes, armed with hook-like claws; the hind feet have four toes and a thumb-like pad. *Cyclopes* can therefore grasp a branch with both hind feet and tail, and habitually poses with the body bolt

upright or at an angle from the branch. It is seldom seen and is believed to feed on honey and grubs from the nests of wild bees.

The armadillos, terrestrial, feeding on insects, roots and fallen fruit, have peg-like cheek-teeth like the sloths. The underparts are covered with a soft skin and sparse hair, but the upper parts are protected by bony shields covered with horn. One species, the apara (*Tolypeutes tricinctus*), is noted for its habit of rolling itself into a ball, like a woodlouse—or a hedgehog. The others cling to the ground or take refuge in thorny scrub if menaced, though dogs, coyotes and peccaries will on occasion turn them over and attack the soft under-belly. The armour consists of a large shield covering the shoulders, flanks and forepart of the body, a similar shield over the hind-part, a head shield and a series of rings covering the tail. Between the hind and fore shields of the body is a number of narrow, transverse shields connected by skin and varying in num-

AARDVARK, OR "EARTH-PIG," OF THE CAPE

The aardvark of South Africa differs from the true ant-eaters in the possession of degenerate teeth. Like the ant-eaters, however, it has become adapted to an exclusive diet of termites, which it licks up and devours in enormous quantities, after having torn open their tough earthen nests with its huge claws.

ber according to the species concerned.

The Giant armadillo (*Priodontes gigas*), of the Brazilian forests, is over 4 ft. long from tip to tail. It has twelve to thirteen bands along the back, double the normal number of teeth, feeds mainly on termites, and has a large claw on the third toe of the fore-feet. The Six-banded armadillo (*Euphractus sexcinctus*), of Brazil and Paraguay, is 18 in. long, with a broad head, small ears and short tail. In southern South America the Hairy armadillo (*E. villosus*) is found. Its armour is almost hidden by a thick growth of hair springing from between the plates.

The Fairy armadillo or pichiciago (*Chlamyphorus truncatus*), of the sandy plains of the western Argentina, is 6 in. long, mole-like, and has twenty or so pink horny plates arranged transversely along the back. The body, even under the horny plates, is covered by a silky white fur. It has large digging claws on the front feet and appears to be completely burrowing. The most remarkable feature is the abruptly truncated hind-end of the body.

The best-known species, the Nine-banded armadillo (*Dasypus novemcinctus*), found from the Argentine to the southern U.S.A., is some 2½ ft. long from tip to tail. One remarkable feature of this species is that all the young in a given litter belong to the same sex and are derived from one fertilized ovum, which divides again and again. Finally, although heavy for its size, this armadillo can cross rivers, not by walking on the bottom as was formerly supposed, but by gulping in air to inflate its intestines and produce buoyancy.

The pangolins (*Manis*), forming the order Pholidota, have the upper surface of the body covered with large overlapping scales, reminiscent of the scales of a pine-cone. The under-surface is, however, soft and sparsely covered with hair, and the animal's natural defence is to roll itself into a ball, with the long tail wrapped round the body. Pangolins are found in Africa, particularly tropical Africa, and in Asia (India, China and Malaya), and range from 3 ft. to 5 ft. in length. Some are terrestrial, some arboreal, but all feed on termites, and although only distantly related to the edentates, they have the same long,

tapering muzzle, long extensile tongue and the other characteristics associated with animals living on a diet of termites. In all these forms sight and hearing are not acute, but smell and taste are apparently very highly developed. In addition, the third toe of the front foot bears an enormously developed claw, for digging out the termites' nests; thus the pangolin, like the Giant ant-eater, is forced to walk on the sides of the feet.

Pangolins are remarkable for two reasons. Firstly, some are tree-dwellers, despite the fact that they live on termites. Secondly, and perhaps more remarkable, is their habit of resting at an angle to the tree-trunk. In the tree-dwelling species the tail is prehensile, but it can also be pressed against the trunk of a tree so that the pointed scales

A ZOOLOGICAL PUZZLE—AUSTRALIA'S PLATYPUS

Before they had a chance of examining an actual specimen, zoologists refused to credit reports of the Duck-billed platypus. For this marsupial animal—a mammal with many characteristics of a reptile—is an exceedingly primitive "living fossil."

ONE OF NATURE'S FASTEST DIGGERS

On the surface of the ground the Common mole appears clumsy and sluggish enough, but in his native element—below ground—he is capable of astonishing speed and agility, being able to "swim" through the earth almost as rapidly as a man can walk. In bodily structure and in habits he is entirely adapted to subterranean life.

dig into the bark. When using its tail in this latter way, the pangolin will often clasp the trunk with the hind-feet and, throwing the weight of the body on to the tail, lean backwards with body rigid. Is this a resting position, or does the pangolin seek refuge in its resemblance to a stump of a branch? Nobody knows.

The aardvark or earth-pig (*Orycteropus afer*) is another termite-eating oddity. At one time it, too, was classed with the Edentata. Now it is placed in the order Tubulidentata for, although it has no front teeth and has the characteristics of a termite-eater, it is markedly different from the rest of the formerly so-called edentates in almost every respect. Aardvarks are abundant in the termite districts of Africa, but being nocturnal, burrowing animals they are seldom seen. The aardvark has a large rounded body, pig-like head, long ears, and small mouth with a long slender tongue. The four toes of the front feet and the five toes of the hind-feet all bear strong claws, and the animal can burrow faster than a gang of men can dig!

BORDERLINE CREATURE

The Duck-billed platypus (*Ornithorhynchus anatinus*) of Australia recalls in many respects Britain's native mole; but whereas the latter is a highly specialized member of a group of advanced mammals, the platypus is a specialized and at the same time extremely primitive mammal. In fact, it has done little more than step over the boundary between reptiles and mammals. Its skeleton, particularly, has several distinctly reptilian features. In addition, it lays soft-shelled eggs, ¾ in. in diameter and dirty-white in colour, instead of bringing forth its young alive. On the other hand, it is a true mammal in having the body covered with hair

and in suckling its young. It resembles the mole, however, in having a torpedo-shaped body, enlarged fore-feet bearing digging claws, a sensitive snout (though this is covered with a horny layer, the "duck-bill"), restless and energetic habits linked with a large appetite, and tunnelling propensities. It will excavate burrows up to 60 ft. long in the banks of the streams in which it swims, filtering its food from the mud, much in the manner of a duck.

MOST PRIMITIVE MAMMALS

Perhaps the most remarkable feature of this animal is its fore-feet, which fulfil the double function of swimming and digging, for they are webbed, the web overlapping the ends of the claws by a fair margin. When digging or walking, however, the web can be folded back out of the way. Other curious features of this most odd animal are the hollow spurs on the hind-feet of the males, which are connected with a poison gland (a combination of the snake's fangs and the bantam's spurs), and the cheek-pouches for storing food.

Together with the platypus, the echidnas, or Spiny ant-eaters, constitute the sub-class Monotremata, the most primitive of mammals. The Common echidna of Australia and Tasmania has related species in New Guinea. Its body would be somewhat mole-like in shape if the spines were removed, and as it also possesses strong, short front legs armed with stout digging claws, we may accurately assume it to be a burrowing animal. Indeed, in soft ground it can burrow so quickly that it sinks out of sight within a few moments. The sensitive snout is long, the mouth tubular and terminal on it, the tongue long and extensile—and it feeds mainly on termites. It has no teeth, but the food is crushed by horny serrations on the back of the tongue which press against hard ridges on the palate. Perhaps the most significant thing is the fact that the female has a pouch on the belly into which she deposits her eggs and in which she carries the young for several weeks after they are hatched.

The marsupials, typically represented in our minds by the kangaroos but embracing a wide variety of other forms, are a more advanced group than the monotremes, though still very primitive. They have fewer reptilian characters and, instead of laying eggs, the young are born at a very early embryonic stage and carried in a pouch or marsupium. In some of the marsupials this pouch is no more than two flaps of skin. In others it opens backwards, and it is only in the kangaroos and phalangers that the mouth of the pouch is in front.

When we think of marsupials our minds revert inevitably to the fauna of Australia. A few pouched animals are, however, found in America, though these belong to entirely different families.

Marsupials are divided into two groups: the Polyprotodontia, having many simple incisors (that is all the name means!) and the Diprotodontia, having fewer incisors. The first are carnivorous or insectivorous; the latter herbivorous or fruit-eating. The Polyprotodontia include four families: the Didelphidae, the Dasyuridae, the Peramelidae and the Coenolestidae.

The Didelphidae, or True opossums of America, include the Common opossum (*Didelphys virginianus*), from whose behaviour we have the phrase "playing possum." It looks like a rat, though in size it is nearer to a cat; and

AMONG THE MOST PRIMITIVE MAMMALS—THE ECHIDNA
There are several species of echidna, all of them insect-eaters and all confined to Australasia. They are covered with sharp spines and equipped with strong claws.

NATIVE OF THE AUSTRALIAN "GUM" FOREST

The "opossums" of Australia are more accurately described as phalangers. Among them, the Ring-tailed opossum is peculiar in building a nest, usually in the fork of a tree. This little marsupial is only active at night, when it feeds on eucalyptus leaves.

when attacked it has the habit of lying apparently lifeless with its hair dishevelled. This does not always save it, however, for it is hunted for food in some parts of the U.S.A.; but, being able to eat almost anything and live almost anywhere, it has been able to hold its own. Of the several South American species in this family, ranging in size from that of a mouse to that of a squirrel, one (*Monodelphys domesticus*) lives in the native huts, in the manner of the house-mouse.

The Dasyuridae are all found in Australia. The smaller of them are insectivorous, the larger carnivorous. The Marsupial mice have tapering shrew-like snouts. One of them (*Antechinus macdonellensis*) can lay up a store of fat in its tail against hard times. The

Crest-tailed marsupial mouse (*Dasycercus cristicauda*), of the Australian deserts, feeds on small mammals and birds. It will eat a mouse or rat from head to tail, turning back the skin as it goes, leaving finally the empty skin turned inside out. In the deserts, too, are the jerboa-marsupials, with long hind-legs and long tufted tails. The dasyure or Native cat (*Dasyurus quoll*), strongly carnivorous, has been heavily persecuted for killing poultry, but it feeds mainly on rats, mice and rabbits. A female may have twenty-four young at a birth, but has only six teats to feed them! The largest Native cat, the Large spotted-tailed or Tiger cat (*Dasyurops maculatus*) is 2 ft. long, with a 19-in. tail; it has a ferocious nature. Finally, the thylacine or Tasmanian wolf (*Thylacinus cynocephalus*),

SPOTTED OPOSSUM, OR CUSCUS

Cuscuses are members of the phalanger family and inhabit parts of Australia and the neighbouring Pacific islands. The Spotted cuscus is a slow-moving animal and has a remarkable prehensile tail, quite naked at the tip, which it uses as a fifth "paw" to grasp twigs and branches. Its food consists mainly of leaves.

once common throughout Australia, now lives only in Tasmania and even there is rarely seen; it may well be, indeed, that this animal is now extinct. It feeds (or should we now say, it fed?) on rats, birds and wallabies. Unfortunately, it developed a taste for sheep and poultry. Its body is 3 ft. long, with a long tail and a dog-like head; the hindquarters bear a few dark, vertical stripes.

Australia has, therefore, its native mice, rats, cats, dogs and jerboas; these are all pouched and very primitive mammals, entirely unrelated to the rodents and carnivores that bear these names in other parts of the world. The family Dasyuridae also includes an anteater and a mole—both pouched and primitive, but again very like the

animals living elsewhere that bear these names. The Banded ant-eater (*Myrmecobius fasciatus*), of South and Southwest Australia, is a marsupial that feeds on termites; and, like all other termite-eaters, it has a long tapering snout, extensile tongue and stout claws. The Marsupial mole (*Notoryctes typhlops*), not discovered until 1888, burrows 3 in. below the surface in sandy soil, but does not leave permanent burrows. It has no eyes and the snout is protected by a horny shield. Otherwise it is very like the Common mole, especially in its enormous appetite and restless activity.

The Peramelidae, or bandicoots, feed wholly on insects. The Long-nosed bandicoot (*Perameles nasuta*) digs in gardens and lawns for grubs and worms.

It will also eat a mouse, but not until it has pummelled it almost to a jelly with its fore-feet. The Rabbit bandicoot (*Macrotis lagotis*), so called because of its large ears, can burrow as fast as a man can dig. When sleeping, it squats with its snout tucked between the fore-legs and the ears folded on themselves.

The last family of the Polyprotodontia, the Coenolestidae, contains *Coenolestes* only, a South American marsupial living in the damp forests of the higher Andes. It has no common name, for it is little known. Insectivorous, it is shrew-like in form and has the teeth of the Polyprotodontia and feet like the Diprotodontia. It is the sort of animal that is the despair of the zoologist, for he does not know how to classify it. Possibly *Coenolestes* is the last remnant of the stock which gave rise to both the Polyprotodontia and the Diprotodontia.

The rest of the marsupials comprise the Diprotodontia, the Australian opossums and phalangers, koalas, wombats, wallabies and kangaroos. They are all mainly vegetarian; their incisors are few in number, those in the lower jaw being particularly large and resembling the teeth of rodents. Another characteristic is the shape of the hind-foot. The second and third toes are small, bound together in a common skin so that they look like a small toe with two claws, and the fourth and fifth toes are large and form the functional foot. The small claws on the second and third toes are used for combing the fur. There are

LIVING "TEDDY BEARS" OF AUSTRALIA

Formerly slaughtered in enormous numbers for the sake of its thick ash-grey fur, the quaint, appealing Koala bear is now protected in reservations. The female carries her single young in her pouch until it is old enough to mount upon her back.

two families of Diprotodontia, the Phalangeridae and the Macropodidae, the second including the wallabies and kangaroos.

The Phalangeridae—the Australian opossums, phalangers, cuscuses and koalas—are all arboreal, feeding on leaves, fruit, flowers, honey, and insects; all, except the koala, have long tails. All have the big toe opposable to the rest, acting like a thumb in grasping. The small Honey mouse (*Tarsipes*) of Southwest Australia is nocturnal, and seldom seen except when a cat brings one in. It feeds mainly on honey. Its muzzle is long and pointed and the tongue is armed with bristles for brushing up nectar from the flowers. The tiny Pygmy flying phalanger (*Acrobates pygmaeus*) lives in holes in the eucalyptus trees of eastern Australia and New

Guinea. Its body has a fringe of hairs on either side, and the tail is feathered.

The Australian or Brush-tailed or Vulpine opossum (*Trichosurus vulpecula*) also lives in the eucalyptus, feeding on its leaves. It is fox-like, with a woolly coat of silver-grey to dark brown and black, much valued in the fur trade. Although most at home in trees, it will also live in rabbit holes in the bush, and has even taken to living in the roofs of suburban houses. The Australian Striped phalanger (*Dactylopsila picata*) of the forests of Queensland is striped black and white, as are its several relatives in New Guinea. The fourth toe of the front foot is long and thin and is used for tapping the bark of rotten boughs in its search for insect grubs, in a manner similar to that of the aye-aye of Madagascar. Having detec-

KANGAROO IN MINIATURE

Though members of the same family as the large kangaroos and wallabies, Rat kangaroos are no larger than a rabbit. They live in nests made of grass.

TREE KANGAROOS OF NORTH QUEENSLAND

Somewhat resembling bears in appearance, the Tree kangaroos lack the exaggerated development of hind limb which distinguishes their exclusively ground-dwelling relatives. They are daring climbers, at home in the loftiest trees.

ted the grubs, the rotten wood is ripped open with the powerful incisors, after which the long sensitive finger is inserted to extract them.

The gliding phalangers spend the day resting in holes in trees, but come out at night to make long gliding flights from tree to tree, and feed on leaves. The largest, the Great glider (*Schoinobates volans*), is the size of a cat. The Ring-tailed opossums (*Pseudochirus*), of Australia and New Guinea, also live in

trees and are nocturnal. They build nests like squirrels, and the end of the tail can be coiled into a ring and used as a spare hand. The cuscuses, the largest of the Australian opossums, have rounded cheeks, small ears half-hidden in the fur, a woolly coat and a prehensile tail. They have often been mistaken for monkeys. Cuscuses are found in northern Australia, New Guinea, the Celebes and the Solomons. They spend the day curled up in the forks of trees, "cussing"

DISTINCTIVE WALLABY

Parry's, or Bennett's, wallaby is found in the highlands of northern New South Wales and Queensland. Its colour is variable, blue-grey in winter, changing to yellowish-brown in summer. A wallaby is, generally speaking, a small kangaroo.

violently if disturbed. When on the move they are very slow and spend their time consuming great quantities of leaves. They are able to give off a most pungent odour.

The best-known phalanger is the Australian Teddy bear or koala (*Phascolarctos cinereus*). Bear-like, 2 ft. high,

with tufted ears and a prominent beak-like snout, it lives in the trees feeding on leaves. A remarkable feature of the diet of the koalas is that animals of one area cannot readily get used to eating the leaves growing in another area. In some cases the leaves from another district have actually poisoned them.

The last family of marsupials, the Macropodidae, includes the wallabies, wallaroos and kangaroos, in which the first toe of the hind-foot is missing, and the fourth and fifth toes are enlarged for leaping. The distinction between these three is bound not to be clear. In general, a wallaby is a small kangaroo, and a kangaroo is a large wallaby, but the use of the two words varies from one part of Australia to another. The wallaroo is merely a stockily built form of kangaroo.

Wallabies and kangaroos take the place, in the Australian fauna, of the large herbivores, deer, antelope, horses and cattle, of the rest of the world, but because they had no large carnivores to contend with they have not specialized in speed. Consequently, with the white settlement of Australia they have fallen an easy prey to man, his gun and his imported animals, and many species have become either extinct or nearly so. The speeds and leaping powers of kangaroos have been rather over-emphasized. Even the largest of these animals rarely exceeds 25 miles per hour, as compared with the 50 or more miles per hour of some antelope and deer. As for jumping, the longest leap observed (26 ft.) is rather less than the best human athlete has accomplished; and although a kangaroo was once seen to clear a 9-ft. fence, more often than not a 5-ft. wire fence has disastrous consequences for it. When feeding, the kangaroo moves on all-fours.

Not all the Diprotodontia are large. The Rat kangaroos are only the size of

BRUSH-TAILED ROCK WALLABY OF QUEENSLAND

Unlike most kangaroos, which chiefly frequent grassland and "brush," Rock wallabies make their homes among the clefts and crevices of stony gullies. The soles of their feet are specially adapted for gripping the rocks over which they scramble.

KANGAROOS TRAVELLING AT SPEED

The kangaroo's powerful hind-legs enable it to hop along at a maximum of 25 miles an hour. The front legs are relatively small, but the kangaroo's tail is built on the same scale as its hind-legs; huge and heavy, it forms, when at rest, a sturdy prop.

rabbits and either walk on all-fours or, at best, merely hop about. The Hare wallabies, on the other hand, are swift and agile. In northern Australia and New Guinea are found the Tree kangaroos (*Dendrolagus*), 3 ft. high and brightly coloured in orange or yellow. They live on the ground but go up into the trees to feed and sleep. If disturbed they may leap 50 ft. from tree to ground. The Rock wallabies (*Petrogale*) live in the barren rock-strewn gullies, feeding on leaves and fruit. The soles of their hind-feet are padded and granulated to prevent slipping on the smooth rock surfaces. Their fur is often brightly coloured and one, the Ring-tailed Rock wallaby (*P. xanthopus*), is in danger of extermination for its valuable pelt.

The Scrub or Pademelon wallabies (*Thylogale*), of small size, are very like rabbits in their habits, for they keep to tunnel-like runways in the long grass or in the dense undergrowth. Another rabbit-like habit is thumping the ground with the hind-feet when danger threatens.

This brief account cannot convey a complete idea of the many different species of wallabies and kangaroos, of all sizes, habits and habitats. We must end by recalling the largest and most familiar of all, the Grey kangaroo (*Macropus giganteus*) and the Red kangaroo (*M. rufus*)—both may epitomize the oddness of the Australian fauna.

Birds of prey

STRICTLY speaking there would be some justification for including under the heading of "Birds of Prey" such modest and seemingly harmless birds as nightjars, swifts and even the delightful little fly-catchers. Shrikes really ought to be included, for are they not, in fact, just as much birds of prey as the modest kestrel which, as often as not, is only on the look-out for such insignificant victims as grasshoppers? For the purpose of this volume, however, the present chapter will be confined to the more dramatic predators—those which feed on other birds and mammals, and especially those belonging to the Falconiformes.

The kestrel (*Falco tinnunculus*) is the least impressive of these birds of prey and is generally regarded as being of a somewhat craven disposition. Yet the kestrel will occasionally attack and overcome such victims as starlings or misselthrushes. Nevertheless, it is completely outclassed by another and rather smaller member of the Falconidae—the merlin (*F. columbarius*).

The merlin is a courageous, hardflying little falcon which measures only 11 to 12 in. in length, is partially migratory, and in winter occurs in southern Europe, Egypt, Palestine and North-west Africa.

It usually makes its nest, or rather prepares the few scrapings on which the eggs are laid, on the ground amidst the heather of some lonely moor. Some-times the disused nest of a crow or the ledge on an outcrop of rock may be utilized. Pipits, larks and ouzels usually abound in such country and on them the merlin chiefly subsists, although instances are on record when doves and plovers have been the victims.

The merlin does not share the kestrel's habit of hovering over some spot where a meal has been espied; it is quite capable of overtaking all but the most efficient fliers such as swifts, swallows or martins, and for this reason does not require the hovering technique, as do slower birds of prey.

The skilful manner in which it can climb, in a straight slanting ascent after a pipit or a lark, must impress anyone interested in the flight of birds. The merlin's approach is quickly spotted by the intended victim, which, instinctively realizing the danger, at once sets out to keep above the pursuer at all costs. With such easy confidence does it rise on those vigorous wings that the chances seem to be all against the little hunter's ever gaining the ascendancy. The merlin is, however, as has already been stated, a most persistent aggressor. Time being of no importance—or so it would seem—it now commences to make for greater height by climbing more gradually and more easily than its quarry.

In the end the unfortunate victim is usually outflown and taken high in the air. Sometimes, however, it will close

KESTREL FEEDS ITS YOUNG

The kestrel is the least impressive of the birds of prey, but it is remarkable for its graceful flight and its habit of hovering. Its chief diet consists of insects, but it will attack other birds—such as starlings and missel-thrushes—when its normal food fails.

its wings and drop earthwards in a desperate effort to reach safety among the heather or bracken below. The manoeuvre generally fails, for the merlin follows at far greater speed and is consequently well placed to deliver the *coup de grâce* with its powerful little talons.

During the Middle Ages, when falconry was the vogue among the nobility of Britain, the merlin was trained and used for the taking of small birds and was known—on account of its delightful disposition—as the "lady's hawk."

There is another little falcon which is gifted with extraordinary powers of flight and which, in certain respects, even outflies the merlin—the exceedingly handsome and beautifully shaped

hobby (*F. subbuteo*). It can be readily distinguished from the merlin by its far more contrastive plumage and by its abnormally long wings—wings that, when at rest, extend beyond the tip of the tail. On the wing the hobby looks like a giant swift. It is essentially a "stooper," that is to say, it relies on a downward swoop or nose-dive from a height to enable it to secure a victim.

The hobby was also used for falconry, but curiously—because erroneously—was considered to be a poor-spirited creature, lacking in determination and courage. In the wild state it feeds largely on beetles and other large insects which it usually takes on the wing. Yet, curiously enough, it is capable of outflying and securing birds, such as swallows and swifts, which are too efficient in flight to fall victims to any other members of the falcon tribe. It is also unusually courageous, in spite of its insect-eating propensities, and will attack any intruder—human or avian—who may approach too closely to its nest. A pair of hobbies "mobbing" a crow that has entered their territory will put on an exhibition of really first-rate and most stylish flying. It is doubtful whether a peregrine could time her stoops more nicely or "throw up" with greater ease.

The hobby invariably makes its home in the disused nest of some other bird—often in that of a crow. Such a nest is usually at a considerable height from the ground and in a position from which the little falcon can swing clear into the open without having to dodge through intervening cover after the manner of the sparrow-hawk, with its shorter, rounded wings.

In many ways the hobby resembles its larger cousin the peregrine (*F. peregrinus*). Both are stoopers, are structurally similar, have the same impressive "moustache" markings, and are wide-ranging in their flight. Unlike the hobby, however, the peregrine never, or very, very rarely, nests in a tree. A ledge of some precipitous rock or cliff is usually chosen, often in a position overlooking the sea.

The peregrine is the largest and most spectacular of the falcons which breed in Britain. In the Middle Ages it was prized so highly by falconers in Britain

MERLIN ON ITS NEST

The merlin is the smallest of the British falcons, but it is sturdy and bold, and will attack and overcome birds that far exceed it in size and weight. It usually makes its nest on the ground amidst the heather of some lonely moor.

PEREGRINE FALCON
The peregrine is the largest of the British falcons. As is the case with most birds of prey, the female is larger and more powerful than the male.

that it was assigned to the earl. As is the case with most birds of prey, the female is considerably larger and more powerful than the male. She it was who was referred to as the noble falcon; the male was known as a tiercel (so called because he is one-third less in size than his sister). It was the falcon which was used for the flight at such large quarry as herons and, even so, the falcons destined to take part in this branch of the sport had to be specially trained. It is extremely unlikely that a falcon, in the wild state, would ever tackle such a large and unattractive-looking adversary. Wild peregrines will, nevertheless, stoop playfully at a heron so that the frightened thing utters a loud "Hank" of terror. The tiercels seem never to indulge in this sort of fun.

A simple method of catching peregrines has proved effective on an island off the eastern seaboard of the United States. The island is nothing more than a sandy spit of land where there is no vegetation except patches of rank grass and some scattered bushes. This island seems to be used as a sort of landing ground by migrating peregrines; at certain seasons of the year one or two or more may be seen perched on pieces of wreckage, wooden cases or branches of trees that have been cast up by the sea.

As soon as a peregrine is spotted, the watching hawk-catcher gets out of his car on the side farthest from the peregrine, taking with him a shovel and a large basket. He and his friends then commence to dig a hole about 4 ft. deep and roughly 3 ft. across. Only the shoulders, neck and head of the catcher are above ground when he sits in this hole. Somebody then hands him a live pigeon with jesses and a short piece of line attached to its legs. The catcher holds the pigeon out in front of him at arm's length and his forearms and hands are buried in the sand by a companion so that only the pigeon is showing. The catcher's shoulders and head are now covered by the inverted bushel basket and the trap is set. The car is then driven away to a distance of two hundred yards or so.

Usually the pigeon proves an irresistible bait; the peregrine comes at it at once and, just as it prepares to enjoy a good meal, the catcher grasps it by the legs. That a wild peregrine should come so readily to such a decoy suggests that it has just completed an exhausting journey and is famished. Birds taken in this way will generally feed on the gloved fist the same evening.

In Britain, peregrines have the reputation of being inveterate pigeon-killers, but it would seem to be a matter of individual disposition. One eyrie may contain the remains of pigeons; another, in precisely the same locality, may contain only remnants of sea-birds—puffins, razorbills, and Black-headed gulls.

All the birds discussed in the preceding pages belong to the falcon tribe or Falconidae and, incidentally, are all British nesters. There are, however, foreign races or subspecies of each.

There are other falcons distinct from *F. peregrinus* and its races which should be mentioned. The lanner (*F. biarmicus*), which ranges from Egypt to the Persian Gulf and South Africa, is much like the peregrine and is equally bold and dashing but has a reddish cap to its head and a pinker breast. There are several subspecies of the lanner.

A much larger falcon which breeds in southern Europe, southern Russia and Asia is the saker (*F. cherrug*). It is of a dull brownish colour, lacks the alert eye of the peregrines and looks, in fact, rather like a huge female kestrel.

GERFALCONS

Far more imposing in appearance are the gerfalcons of the north. They consist of the Norway falcon or gerfalcon (*F. rusticolus rusticolus*) which inhabits Norway, Sweden, Lapland and North Russia; the Iceland falcon (*F. rusticolus islandus*) which breeds in Iceland but which migrates occasionally to Europe and, handsomest of them all, the Greenland falcon (*F. rusticolus candicans*). The two first-named are very similar in appearance, though the Iceland falcon is generally a good deal lighter in colour. The Greenland falcon is larger than the other two and is subject to much colour variation. One form is completely white except for small dark spots. It has been recorded as a visitor to the British Isles and the continent of Europe. This last type was much sought after by the falconers of

old and commanded high prices, but, although its habits are very similar to those of the peregrine, it lacks (as do the other gerfalcons) the determination, dash and energy of the latter, in spite of its larger size and greater strength. The esteem in which it was held by falconers was in all probability due to its magnificent appearance.

SPARROW-HAWK

Whilst the chief characteristics of the falcon tribe are long-pointed wings, dark eyes and somewhat short tails, those of their allies, the hawks, are rounded wings, yellow eyes and long tails. Hawks are also less engaging than falcons. The yellow eyes of the sparrow-hawk (*Accipiter nisus*)—the only true British hawk—seem, rightly, to suggest a mistrustful, wayward and shifty disposition.

It dives with such rapidity at some unsuspecting quarry, which it snatches with its spindly foot, that the business of securing a meal is over before the wretched victim has had time to realize what is going on. But—and this is one great difference between the methods of the hawks and those of the falcons—should this first impulsive dash prove to be unsuccessful, the sparrow-hawk does not persevere in the chase as would a merlin or a hobby.

It may persist, in a rather half-hearted way, for a few yards, but, unless the fugitive is in poor fettle, soon retires to some convenient perch whereon it awaits the moment for another chance. Sometimes, keeping within a few feet of the ground, it will skim rapidly towards some hedgerow or thicket, swerving with the utmost ease to avoid any obstacles it may encounter, so as to make a surprise attack on any suitable quarry that may be on the other side. When close to such cover it will suddenly shoot up and over the top in the hope of spotting something worthwhile. Woe betide the blackbird, thrush, partridge or wood-pigeon that may be happily feeding or resting within striking distance. The sparrow-hawk's long legs are extremely effective in enabling the bird to snatch up quarry even after the latter has dived into thick cover. The sparrow-hawks (like all hawks) kill their prey with their talons; the business of killing tends, therefore, to take longer than it does with the falcons, which kill quickly and efficiently with their bills.

There is a greater difference in size between the male and the female sparrow-hawk than is the case with a good many of the birds of prey. It is the considerably larger female that secures such sizable quarry as partridges and wood-pigeons: the male captures such small game as finches and tits.

SPARROW-HAWK'S NEST

In the past a certain amount of controversy arose as to whether this hawk builds a nest of its own or utilizes the abandoned home of some other creature. It is now accepted that it generally builds an entirely new nest, though sometimes it is not above taking over a disused squirrel's drey or another bird's nest. In either case it spends some time in renovating and touching up before— as it were—moving in. Whilst the nest is undergoing construction the owners may be seen soaring at a considerable height—particularly when the sun is shining; up to the time when the female broods they spend a part of most days in thus enjoying themselves. It is, in fact, the sight of a sparrow-hawk soaring that often leads to the discovery of its home.

When the young ones arrive they are fed by the female on food caught by the male and brought to the vicinity of the nest. When he arrives on some near-by branch with food in his foot (and if it is a bird it will usually have been quite carefully plucked) he utters a soft "pee-oo, pee-oo," repeated several times. Whether his mate is brooding the family or is otherwise engaged she at once flies to him to take the offering. Very occasionally he will bring the catch to the nest himself, place it at his mate's feet, bestow a glance at the growing family and be away again.

FEEDING THE YOUNG

Hawks, as well as other birds, are largely creatures of habit. It sometimes happens that a female sparrow-hawk, with a family to care for, is shot or trapped or otherwise comes to grief. In such cases the male may continue to procure food for the young, bringing the various catches to the nest and leaving them there. He seems instinctively to realize that the little ones need food, but certainly has no idea as to how it should be distributed.

The sparrow-hawk is not popular amongst the gamekeeping fraternity, a fact which is quite understandable, for it is the one bird of prey that will make really serious inroads on the numbers of young pheasants. Not that, generally speaking, it is specially partial to this type of food—it would probably enjoy jay or woodpecker or cuckoo just as much—but young pheasants, in a wood where they are being cared for, must seem to the hawk so plentiful and so easy to catch as to be quite irresistible. Having once fallen, the sparrow-hawk probably continues on the downward path. Just as one peregrine's eyrie is littered with pigeon's feathers and another with nothing but those of sea-birds, so one sparrow-hawk's nest contains the remains of woodland birds and

SPARROW-HAWK ON ITS NEST

*Although the sparrow-hawk is only about a foot in length, it is one of the boldest of
the birds of prey. Its diet consists mainly of small birds, but it will make serious inroads into young pheasants and other game birds. Like all the hawks, it kills its prey
with its talons; falcons by contrast kill with their beaks. The female sparrow-hawk is
considerably larger and more powerful than her mate.*

285

another is piled with the feathers and bones of young pheasants.

On account of its swiftness and courage the sparrow-hawk is much prized in India for use in falconry—or rather for hawking, for falconry is, properly, the sport with the long-winged falcons. In Britain and in some countries in Europe, it has been much criticized because of its sulky, unreliable disposition. The reason for this divergence is doubtless due to the different methods of training the birds.

METHOD OF HAWKING

The practice of "throwing" the short-winged hawks is invariably adopted in India. Such hawks are quick enough off the mark, but when thrown properly do gain an immense impetus. The hawker, generally in line with a number of beaters, walks slowly forward until a quail rises from the rough grass ahead. At once the little hawk is thrown, as a native throws a spear, in its direction; the hawk shoots forward on half-spread wings and closes with the quail as neatly as a bee-eater closes with its favourite quarry. A halsband (a strip of leather which encircles the hawk's neck) prevents the bird's neck and back from being put out of joint or receiving a nasty jar.

The European sparrow-hawk, or bashah, is much preferred by Indian falconers to the native shikra (*Astur badius*), a small type of goshawk. Although the latter is a more docile creature in the early stages of its training it is not to be compared with the former. The bashah is faster and more courageous. Goshawks are likewise caught in the hills on migration, are handled in the same way and are equally tame. In the wild state the goshawk resembles the sparrow-hawk in many respects: it has wonderful

acceleration; it inhabits forests and with its rounded wings can turn in a very small space; it catches its victims by the same methods, and it builds its nest in a tree.

There are a number of species of the goshawk in various parts of the world. In America one occurs that is about the same size as the European type, but has smaller, less powerful feet and is of a less bloodthirsty character. It is known zoologically as *Astur atricapillus*. It has been trained and used for hawking in the United States, as have two members of the Accipiter family: the Cooper's hawk and the Sharp-shinned hawk. They are both very like the British sparrow-hawk in hunting and nesting habits, in appearance and in general behaviour. The first is, however, a good deal larger than the sparrow-hawk and the second slightly smaller.

In Africa there are two quite small goshawks; the Little Banded goshawk, or South African shikra, which is not much bigger than a missel-thrush, and the Gabar goshawk, which is about the size of the European sparrow-hawk.

AFRICAN GOSHAWK

The African goshawk (*Astur tachiro*) is the same size as its European relative and is just as dashing; all goshawks, in fact, have the same disposition and general habits as have the sparrow-hawks.

There is one other particular and strange goshawk of South Africa which deserves special mention although it is not actually listed among the Asturs. It is the Chanting goshawk or blouvalk (*Melierax musicus*). This is a long-winged, sluggish-flying hawk which feeds on insects and small reptiles captured as they run about the ground. It is quite a common bird in its favourite localities and may, not infrequently, be seen perched on a telegraph pole or branch of a dead tree which it is generally unwilling to leave. It seems that the stories of its vocal accomplishments are no myth. Ornithologists have reported that it sings loudly and well.

The Chanting goshawk resembles another and equally curious bird of South Africa—though not a true goshawk—which is unique and has a family all to itself. It is the Harrier hawk or gymnogene (*Gymnogenus typicus*). The sides of its face are bare of feathers, the skin being of a reddish-yellow colour. It has long legs and a very narrow head which it pokes into the hiding-places of lizards, spiders and insects. It occurs sparingly in wooded country and has been reported from eastern Transvaal to Cape Province.

The harriers, of which there are some sixteen species, are birds of long and slender form. They have long legs and tail and a facial disk or ruff which imparts a quite owl-like expression. Their plumage is, generally, soft and loose and they catch their prey by quartering the ground and suddenly dropping on to it. These two characteristics both suggest an approach in character to the owls.

There are three British species: the Marsh harrier (*Circus aeruginosis*), the Hen harrier (*C. pyaneus*), and the Montagu's harrier (*C. pygargus*). They are all migratory in winter, ranging as far as South Africa or India. Harriers are remarkable for the great difference in colour between the two sexes, the males being much more beautifully coloured than the females. All these harriers build their nests on, or near to, the ground—the Marsh and the Montagu's in damp surroundings, such as reed-beds or among clumps of rushes; the Hen on drier, more open moorlands.

It would seem that the harriers again resemble the owls in their tendency to lay their eggs at intervals; the result is that the young in one nest are often of different sizes. Harriers always hunt on the wing, skimming along at no great height.

One of the most interesting characteristics of the harriers is the "pass" of food from the male to the female. Many people interested in birds must have seen the male Montagu's harrier returning from a foraging expedition with a victim in his foot.

The male announces, with a little "tew-tew," that he is the bearer of good things; the female, on hearing his cry, will rise from the reeds and circle higher and higher until she is almost

GOSHAWK

The goshawk resembles the sparrow-hawk in many respects, and it catches its victims by the same methods.

level with the male, following rather below and behind him. When he drops the food, she swings up, turns almost on to her back and catches it with the greatest dexterity.

Whilst the harrier chicks are small the female is almost always at the nest and the male does all the hunting. When, however, the young are acquiring feathers she leaves the nest for longer and longer periods on hunting expeditions of her own—a technique that is employed by other members of the hawk tribe.

CHANGING PLUMAGE

The great differences in the colour of harriers, together with the curious changes of plumage at various ages, presented ornithologists with a problem as to which species a particular harrier might belong to. One form, the Pale harrier (*C. macrourus*)—which breeds in southern Europe, Russia and central India—is lighter in colour than the British species; whilst another—the Black harrier (*C. maurus*)—is very much darker, being black except for a white patch above the tail and a few greyish-white markings. It is an African harrier and appears to be on the verge of extinction.

In the United States there is a form of harrier which corresponds with the British Hen harrier, but is distinguishable by the more decided grey of the upper parts; it is the Marsh hawk (*C. hudsonius*). Actually, of course, it is a harrier and its name is no doubt due to the habit of early settlers of naming birds which were new to them in accordance with what they knew about similar birds in Europe.

In certain respects owls resemble the harriers. Both birds are inclined to be crepuscular in their activities; both have curious facial disks; both may be seen quartering the ground in search of victims and both may lay their eggs at intervals so that young and eggs are sometimes found in the same nest.

There is a large variety of owls— some two hundred species—in widely dispersed parts of the world. They range from the tiny Pigmy owls—no larger than a quail—to the powerful eagle-owl (*Bubo ignavus*) which is larger than a buzzard. Most species hunt only at night, but some will secure a victim in daylight. All are carnivorous and provided with strong, hooked beaks and toes furnished with sharp, curved talons. They feed on such fare as mammals, birds, reptiles, beetles and other insects. Their soft, fluffy plumage enables them to proceed silently when on the wing—a fact which is of the greatest advantage to them when closing with their prey.

Most owls are useful to the farmer and keeper of poultry, for their food consists very largely of rats, mice and other "vermin." Some species, however (the Tawny owl, for instance), sometimes acquire the habit of preying on game birds and, by doing so, tend to bring the whole owl family into disrepute among gamekeepers and their kind.

OWLS OF GREAT BRITAIN

Five different species of owls nest in Britain: the Tawny or Brown owl (*Syrnium aluco*); the Barn owl (*Strix flammea*); the Long-eared owl (*Asio otus*); the Short-eared owl (*Asio accipitrinus*), and the Little owl (*Athene noctua*). Of these the Tawny owl is the largest and most courageous (there are many instances of a Tawny attacking a human being); the most beautiful and least harmful is the Barn owl; the quaintest—with its curious "ears" or "horns"—is the Long-eared; the rarest and most diurnal is the Short-eared,

LITTLE OWL

Of the five species of owls which nest in Britain, the Little owl is the smallest, being only about 7-8 in. long. Formerly a rare visitor, it was imported about fifty years ago, and is now very well established, even being regarded as a menace. Its increase may be largely due to its inconspicuous appearance and unobtrusive habits.

whilst the smallest, and in many districts the commonest, is the Little owl.

Until some fifty years ago the Little owl was known only as a rare visitor to the British Isles, although common enough on the Continent. Various ornithologists, at about that time, imported and liberated Little owls in the hope that they would become established as a nesting species. Their efforts turned out to be all too successful, for today the Little owl is in many districts the commonest of the owls, and is generally regarded as a menace.

Whether, however, it is more "harmful" than "beneficial" is a matter of opinion. That it should have increased to such an extent in such a comparatively short time may be due to its insignificant size, to its habit of hiding and "lying doggo" in the hollow in which it has taken up its abode, and to its resemblance to a piece of dead wood as it sits motionless on some branch or post.

Such a conspicuous bird as the large and handsome Snowy owl (*Nyctea Scandiaca*) generally comes to an untimely end on its rare visits to the British Isles and would not survive if attempts were made to introduce it as a nesting species—unless, indeed, such an attempt were made in, for instance, the Orkneys or the wilder parts of Scotland.

CHARACTERISTICS OF OWLS

All owls are characterized by the dense feathering of the head and neck, which is so pronounced as to give the bird the appearance of possessing an abnormally large head ; by their soft, fluffy, plumage; by the fact that they invariably perch with two toes in front and two behind (though the fourth toe is reversible), and by their great round, glaring eyes, limited in movement.

For centuries the owl has been regarded as a bird of ill-omen, a forerunner of disaster, and even in these enlightened times it is regarded by superstitious people as being an uncanny, ghostly sort of bird that is best avoided and whose cry forebodes some dire calamity. The majority of us, however, certainly award the owl a high place among the most interesting and amusing birds of the world.

PERILS OF MIGRATION

Some of the birds of prey are astonishingly common in the United States; which is rather surprising since, at certain seasons, they follow migration routes in their hundreds and are shot by the score at well-known strategic points. Buteos—birds of the buzzard type—are often the victims and probably offer an easy target as, unless high in the air, their heavy-winged and sluggish movements make them conspicuous. Yet the buzzard, wheeling high in the sky with scarcely a movement of its wings, is just as impressive a sight as is the eagle; in fact, it needs the eye of a practised observer to be able to distinguish between the two.

The only buteo which commonly nests in the British Isles is the buzzard (*Buteo buteo*). The Honey buzzard (*Pernis apivorus*) and the Rough-legged buzzard (*Buteo lagopus*) are occasional visitors to Britain. Both are very rare.

Honey buzzards are peculiar in that they feed largely on the comb from wasps' nests as well as on more normal food and are far more beautifully coloured than the buzzard. Rough-legged buzzards have legs feathered down to their feet (the other two have bare tarsi) and frequent river-banks.

In many respects, even when scrutinized at close quarters, the buzzard

BARN OWL BRINGING IN ITS PREY

A male Barn owl with a mouse firmly gripped in its beak is seen flying up from a window in the tower of an English country church to its nest, built high above the bells. This high-speed photograph, taken by flashlight, has caught the owl's powerful wings on the up-beat. Of the five species of British owls, the Barn owl is the handsomest.

markedly resembles the eagle. It nests in trees or on a rock; it builds its own nest; it lays two and rarely three eggs; it is given to decorating its home with sprigs of greenery; the young are much given to fighting each other, and both eagle and buzzard eat carrion as well as prey which they catch themselves.

Such a large bird cannot be expected, of course, to rear its voracious young on such insignificant food as beetles. It takes moles to some extent in dry weather, when these little animals are easily picked up, but its main diet appears to be small rabbits. In one buzzard's nest thirty-five rabbits were found; naturally, the youngsters could never hope to consume so much food before it began to deteriorate, and it is interesting to know that whereas the rabbits on top of the pile were quite fresh, evidently having been secured the same day, those at the bottom were little more than a mass of maggots. All these young rabbits had been roughly plucked and most of them had had their intestines removed.

In a part of Britain in which the kite (*Milvus milvus*) still nests, buzzards are quite numerous. The latter seem to resent the approach of the kite towards their territory, for when both birds nest in the same vicinity it is not unusual to see the buzzard stooping at its distinguished neighbour.

CITY SCAVENGER

In the Middle Ages the kite was exceedingly common in the City of London, where it served a useful purpose by acting as a scavenger in streets that lacked the sanitary equipment of today. With the introduction of drainage systems the kite retired to more rural surroundings, where it was without the protection that cities afforded it. Doubtless it was often destroyed,

and it is today one of the rarest of British birds.

To its detriment the kite often elects to nest in the proximity of human dwellings rather than in the not-far-distant mountain fastnesses. The nest is composed of sticks mingled with clods of turf, clumsily arranged sheep's wool, pieces of paper and cotton-rag. When the young kites have hatched (and there are generally two in the family), various types of food will generally be found lying on the side of the nest: several young rabbits, a vole, a half-eaten young bird, and some lambs' tails, for instance. It would, therefore, seem that the kite is not altogether a scavenger, but that it sometimes kills for itself.

BLACK KITE OF INDIA

The Black kite is a rare visitor to Britain. It is one of India's most useful scavengers, picking up any scraps of food it can espy.

It appears to feed on almost anything edible, from earthworms on the lawn to slices of meat or pieces of pie from a soldier's plate. It secures the latter by a sudden and unexpected swoop from above; snatching up the prize with the greatest dexterity in its little foot as it swings by. It will often transfer some small portion of food to its beak whilst still on the wing.

Although a whole-time scavenger, it will not hesitate to stoop at such a rival as an eagle, but, strangely enough, seems not to bother itself about any vultures that it may encounter—perhaps because the vulture is not a killer and, consequently, not to be dreaded.

Regarding the possible killing propensities of the vultures, it is perhaps opportune to mention the one vulture that was at one time regarded as an eagle and, therefore, as a hunter. It is

A BUZZARD BRINGS FOOD TO ITS YOUNG

The buzzard closely resembles the eagle in many respects. It builds its nest in a tree or on a rock and decorates it with sprigs of greenery. It rarely lays more than two eggs, and when the young hatch out they are much given to fighting each other. The parent bird feeds the chicks on such food as moles and small rabbits, which it plucks and from which it often removes the intestines. Huge quantities of food may accumulate in the nest,

293

THE KITE, ONE OF NATURE'S SCAVENGERS

The kite is less predacious than most birds of prey, being by nature a scavenger, with an appetite for almost anything edible. Nevertheless it sometimes kills other birds, especially when it has a voracious family to feed, and at such times it will wreak havoc in poultry-yards. In the Middle Ages kites were common in the City of London, but with the introduction of the drainage system they retired to more rural surroundings.

the Bearded vulture (*Gypaetus barba-tus*)—so called because of the tuft of black bristles under its chin—which is quite common on the North-West Frontier of India. Sometimes called the lammergeier, it is one of the most imposing birds in the world, with its vast wing-spread, tawny breast, orange head feathers and majestic gliding flight.

It frequently feeds on the rubbish dumps of military camps in the hills or on the bones of slaughtered cattle outside such places as Simla, Mussoorie, or Naini Tal.

THE OSPREY

Like the Red kite, the osprey (*Pandion haliaëtus*) was, some forty years ago, on the verge of extinction as a British nesting species, but, unlike the former, was finally exterminated in Britain by the activities of collectors. At one time a number of pairs of ospreys nested annually in Scotland, but in the end only one pair survived. Their huge nest was built at the top of a small oak-tree, growing on an island surrounded by the waters of a loch dramatically situated in wild, mountainous country. Every precaution seems to have been taken to preserve this last remaining pair, but all were unavailing. Collectors continued to steal the eggs each year and the osprey eventually died out as a nesting bird in Britain. During the intervening years many ospreys have been seen—and destroyed —in various parts of Britain, and it is to be hoped that, with the modern and more reasonable interest in wild life, they will once again nest in their old haunts.

The osprey feeds entirely on fish which it catches by hovering, after the style of the kestrel, over rather shallow water at a height of some forty feet and dropping feet and head first into the water. Its hard feathers do not become waterlogged, and soon after leaving the water the bird will steady itself in the air and give its feathers a thorough shaking. Then, with the head of the fish pointing forward, it continues on its way. That it can succeed in holding such a slippery object as a fish may seem surprising, but the osprey's feet are specially adapted for the purpose— the toes, on the underside, being furnished with horny spicules.

The osprey is widely distributed in the world and is to be found nesting in Russia, Spain, Egypt, Africa, India and other regions. It is surprisingly common in the United States, particularly on some of the islands off the eastern seaboard. On one of these islands the enormous nests are to be seen amongst the branches of large thickly foliaged trees, at the tops of dead or dying trees, which sometimes collapse under the weight, on bushes a few feet high, on upturned tree-roots, on walls, and even on the seashore. It is worthy of note that although some hundreds of pheasants are reared every year on this island, not a single instance of one of them having been taken by an osprey has ever been recorded.

NESTING MATERIALS

The osprey, like the kite, collects strange materials with which to decorate or otherwise improve its nest: pieces of board, straw bottle-cases, scraps of paper, seaweed, the dried-up remains of a dead bird—almost anything which it spots amongst the wreckage littering the beach and which it can pick up in its stoop and is strong enough to carry away. As with the other birds of prey, it is the male that usually does the hunting whilst the young are small and the female is at home. The food is passed from his claws to hers.

THE OSPREY, OR FISHING HAWK,

Ospreys feed entirely on fish, which they catch by diving into the water from a height of about forty feet. Their feet are specially adapted for gripping their slippery prey, being equipped with horny spicules on the underside of the toes. A fish, when caught, is carried with the head pointing forwards so as to reduce wind-resistance. Ospreys

BRINGS HOME ITS CATCH

are widely distributed throughout the world, but they no longer nest in Britain owing to the activities of egg-collectors. The osprey's nest is a huge, untidy structure, containing a curious medley of materials—sticks, wool, paper, seaweed, straw—and appears to be placed indifferently upon trees, bushes, walls, or even on the ground.

WHITE-TAILED SEA EAGLE

The White-tailed sea eagle (Haliaëtus albicilla) *is also known as the erne. It no longer nests in Britain, but is still to be found on the continent of Europe and in Asia. Like other species of sea eagle, it feeds chiefly on fish and water-fowl, but also likes a meal of carrion—of which it is said to eat sometimes so voraciously as to be practically incapable of flight after its meal. Its plumage, save for its white tail, is mainly brown.*

Although the osprey does not attack creatures other than fish in order to keep itself or its family supplied with food, it will frequently attack larger birds, but for a different reason. The objective may be a heron, a Short-eared owl or a Marsh hawk. The osprey is obviously sceptical of the other's intentions and will stoop at the intruder—even delivering a clout as it shoots by in an endeavour to scare it away. Occasionally it succeeds in delivering such a blow as to put its foe out of action—perhaps with a broken wing. Even the White-headed or Bald eagle, emblem of the United States, may be greeted in the same way; the osprey is, however, careful to "throw up" after each stoop so as to be out of harm's way.

EAGLE SNATCHES PREY

Sometimes the boot is on the other foot and the Bald eagle—also for a different reason—stoops at the osprey. This occurs when a high-flying eagle sights an osprey laden with a fish, making for some feeding-spot. This is the eagle's chance. Down it comes at full speed towards the osprey, which is doomed to lose its plunder. The sight and sound of its rapid approach must have an unnerving effect on the surprised osprey, which may manage to avoid the first stoop but which still will be awkwardly placed, for the eagle throws-up again easily and is ready for another shot. In desperation the osprey drops its fish, shifts aside and experiences the humiliation of seeing the eagle catch the fish before it reaches the water or land below.

The American White-headed eagle (*Haliaëtus leucocephalus*), although a buoyant and adroit flier, cannot be considered a dignified bird. It feeds largely on carrion and often on dead fish. It resembles the vultures in other respects,

too: its large sharp beak, the long neck, the comparatively small feet. It does kill for itself, but its prey often consists of fish, easily caught in very shallow water, or of weak or wounded victims. This eagle invariably nests in a tree and generally lays two eggs. The young are a dull brown all over when grown. They do not acquire the white head and tail for four or five years.

In a hard winter Bald eagles—both mature and immature—may be seen perched on slabs of ice drifting slowly downstream in the Hudson River and within a few miles of New York City.

The Bald eagle is one of the sea eagles, a family of which another species once nested in Great Britain—the White-tailed sea eagle or erne (*H. albicilla*); this bird no longer nests in Britain, but is still to be found on the continent of Europe and in Asia. All the sea eagles, and there are quite a number of varieties, feed chiefly on fish and water-fowl and all enjoy a meal of carrion. The largest of this group is the huge Steller's sea eagle (*H. pelagicus*) of eastern Siberia, north China and Japan, whilst the smallest is the prettily-marked, white-headed African sea eagle (*H. vocifer*) which may be frequently seen near the rivers of South Africa.

GOLDEN EAGLE

Of all the eagles, the Golden eagle (*Aquila chrysaëtus*) is probably the most famous. It is probably less rare today than it was fifty years ago. The shortage of gamekeepers, the growing interest in wild creatures and the wider knowledge of their ways have no doubt helped to save it from the fate of the sea eagle and the osprey. It is still destroyed by some who are interested in sheep-farming because it has been known to take lambs, and by game-

GOLDEN EAGLES IN THEIR EYRIE

The Golden eagle is the largest and noblest of the European birds of prey. It attains a length of almost 3 ft., has a wing-span of about 7 ft., and weighs about 14 lb. when fully grown. Its normal diet consists of hares, rabbits, young deer, game-birds and the like, but eagles nesting near farms are apt to help themselves to lambs, pigs and poultry. For this reason it was formerly outlawed, but now seems to be maintaining its numbers.

keepers because it kills grouse. Nevertheless, it is holding its own very well.

The Golden eagle is widely distributed in the world and occurs in Europe, Asia, Africa and America. It builds its nest, or eyrie, either in a tree or on a rocky ledge. Two eggs are usually laid and the young, when first hatched, are covered with a light-greyish down.

QUARRELSOME EAGLETS

While they are still quite small a curious urge to attack one another seems to overcome them—or one of them. They will square up to one another pugnaciously and with much twittering and head-dodging try to get a beak-hold on the opponent's face. At this age their little legs, with which they will do all their attacking when they are older, are not manoeuvrable and it seems they must attack with something. At last one may get the upper hand and, having seized the other by the back of the neck or some other vulnerable part of the body, will proceed to shake it from side to side as a terrier shakes a rat. If the weaker one manages to break away, it scrambles across the nest on its shaky legs, but is soon overtaken by the aggressor which, once more getting a hold, proceeds to bite and shake until the unfortunate victim is battered beyond resistance.

It has been suggested that the photographer or bird-watcher is the cause of such fights. The reasoning of those who put forward this suggestion is that the presence of the photographer's "hide" arouses the suspicion of the parent eagle to such an extent that it becomes too scared to bring food to the nest, and the result is that the starving young, in desperation, set upon each other in the hope of securing a meal. This, however, is not so. The fighters are often surrounded by the bodies of hares, rabbits and grouse. Furthermore, one of the parent eagles may bring yet more food to the nest whilst the fight is proceeding, but the combat continues.

An instance is recorded of a Golden eagle's eyrie slipping from its ledge on a cliff during a storm and crashing, with the two well-grown eaglets that inhabited it, on to the rocks below. It is interesting to know that the eaglets were unhurt and that their parents continued to supply them with food as though nothing untoward had occurred.

For some weeks after they have left the nest young Golden eagles continue to be fed by their parents. As they gain strength and flying ability they undertake journeys farther and farther from their old homes, and attract the attention of their parents by uttering a quickly repeated, shrill "kew-kew-kew." It is probable that this practice is followed by some of the other members of the Aquiladae.

VERREAUX'S EAGLE

As close as any to the Golden eagle—as far as habits and general behaviour are concerned—is the fine Black eagle (*Aquila verreauxi*) of South Africa. This eagle is often called, in its native country, the Verreaux's eagle or dassie-vanger (dassie or rock-rabbit killer). It is jet black except for a pure white band down the centre of the back. Its food consists mainly, as its name suggests, of dassies or rock-rabbits, but it also eats lambs, young pigs and kids.

There are in Africa a great many other members of the eagle family. For instance, the curious Bateleur eagle (*Terathopius ecaudatus*), with its enormous head and tiny tail, which combine to make the bird look, when on the wing, as though it is flying backwards;

CROWNED EAGLE AND

With the possible exception of the huge Harpy eagle of South and Central America, the Crowned eagle of Africa is the world's most formidable eagle. Hawk-like in form and habits, it nests in trees and dense forests and can make its way with astonishing dexterity through thick cover. It lives to a great extent on buck of various kinds, but

FAMILY ON THEIR NEST
it also kills monkeys, which it catches by diving silently down from some vantage-point high up in the branches of a tree. So deadly is this swift and unexpected form of attack that the victim succumbs at once. The young of the Crowned eagle, of which there are usually two at a time, fight viciously—often till the death of one of them ensues.

303

the Black-breasted Harrier eagle (*Circaëtus pectoralis*), which, in spite of its magnificent appearance, is of such a meek disposition as to feed mostly on small rodents, lizards and snakes; the curious Crested Hawk eagle (*Lophaëtus occipitalis*), which also subsists on insignificant creatures and has such a long crest that, seen at a distance, it looks like a cockatoo.

Far more dignified and powerful is the splendid Martial eagle (*Polemaëtus bellicosus*), one of Africa's most impressive birds. It has a wing-spread of 8 ft. and is much given to soaring at vast heights. It frequents the open plain country and feeds on meerkats, hares, small buck and lambs. It builds its nest in an isolated tree, generally fairly near the ground, and lays a single egg.

The Martial eagle differs from the true eagles very considerably. In many ways it resembles the hawks and is sometimes referred to as a Hawk eagle, though known locally as the lammervanger (lamb-killer). Its habit of soaring conspicuously is liable to disclose the whereabouts of its home and bring it to grief at the hands of the farming fraternity. It has, in fact, been nearly exterminated in certain districts of Africa.

The magnificent Crowned eagle of Africa (*Stephanoaëtus coronatus*) is more numerous, probably because it makes its home in dense forests and is, in consequence, seldom seen. This is Africa's most formidable eagle; it might be said to be the most formidable eagle in the world—with the possible exception of the huge Harpies of South America. The Crowned eagle is even more

GOLDEN EAGLE ARRIVES AT ITS NEST

The Golden eagle is generally regarded as the "king of birds." Its body feathers are blackish-brown in colour, but those on its head and the back of its neck are golden, and it is from these that the bird takes its name.

THE POWERFUL MARTIAL EAGLE

The Martial eagle (Polemaëtus bellicosus) *has a wing-spread of 8 ft., and is much given to soaring to great heights. The specimen seen above was brought to England by Capt. C. W. R. Knight, author of this section, who has trained it to hunt like a hawk.*

hawklike in its form and habits than the Martial. It builds its nest in a tree; it secures its victims by an unexpected dash, and can, with its rounded hawk-like wings and long tail, make its way through cover with astonishing dexterity. It is, in fact, like a huge sparrow-hawk. It resembles the Golden eagle, however, in that it lays two eggs, and the young, when small, develop the fighting urge. Each of two nests recently discovered, both built in yellow-wood trees and at a height of some 70 ft. from the ground, contained, in the first place, two eggs: two eaglets duly hatched from each pair, and in both cases fighting took place which ended in the death of one of the eaglets. On one of the nests the survivor was a female; that on the other nest, however, was a male.

This fierce and dashing eagle feeds to a great extent on buck of various kinds and monkeys. The Crowned eagle's method of accomplishing the feat of catching the swift-moving and alert monkey is most efficient. It selects a bare branch, high up in a tree on fairly open ground, and on it waits until a potential meal appears below. When an unsuspecting band of monkeys emerges from the bushes into the open, the eagle leans intently forward, launches itself into the air, drops in complete silence and lands on the selected victim with a crash that sends the rest of the party away screaming in terror. Because of the suddenness, the power and the speed of its attack the Crowned eagle is known amongst the natives as the "leopard of the air."

REED-WARBLER WITH ITS FLEDGLING

The reed-warbler's nest is suspended from upright reeds, near streams and rivers.
The hen alone builds, although the cock assists in feeding the young; he may, indeed,
be left to feed the fledglings entirely by himself. This English song-bird is reddish-brown
above, yellowish-white beneath. Intensive and continuous study of reed-warblers has
shed much light on the holding of "territory" and other riddles of bird behaviour.

Perching birds

PERCHING is a habit found in almost all the orders or main divisions of the class of animals which we call birds. The principal exceptions are the orders which include the flightless land-birds, such as the ostrich and emu, and those in which are found the more oceanic sea-birds, such as the shearwaters, petrels and albatrosses; also penguins, and auks and guillemots, or other waterfowl which spend almost all their lives in their chosen element, such as the grebes and divers.

Herons, storks and cranes, on the other hand, spend a lot of time on perches, as do many gulls. Some waders, such as the Common snipe and redshank, often settle on posts, and the Green sandpiper actually breeds in the old nests of other birds in trees. Some ducks in other parts of the world perch regularly; British mallard often nest in old trees and actually perch on branches, while the habit is so common amongst the game-birds and so regular in the pigeons and doves that both these groups are being covered by this section.

The birds of prey, nearly all of which perch, have been dealt with in the previous section.

"Perching birds," therefore, in the sense in which we are using it, is a very wide term. Essentially it refers to the huge order of Passerine (*passer* = sparrow) birds, which contains the true song-birds, but this section also covers the group of orders—poorly represented in Britain—some of which are called the near-Passerines. These include a great many colourful birds: kingfishers, woodpeckers, hoopoes, rollers, parrots, hornbills, which, generally speaking, nest in holes and lay white eggs, together with cuckoos, and such diverse and remarkable orders as the swifts, hummingbirds and the nightjars.

Some nine thousand species of birds are known to science throughout the world; of these over five thousand are passerine, and it is very likely therefore that they also comprise the numerical majority of individuals. In origin they are as old as most other bird orders: a passerine ancestor, *Osteornis*, dates from Eocene times, sixty million years or so ago.

Ancestors of the typically passerine tits and warblers, and of the near-passerine hornbills and woodpeckers, date from thirty-five to forty million years ago, while many modern genera appear in French deposits of late Miocene times. Some of these represented orders such as the trogons, unknown in Europe since the Ice Age.

The success of the Passerines continues, for they have adapted themselves to human association better than any other group, and man has rewarded some of them with a kindness he now regrets, for introduced house-sparrows and starlings have swept over America

YOUNG CHOUGHS AT HOME IN CORNWALL

The chough is found throughout a large part of Europe and Asia, but is much less common in the British Isles than formerly, owing, possibly, to persecution by man and by birds of prey. It has black plumage, with red legs and beak, and it usually nests in crevices of sea-cliffs and precipices, far from human habitations.

in the past fifty years, while the nostalgic desire of the settlers in New Zealand to surround their homes with familiar British birds has contributed to the banishment or extinction of native kinds. There are many other species which have come to meet civilization halfway and may be seen in the parks and open spaces of the great cities of Europe and America.

But Passerines also penetrate into the extremes of remoteness: in South Georgia the Antarctic pipit is to the breeding-ground of the Wandering albatross what the rock-pipit is to gull colonies; in the Aleutian islands ravens foraged in war-time American camps; the snow-bunting in Spitzbergen replaces the house-sparrow in human settlements; choughs have been seen at enormous heights in the Himalayas; there are several species of chats which live in the deserts of Africa. Only mid-ocean is free of them, for the Passerines, and indeed all the groups covered by this section, are naturally land-birds.

In view of this adaptability and tolerance it is not surprising that many of the "common or garden" British birds are Passerines. The often seen, more frequently heard, Green woodpecker, most adaptable of its order in its behaviour, is a near-Passerine, while the wood-pigeon and stock-dove, the pheasant, partridge and grouse are also for our present purposes included in the category of "perching birds."

It would take the entire space allotted to this chapter just to list all the orders, families and genera—let alone the actual species. J. L. Peters, the American ornithologist, has published six volumes of his *Checklist of the Birds of the World* and has not yet reached the Passerines! But, to take some examples from the orders he has listed, the game-birds (Galliformes) have eight families of existing birds, of which two are represented in Britain, though members of two others (guinea-fowl, turkeys) have been introduced under domestication, for this is the order which has given man not only his tame poultry and his wild "sporting birds," but also the ornamental, if raucous, peacock.

The pigeons (Columbiformes) have three families, but one contains fifty-nine genera. The doves have given their name to a quiet shade of grey, but some tropical fruit-pigeons are brilliantly coloured. The family is peculiar in feeding its young, normally two in number and hatched from white eggs in an open nest, on "pigeon's milk," composed of the cells lining the crop, which become rich in fat and are shed to form a cheeselike substance. The famous dodo was a near relative of the pigeons, and the third family consists of the sand-grouse, which in their habits are more like game-birds.

The great order of parrots (Psittaciformes) has about six hundred species, mostly tropical, so that none occurs wild in Europe. But captive parrots,

KEA PARROT OF NEW ZEALAND

The Kea parrot is a strange example of a wild creature altering its dietary habits. Before the introduction of sheep into New Zealand it fed upon fruit and berries, but it changed its diet and became a serious pest to sheep-farmers. It attacks live sheep with its powerful beak, devouring the fat that surrounds the kidneys.

lories, cockatoos and macaws are amongst the best known of all birds to the man in the street and the child at the Zoo. Parrots range down to pygmy species less than three inches long and include both the Kea parrot of New Zealand, which has learnt to attack sheep, and an East Indian group which roost upside-down like bats. Occasionally parrots have got loose or been released and lived at large in Britain for a time; one of the writer's ornithological nightmares was caused by three Indian Ring-necked parrakeets flying over a Midland wood on an afternoon in January.

The Cuculiformes are divided into the African plantain-eaters or turacos and the cuckoos. The European cuckoo is such a by-word that it is hard to re-member its parasitic habit is not found throughout the family, which in America includes also the roadrunners and the tropical anis. American cuckoos tend to build very slight nests, and the Black-billed cuckoo, a very rare wan-derer to Britain, shows a tendency to parasitize other birds. The most pecu-liar of the Caprimulgiformes, the oil-bird, is being dealt with in another section; the other four families in the order are different groups of nightjars, birds of the dusk, with cryptic colouring to help them escape notice in daytime. The transition from them to the swifts (Apodiformes) is fairly easy for anyone familiar with the British species to follow, but the swifts feed by day, en-tirely in the air, and cling rather than perch on the sides of buildings and

TREE-PIPIT FEEDING A YOUNG CUCKOO

The cuckoo is a migrant which passes the winter in Africa, reaching the British Isles in spring. It is notorious for laying its eggs in the nests of other, and smaller, birds. The young cuckoo is assiduously fed by its deluded foster-parents.

KEEN-SIGHTED BIRD OF THE DUSK

The nightjar does not build a nest, but merely deposits its two marbled eggs on the ground. This brown-grey bird, a summer visitor to Great Britain, has large, staring eyes that are adapted for vision in the twilight. By day it rests upon the ground, protected by its "cryptic" plumage. It eats insects, taking them in swift flight.

cliffs. Eastern swiftlets build the celebrated edible nests out of their own saliva; the nests are only used in soup to thicken it—they are not really palatable in themselves. The humming-birds are also in this order, one huge family of about a hundred genera and five hundred species, confined to the New World. While their general form and brilliant colours are well known, there is great variation in size, shape and in colour, which tends to be duller outside the tropics. Humming-birds take not only nectar, but minute insects from the flowers they visit.

The colies (Coliiformes) are also called mouse-birds from the appearance given by their short, thick body-feathers and long tails. They are a small order of about five species found in the bush in Africa; they roost clinging to their perches, but not upside-down like bat-parrots. Another tropical order is that of the trogons (Trogoniformes), whose fossil relatives have been found in Europe. A number are found in the forests of Central America, where the quetzal has become the symbol of Guatemala and better known to British philatelists than to bird-watchers.

The Coraciiformes are an extraordinary mixed bag, divided into several sub-orders. There are the kingfishers (not all of whom feed as their name suggests, for some species hunt insects on land), and their relatives the todies, five species of small green and red birds restricted to the West Indies. The motmots of Central America are recognized by their long middle tail-feathers with "blobs" on the ends, while the hornbills are famous for their unique breeding habits: the female walls herself or is walled in to incubate the eggs and carry through her own moult at the same time, the male bringing food to her and to the young.

Last before the Passerines come the Piciformes, which include exotic families like the jacamars, puff-birds, barbets, toucans and honey-guides, as well as British woodpeckers and wrynecks. Honey-guides really do show man the nests of wild bees and then take the larval stages of the insects while he takes the honey. The woodpeckers, like the kingfishers, do not all live up to their name; the British Green wood-pecker, for example, is becoming more and more a bird of open country, where it feeds on ants. Their little eastern relatives, the piculets, behave more like nuthatches than woodpeckers.

Dr. Wetmore, whose survey of the bird orders has formed the basis of the above paragraphs, and whose classification Peters largely follows, has listed sixty-nine families of Passeriformes, of which fifty-three are Oscines, or true song-birds. The remaining sixteen range from the South American oven-birds, which may build their extraordinary mud nests high on poles, through the tyrants, which replace our flycatchers in the New World, to the lyre-birds. Many of them are families confined to the southern hemisphere, and none is represented in Europe.

PRIZED DELICACY OF THE FAR EAST

Some species of swift build their cup-shaped nests entirely of mud; others, of straw and feathers cemented with saliva. But the nest of the Esculent swift, of the Far East (here seen built on the face of a cliff), is comprised entirely of dried saliva. This is used for the purpose of thickening "bird's-nest soup," a Chinese delicacy.

JEWEL-LIKE HUMMING-BIRD

The tiny humming-birds can be fittingly described as "feathered jewels," for most of them have plumage that glows with iridescent colours. The "humming" note is caused by the rapid beat of their wings. The Sword-billed humming-bird (ABOVE) hovers over trumpet-shaped flowers, seizing tiny insects from their depths with its long bill.

There is general resemblance between the Passerines of Europe and North America; most of the British families: larks, swallows, crows, titmice, nuthatches, creepers, dippers, wrens, thrushes, kinglets or goldcrests, wagtails and pipits, waxwings, shrikes, starlings, weaver-finches (which include the sparrows) and true finches are found across the Atlantic—the sparrows and starlings having been imported—some of them represented by the same species. The British warblers are replaced by a very similar family, and there are a number of additional families, as might be expected from the greater area and variation in latitude.

Other families, such as the bulbuls, are found much farther south in the Old World, while some are confined to small areas. The Australian bowerbirds are described elsewhere, as are the African Picathartes, the birds-of-paradise of New Guinea, and Darwin's finches (Geospizinae), so important in the study of evolution.

In view of this and of the vast range of birds briefly reviewed above, and to which it is impossible to do descriptive justice, the rest of this section will be devoted to some of the chief aspects and problems of bird behaviour most clearly seen in the lives of the Passerine and related birds; examples will be taken mainly from the familiar species of western Europe.

Another reason for this approach lies in the fact that, since Passerines are relatively tolerant of man and of the way in which he has modified the countryside, they have become favourite subjects for intensive study in the two areas, Europe and North America, which are most profoundly affected by human enterprises and are also those in which scientific ornithology is most highly developed. Moreover, the fact that Passerines live so close to man challenges his powers of observation, for they are generally small, active and elusive birds.

The house-sparrow, the closest human associate of all, is still a "bird of mystery," pointed out by each generation of ornithologists to their successors as a worthy object of study. But it is only necessary to try to watch a London sparrow for a few minutes to realize how difficult a detailed chronicle of its activities is likely to be; even to count the number of pairs nesting in a group of buildings and to find the sites may be a laborious task; many sparrows' nests are well hidden in holes and crevices and are only revealed when the young are being fed.

All the same, it is largely through close study of a few Passerine birds that we have acquired much of our knowledge under the main headings of migration and homing; song and territory; courtship and breeding biology; moulting; roosting; flocking and winter routines.

MARVELS OF MIGRATION

Migration is perhaps the outstanding activity associated with birds. Other creatures—insects, fish and mammals—migrate, some of them spectacularly, but the phenomenon is seen at its highest development in birds and has caught the imagination and attracted the attention of leading naturalists, not all of them ornithologists in the narrow sense, for ages.

Although visible migration has been known since classical times, the most remarkable speculations were put forward in the Middle Ages and thereafter to account for the annual appearance and disappearance of certain well-known birds; for though on the whole

the summer visitors to the northern hemisphere are less familiar than are the residents, the swallow, nightingale and cuckoo, and to a lesser extent the corn-crake, have been enshrined in poetry, literature and public regard.

SOME ANCIENT FALLACIES

So the swallows and their relatives, the martins, were supposed to dive below the waters of a lake or pond and hibernate in the mud; the cuckoo became a sparrow-hawk, and the corn-crake crept into a stone wall and "lay up." The first idea probably derives from a fanciful notion based upon the observation that swallows dip to the surface of a pond at dusk; but there is an undoubted superficial resemblance between cuckoo and hawk, and corn-crakes and other birds have been found from time to time in holes in walls, though they were probably injured birds unable to migrate. Astonishingly, hibernation has now been proved for some individuals of the American poor-will, a species of nightjar.

Gilbert White, in Britain, is always associated with the "debunking" of some of these beliefs during the eighteenth century when the real nature of migration—as astounding in its way as any metamorphosis of cuckoos and hawks—was recognized; in the next century the first attempts and experiments designed to explain it began to be made.

Today we know the when and where of migration fairly well, at least in the regions where birds are most studied; we know at what times each species may be expected to flood back into its summer range and when it will depart. We also know, though not completely, its destination in winter and, still less completely, by what stages it travels.

To clear up the last point first, the

KINGFISHER HOLDING A FISH IN ITS BEAK

In colouring the kingfisher is outstanding beside most British birds. Green, brown, white, orange and the famous "kingfisher blue" compose its brilliant plumage. The small fish which are its prey are swallowed whole, the bones being disgorged later.

OWNER OF AN OUTSIZE BEAK—THE TOUCAN

The many species of toucan—all of them hail from South and Central America—are predominantly fruit-eaters. In spite of the imposing dimensions of the grotesque beak (of brilliant red, yellow, green or blue), it is surprisingly light and quite manageable.

human love of definition, of tidying up the world of nature, has led to various rather ill-judged maps indicating with lines and arrows cut-and-dried flight lines by which migrating birds are supposed to travel. It is much more probable that migration occurs on a broad front from summer range to winter range, and is canalized over that front according to geographical features: mountains, deserts and seas are bar-riers, great river valleys and coasts are favourable, both because they are easy to follow in flight and because feeding stations are more likely to occur along them. It is inevitable, therefore, that there are greater concentrations of migrants in some regions; whether we are justified in talking about routes and flight-lines is another matter.

These aspects of migration have been studied in two ways, by direct observations and by catching and marking birds, usually with numbered metal bands or rings which are fixed round the tarsus or shank. Occasional marking of wild birds is several hundred years old, but it has only become widespread in the past fifty years. Now hundreds of thousands of birds are marked annually in Canada and the U.S.A., and tens of thousands in Britain, western Europe and Russia. Naturally, the easiest groups to mark are those which can be easily caught as adults or ringed as young birds in the nest. Ducks can be caught in large numbers as adults in decoys, but small perching birds can both be trapped as adults and marked in the nest. Unfortunately, the percentage of "recoveries" (that is to say, the percentage of ringed birds that are ever traced) is very low for these small birds (usually much less than 1 per cent), whereas ducks and other birds that are often shot show high (10 to 15 per cent) returns. Naturally, recoveries of perching birds are of great interest and, few as they have been, they have thrown a great deal of light on the journeys and winter ranges of the hordes of song-birds which make the northern spring so wonderful an event.

DIFFICULTIES OF RECORDING

The Pied flycatcher, a somewhat local summer visitor to Britain and northern Europe, is a species which the writer has had some opportunity of observing and marking in recent summers. Four hundred and fifty young were marked in 1947 and 1948, but by the end of the 1949 breeding season only two had been recovered and two more seen in the area where they were hatched, while of twenty adult females caught on the nest and ringed, three had been recovered, one of them twice in successive years. Results have been similar in

Finland; high percentages of adults have been recovered, but only 1 per cent of nearly nine hundred young marked were found again. One of the writer's birds has been recovered abroad, on its way through France in its first autumn; of nearly two thousand Pied flycatchers ringed in Britain up to 1948, it was only the second traced overseas.

BIRD OBSERVATORIES

This example shows the amount of effort needed to secure a small return for ringing migratory perching birds in the nest. More promising is the work at bird observatories, where adults are caught in large traps—mostly of the funnel type called "Heligoland traps," after the original evolved by German naturalists at the pioneer observatory on that ill-fated island, once the outstanding place at which to observe migrating Passerines in Europe. There are now seven observatories on islands and headlands round the British coast and others are planned. The observatories, where birds are *observed*, have succeeded the old-time *collections* made by shooting or from the casualties at lighthouses. Nowadays it is very rare for a Passerine to be killed anywhere in Britain in order to identify it, but there is still mortality at lights in spite of protective devices.

While these various methods have combined to give us some idea of the "anatomy" of migration, its "physiology" is still largely a mystery. *How* do birds migrate? It is obvious that the power of flight is their means, but for many of them migration must involve flights of far greater length than any they are seen to carry out at other times. The minute goldcrest must cross the North Sea in thousands, for its Continental race is common on the British east coast on passage, and the even

WATER SONG-BIRDS

The dipper, or water-ouzel, is unique among aquatic birds in having a melodious song,
which is quite unlike the harsh cries and garrulous quacks by which most water-fowl
express themselves. Entirely at home in the water, it swims below the surface, using
its wings. It even walks upon the bottom in its search for aquatic insects.

smaller Ruby-throated humming-bird is credited with prodigious flights over the Caribbean Sea. But if that part of the "how" seems remarkable enough, we still have to consider "how" in the sense of the method of navigation by which birds guide themselves. This "homing instinct" has led scientists to many experiments, some negative and others inconclusive in their results. Much of the evidence is contradictory. Landmarks cannot guide birds in regions where they have never been before (for example, when experimentally released miles outside their normal range), yet it seems certain that birds do look for and use landmarks in regions with which they are familiar. One idea is that birds will circle in widening spirals after

release until they pick up a known landmark, which they might see a hundred miles away in good visibility; another is that they scatter radially and only those which chance to fly approximately in the direction of the home region are successful in returning; recoveries of racing pigeons from long distances tend to support this. Various compromises between and modifications of these two theories have also been put forward.

Another body of suggestions involves the earth's magnetic field as the guiding agent, but experiments with birds carrying magnets strong enough to neutralize the earth's field, and with unmagnetized "control" birds, have not been satisfactory. But one interesting

THE MISSEL-THRUSH, OR STORM COCK

This female missel-thrush was photographed during one of the very brief intervals
which elapsed between ramming food down the throats of her voracious nestlings
and setting out in search of further dainties. Larger than the Song thrush, with a more
boldly spotted breast, the missel-thrush feeds largely on berries, especially upon those
of the mistletoe. It is notable for singing loudly in wild, stormy weather.

RED-BACKED SHRIKE, OR BUTCHER BIRD

The shrikes provide an example of "provident" behaviour rare among birds, for they store food for future use by impaling insects on long thorns adjacent to their nests, though often they do not eat them. The British Red-backed shrike stores bees, beetles and other insects. The rarer Great Grey shrike takes mainly small birds.

result came from the release of Hooded crows in Europe many miles south and west of their breeding range. A number were found in the right direction, but still many miles to the west. They had been able to find a south-north line, but not to make the necessary lateral adjustment.

"RECEPTOR" POWERS

Other theories have postulated "receptor" powers so highly sensitized that it is difficult to believe in them until more simple explanations have been shown to be inadequate; and even when homing has been explained, there is still the problem of the juveniles of certain species which at the age of a few weeks set off on their first southward migration ahead of the adults.

After "how" comes "why." What is the reason for this tremendous movement, with its attendant risks, of millions of birds, many of them small and frail, twice a year up and down the world?

The immediate aspect of "why" is the physiological mechanism which sets birds off on migration. Experiments with North American Passerines have suggested that variation in the amount of light is an important controlling factor, but whether it directly affects the internal secretion which stimulates changes in the organs, deposit of fat and the other conditions necessary for migration, or whether it causes increased general activity, which in turn releases the secretion, has been a matter of contention. The second would seem the more logical sequence. But variation in the amount of daylight does not explain the considerable migrations of birds within the tropics, where the day-length remains much the same, and the general suggestion has been made that migrations result from an internal condition of the bird promoted by various external factors, of which light may be one.

How the habit arose is a more remote problem. It must have "survival value" for those species which have adopted it, that is to say, it must, on balance, benefit the individuals in each species by improving both their chance of survival in winter and of raising a family in summer. But, as Dr. Landsborough Thomson has pointed out, to say that birds migrate to avoid unfavourable conditions, for example, the northern winter, seems to credit them with an intelligence of human standard, since many species leave their breeding range months before the severe weather begins.

THE URGE TO MIGRATE

Birds, therefore, must migrate because of an inherited disposition to do so, a disposition evolved through thousands of generations, in which the migratory individuals have constantly been at some advantage. Since where a bird breeds is generally regarded as its ancestral environment, it has been supposed that species which are now summer visitors to the Northern Hemisphere once resided in regions made uninhabitable by the Ice Age, and which they are now able to colonize only in the short summer; others take the opposite view and see the spring migration as an annual attempt to extend the breeding range.

One of the first signs of each spring's migration into the Northern Hemisphere is the song of the new arrivals. Next to migration, it is probably song that has aroused most human interest in birds and, whereas specialized study of migration is largely a matter for biologists, the study of bird-song is a field in which the amateur excels.

Song is pre-eminently the attribute of the perching birds. Although we may admit that the bubble of the curlew, the bleating of snipe, the crowing of the domestic cock are all songs in one sense, true song is found only in the Passerine birds and is most attractive in those which breed in temperate regions.

BIRD-SONG AND DISPLAY

That the complex phrases which Passerines have developed give their utterances so pleasing a significance to the human ear is possibly a matter of chance, but there is no doubt that song is better developed in those species with duller plumages and that temperate woodland is peopled largely by brown, grey and dull-green birds, hard to see, but, in spring, easy and delightful to hear. Song is an alternative means of advertisement to bright colours, and it is noticeable that most of the few British near-Passerines, which have no true songs—the woodpeckers, kingfisher, and the rarer hoopoe, bee-eater and roller—are conspicuous for their vivid plumage or striking appearance.

Many observers have noticed variations in the song of the same kind of bird in different parts of its range. The modern technique of recording songs on disks may enable us to compare such regional differences in a way never possible before, and it is suggested that song can be used to detect relationships between races or even species just as resemblances in anatomy, plumage or habits are used for this purpose.

Some bird-books suggest that the songs of races which inhabit wild country, for example, the Hebridean song-thrush and the St. Kilda wren, two of the best known British subspecies, are also "wild and ringing," matching the scenery. This may not be as absurd as it sounds, for it is quite likely that the carrying power of songs uttered in noisy and windy surroundings—against the roar of the waves or the endless winds that sweep the Hebrides—has to be greater than that of songs on the mainland, if the songs are to have their proper advertising value.

Whether birds have lived in modern cities long enough to develop songs which can compete with traffic is doubtful, especially as the motor-car has only recently increased the bedlam of city streets, but it may be noticed that the Black redstart, recent colonist of British towns, prefers high songperches where it is above the roar of the streets.

As well as regional variations within a species, individual birds may have peculiarities of song, which are recognized annually by bird-watchers. Many species are able to mimic other birds and enrich their songs in this way, even incorporating non-avian noises—train whistles and dog barks—so that it is difficult to believe that there is not some element of enjoyment, or at least some element in addition to the primary function, in bird-song.

SURVIVAL VALUES

It is true that, to discern the biological advantage to the individual of a certain behaviour pattern, we must submit all behaviour in nature to the test of survival value, but there is no need to assume that its primary functions occupy a creature twenty-four hours out of twenty-four: there must be room for what in our way of life we call recreation, but which some biologists are reluctant to call by that name even in the case of the higher animals, not realizing perhaps that, as there is an indirect survival value in

EUROPEAN HOOPOE AT ITS NEST-HOLE

The hoopoe is found over a great part of Europe and Asia. When it visits Great Britain its striking plumage, its long slender bill and, above all, its remarkable erectile crest of black-tipped feathers, make it conspicuous among native birds.

human leisure, the same may be true for "leisure" in other living things.

So, though we accept the biological concept of song as a means of securing a mate, holding a territory, threatening a rival or even expressing alarm, we do not have to imagine that every phrase that issues from a bird's beak, every local and individual variation, is necessarily of immediate survival value to it; if we like to say that a bird "enjoys" singing, we are not being unscientific, since at its own level of feeling a healthy animal presumably enjoys doing most of the things which normally occupy its days.

In perching birds song is closely bound up with the idea of territory, and the pioneer work on territory was done by ornithologists working with small passerines, especially warblers, perhaps the most difficult group of common birds to observe. Briefly, "territory" is an area defended by one or a pair of birds against individuals of their own and sometimes of other species. It need not necessarily contain the nest and it may be taken up outside the breeding season altogether. P. H. T. Hartley has recently described the winter territories of the Mourning chat, a close relative of the British wheatear and hence not far removed from the highly territorial robin. Because these Mourning chats fought with Hooded chats, another close relative of similar feeding habits, Hartley suggests that territory was established in order to secure its occupier an adequate food-supply, behaviour obviously of survival

WONDERFUL NESTS OF THE WEAVER-BIRDS

The nests built by the weaver-birds of India are marvels of ingenious construction. Each pair weaves a round, compact abode securely laced together with long grass fibres. The Sociable weaver-birds of Africa weave communal nests, housing many birds.

value, and it is tempting to believe that this is the underlying reason for all territorial practice. On the other hand, P. E. Brown and Miss M. G. Davies, in their recent study of the reed-warbler, have shown that this species feeds a great deal outside its specialized reed-bed territory; this evidence supports the view that territorial practice has been evolved by certain species primarily as a means of population control, to secure an even distribution of the species over suitable habitat, with the added advantage of avoiding mass slaughter by predators such as may befall colonial nesters. This may also secure for each pair or brood the chance of an equal food-supply, but the territory is not necessarily itself of food-value. Followers of this theory

argue that if territory was itself of food-value, then the occupier would have to defend it not only against its own species, but against all others with like food habits, which brings us back again to Hartley's chats. But only rarely in the breeding season do two species in the same habitat have the same feeding habits: detailed observations show small but important differences in the food "niches" favoured by each species, except when there is abundance, as in the periodic plagues of leaf-eating caterpillars.

Although the perching birds show territorial practice at what is probably its highest development, they also show examples of colonial and, in tropical species, of communal nesting. House-martins often jam their nests together under the eaves, several pairs of helmet-shrikes co-operate in building a nest, while the huge structures of the African Sociable weaver-bird may be shared by two or three hundred pairs. But where experiments have been carried out with other colonial birds—for example with gulls—it has been found that the pecking radius of the sitting bird constitutes an individual territory within the colony.

The male of a typical Passerine species has two jobs to do when he has occupied a territory: the first is to keep it from other males, the second to secure a mate to share it with him (some species pair for life, or at least are paired before they take up territories). The devices he uses to attain these objects may appear rather similar, and a certain amount of confusion exists amongst some observers between threat displays designed to keep off rivals and courtship displays designed to attract a female.

COURTSHIP DISPLAY

The dual-purpose use of the same organs or actions should not surprise us, for it is commonplace in nature; in fact, it is surprising that the robin does not use his red breast in courtship: the peculiar swaying performance with head stretched and breast exposed is a threat.

As we have already seen, the songbirds are not, with certain exceptions, brilliantly coloured and cannot display remarkable plumages as do many of the game-birds. But it is a poor bird that has not some feature to show off. A modification of courtship display is the greeting ceremony used by some birds after pairing. "Courtship feeding" is common amongst many Passerines and becomes more directly utilitarian when the male feeds the sitting female, as in the tits. The

male may also have a routine to persuade the female that she should return to brood the eggs. The anxiety of male wood-warblers and tree-pipits, for example, has several times in the writer's experience led to the discovery of well-hidden nests that would not otherwise have been discovered.

NESTING HABITS

Courtship and associated behaviour patterns carry over, therefore, into the actual nesting period, the core of the bird's year, and in this, as in their courtship, the vast number of species covered by this chapter shows great variation, in the part played by the sexes in the cycle, in the type of nest used, in the colour of the eggs and in clutch-size. The British Passerines alone show cases where both sexes build (crows), where the male only helps at the beginning (Golden oriole), where he does the final lining (Bearded tit), where he accompanies the female but does little or no building (goldfinch), or where he takes no part at all (redstart and nightingale); nests vary from the warm and elaborate ball of the Long-tailed tit to the simple grass cup of the skylark, eggs from the white of the dipper to the glorious mottlings and colour-range of the tree-pipit, clutches from the three or four of the larks to the double figures of the tits. Incubation and nestling periods might be expected to vary with the size of the bird, but the open-nesting warblers may get their young out into the world nearly twice as quickly as the tits, secure in their nest-holes, and their larger eggs even hatch more quickly.

Both incubation and care of the young show, like building, a range of parental participation. In the reed-warbler, subject of a detailed study already mentioned, the hen alone builds, but both

SKYLARK FEEDING HER YOUNG

This brownish, somewhat drab little bird makes its nest upon the ground, usually in an open field or on heathland. The skylark normally sings when on the wing, and it commonly ascends to a very great height with scarcely a break in its limpid song.

sexes sit on the eggs, though the male's total occupancy of the nest is less than a third of the female's share, at least during the hours of daylight; his spells of sitting are also shorter and he does not settle down on the eggs so "comfortably." Once the eggs are hatched the male does less than a sixth of the covering of the brood. But he does nearly his fair share of feeding the young during the nestling period and probably most of it in the fledgling stage, when the female may be beginning a second nest, perhaps with a new mate. He also, as in many other species, feeds the chicks via the female. In a warbler of a different genus, the willow-warbler, studied by D. J. May, the males do not appear to incubate at all, but share the feeding of the young.

Generally speaking, incubation by both sexes is common amongst Passerines though not universal, but feeding the young is normally shared. This is also true of most near-Passerines and of pigeons. The game-birds present a very different picture and show that when the sexes are not alike in plumage the male tends to do nothing towards hatching the eggs or rearing the young, presumably because he is too conspicuous or even physically unable to brood properly. In the few British game-birds we find that where the sexes approach each other, as in the Red grouse and Common partridge, the males do help with the young, and a stranger suggestion in the case of the French or Red-legged partridge is that the female lays in two separate nests, one of which is brooded by the male. As an exception to the rule, a cock pheasant has been known to incubate, and the writer has seen both cock and hen with a brood of well-grown young.

Whereas in the Passerines, near-Passerines and pigeons the young are helpless when hatched and have to be fed in the nest for several days or weeks, young game-birds are "nidifugous," leaving the nest almost as soon as they are dry from the egg, and able to feed themselves with the help of the mother.

The sand-grouse, relative of the pigeons, shows an intermediate stage: as in the pigeons, both sexes are said to incubate, but the young, like those of most ground-nesters, are nidifugous. The nightjars, on the other hand, mainly lay on the ground, but still have young that are relatively immobile.

On the whole, larger birds have fewer broods than small ones, because it takes them longer to rear their young to independence; in the Passerines, therefore, occur most of the double- and treble-brooded species. Many of the commonest British birds (greenfinch, yellow-hammer, house-sparrow, black-bird, robin, wren and swallow) have two or more broods, but this is not necessarily the reason for their abundance; the chaffinch, probably the commonest of all, is normally single-brooded, and so are the tits, though they have larger clutches. While the modern view is that the size of a bird's clutch, and the number of broods it has, are controlled by the food supply (that is to say, a bird's average clutch

MALE CHAFFINCH HELPS TO FEED THE BROOD

Among birds division of labour varies widely. In some species incubation is shared by both parents, while in others it is the female alone who sits. Even nest-building may be accomplished by one parent alone. But feeding the brood is usually shared.

represents the maximum brood that it can expect to raise under normal conditions), much remains to be done on the whole relationship of bird populations to the availability of food.

Flocking is a characteristic of almost all bird orders; in the perching birds it is a very general habit, perhaps least marked in some near-Passerine orders, such as the woodpeckers. The advantage of flocking is that there is more chance of finding a food supply and better protection from enemies; its disadvantage is that failure to find food may lead to wholesale disaster. A number of species, therefore, have adopted the solution of solitariness, which some of them emphasize by taking up hard-and-fast winter territories as individuals.

MOULTING AND ROOSTING

Two other little-studied subjects may be mentioned here—moulting and roosting. Moult plumages are, of course, well known to museum workers, but the duration of moults and their effect on the life and habits, particularly of the groups of birds with which we are concerned in this chapter, have as yet attracted very little attention. Roosting calls to mind the problem of the swift. So mysterious is the disappearance of the non-breeding population at night—for this species does not breed until its second year—that the old theory of roosting on the wing is not yet entirely ruled out. It is known that breeding birds roost in the nest-hole and that some others find shelter elsewhere, but they must descend silently after dusk, for many observers have lost sight of swifts circling high in the evening sky; evidence of their descent in the dusk is very difficult to obtain.

If the swift's roosting is baffling, there is still much routine observation

to be done on the habits of many common birds at night. Communal roosts have been studied because of the establishment of some striking examples in the middle of cities. The starling roosts in London, Birmingham and elsewhere are a recent development; it is well within living memory that the London roosts were formed first in trees and then in buildings. The roosts remained undeterred by the occasional air-raids of the First World War and survived the sustained uproar of the Second World War. The two main roosts are around Charing Cross and in the City, and it is probable that they attract the starlings of all London's most built-up districts. But whether these hordes are swelled by immature birds, or by winter visitors from elsewhere in Britain, or by immigrants from overseas, has not been settled.

A more surprising urban rooster is the Pied wagtail, which has a famous site in the middle of Dublin.

But while these and other isolated instances come to mind, many reputable bird-books omit all reference to roosting habits and it remains a field in which any nocturnally-minded birdlover can easily make his name by careful investigations and recording.

RHYTHM OF NATURE

During the winter, birds follow routines regulated by light, weather and food supply. In Britain and other highly cultivated countries the routine is largely dictated by man and it has been suggested that he has even succeeded in replacing the sun's time by his clock as far as urban and suburban birds are concerned: the times at which he makes food available are bound to become all-important to birds which depend mainly or wholly on these sources. In the country the rhythm of

FORK-TAILED TYRANT FLYCATCHER

The Tyrannidae *group, to which this South American bird belongs, is confined to the New World. Its members live mainly on insects, which they catch on the wing. These Tyrant flycatchers should not be confused with the Old World flycatchers.*

agricultural operations certainly controls the movements of many perching birds: ploughing makes one field attractive to rooks and jackdaws; the spreading of straw as cattle-fodder brings finches and buntings; threshing creates another great focus from which many species profit; cutting a moorland drain may cause stonechats to perch on the spades like robins in a garden.

In the woods the roving bands of tits and their allies suggest a more natural pattern of daily behaviour: each party seems to work round its beat on a time-schedule, and it is probable that this sort of rhythm characterizes the birds' day in tropical forests and other virgin habitats not yet intensively studied. It is a less exciting period than that of the breeding cycle, but may just as well provide clues to the central problem with which ornithologists wrestle: the working of the bird's mind.

Far removed though they are from us, the perching birds, and above all the small, restless, vivid song-birds, apparently so free and yet firmly fettered by inherited patterns of behaviour, have reached the top of their evolutionary branch and are worthy of the close attention that they are now receiving from professional zoologists as well as from amateur bird-watchers and bird-lovers all over the civilized world.

NESTING KITTIWAKES ON THE WELSH COAST

Although the kittiwake lives mainly in the Arctic regions during the summer months, its southern limits include the British Isles, where it nests on rugged cliffs and islands. One of the prettiest members of the gull family, it takes its name from its cry, which resembles "kittiwake" pronounced slowly. It feeds chiefly upon fish.

Water birds

EAR the middle of the nineteenth century there were found in the lithographic limestone of Bavaria two very complete fossils of a bird which, although it had still retained many reptile characters (such as rows of teeth in its jaws and its long, lizard-like, jointed tail), seems nevertheless to have been clothed with true feathers. It is the earliest bird so far known, though it cannot be the oldest of all birds. It seems, however, that after birds had established themselves on land and acquired a covering of feathers they turned, at a comparatively early stage, to the sea for a living. That is shown by the fact that the earliest sea-birds whose fossil remains have been found still retained reptile-like teeth, and that one group had, while the chalk formations were still being laid down, become practically wingless and entirely flightless. At the same time there existed toothed sea-birds with full powers of flight and with wing skeletons nearly resembling those of modern birds, and they may have been the immediate ancestors of some groups of living sea-birds.

This turning to marine feeding-grounds was doubtless a matter of slow, or comparatively slow, stages. There might be first the exploration of the beaches and the search along the shore for small creatures or other food cast up by the tides. Then the venturing into the shallows, then the effort towards propulsion with the feet and the gradual expansion of the toes and the coming of the webbed feet.

The origin of the duck tribe (Anseres) is not so ancient, as geological time goes, compared with that of other groups of sea-birds, but they serve as a useful starting-point, for they are, in general structure, the sort of bird one would expect to live on the margin of sea and land—"one foot on sea and one on shore," as it were. All of them have comparatively short, strong legs with fully-webbed feet, and they are perfectly adapted for an aquatic life, particularly for surface swimming. Most have broadish, rather flat beaks, admirably adapted for shovelling up small creatures, such as snails, shrimps and worms. Gathering such food may have been the primary purpose of these beaks, but they have been turned to other foraging and many members of the tribe are almost entirely vegetarian. Their beaks are bordered by a fringe of small, thin, horny plates which allow water to escape, but retain the small creatures on which many species feed and which, in the case of vegetable-feeders, are useful for cutting herbage.

Their distribution is almost world-wide, and while some species live and hunt chiefly on the shore and in the sea,

331

many have turned to fresh water and some seem inclined to desert the water for the land. Except for those great spring and autumn journeys which the migratory species undertake, the duck tribe are not, in general, given to long flights and their flying is characterized by regular and fairly rapid wing-beats.

THE STATELY SWANS

The largest of the Anseres are the swans. As a rule, the length of a bird's neck corresponds to length of leg, so that the bird can bring its head to the ground to feed while standing upright. The long neck of the swan enables it to get its head down into the water to reach the weeds on which it largely feeds, while its body remains afloat. Swans fly well, with slow, regular wing-beats and neck outstretched. The commonest British species is the Mute swan. Others are the Whooper swan and Bewick's swan, both of which are winter migrants to Great Britain, though the former has been known to breed in Scotland.

Geese, which are much more numerous than swans, have to a great extent become land birds. They still retain their webbed feet and swim well, but they spend much time and get most of their food, which is largely vegetarian, on land. Grass enters the diet of some species and the domestic forms can be fed almost entirely on grass, which they crop closely. Geese are among the more intelligent of birds and they are also distinguished by a great capacity for friendship. Many stories have been told of the alliances geese have made with animals very unlike themselves, such as horses, donkeys and cows. A striking example occurred some years ago in the Scottish National Zoological Park at Edinburgh; an Egyptian gander forsook wife, family and home and attached himself to a female sea-lion. He seemed devoted to her and scarcely ever left her for the remaining years—about seven—of his life. He was ultimately killed by the sea-lion's son!

Still more numerous are the species of ducks, and they cover almost the whole range of habitat and habit. Some live almost entirely on inland fresh waters, some perch in trees, some live near the shore, and all are ready to change their location according to circumstances and food supply, for, while most species are mainly vegetable-feeders, they all relish worms, molluscs and crustaceans when they can get them. Some species live almost entirely by the sea and shore, and some have, by becoming divers and by invading the feeding range of other families, brought themselves well within the scope of this section.

We may, perhaps, trace the beginning of the habit of diving, at least among the ducks, to that practice which is known as "up-ending," or "tilting"; the bird pushes its head under water and feeds on the bottom, as far as the length of its neck will permit, half the body being above the surface with the tail pointed skywards and the position maintained by paddling with the feet. This is possible only in shallow water, but it is easy to imagine how a duck, tempted by food just a little deeper than it could reach, might go right under and paddle down to reach its object. The surprising thing is that all ducks do not dive for food.

SEA-DWELLING EIDER

Among species which are regular divers are pochard, Tufted duck, scaup, golden-eye, scoter, and eider. The last is one of the most interesting; it is a completely marine duck and rarely travels inland from the shore. It breeds on many parts of the Scottish coast and

MUTE SWANS ON AN ENGLISH LAKE

The order Anseriformes includes ducks, geese and swans, of which swans are the largest. Their long necks enable them to reach down under the water for the weeds on which they feed. The Mute swan is the commonest of British species.

islands and on the coast of North-east England. Outside the breeding season it travels well out to sea and in winter probably sleeps there. It feeds on small crustaceans, molluscs, and so on, and dives to a considerable depth, sometimes to as much as 30 ft. It propels itself under water chiefly by its webbed feet, but some observers have stated that it sometimes uses its wings as well. The male in full breeding plumage is a handsome bird; its breast is a pinky-buff, the back pure white and the lower part and top of the head black with some bright green feathers on the neck. The nest is lined with large quantities of down, which is collected for stuffing quilts and cushions.

Now we come to a group of birds which, while far better equipped for life at sea, still keep that one foot (and sometimes rather more) on shore—the gull tribe. All are birds of powerful and long-enduring flight, rising by beats of their long wings, but often soaring and gliding in the air with scarcely a movement of their wings. They are equally at home on the surface as in the air above, swimming easily with their broad, webbed feet, picking up fish from the shoals which approach the surface, but with little inclination to diving.

Gulls, perhaps because they are so numerous and so tax the food supply heavily, seem always hungry and voracious. They feed on fish, molluscs, crustaceans—even insects and offal—anything they can find, in fact, and the larger species are not above attacking other birds and small mammals.

The skuas are, in general, brownish in colouring, unlike the pure white and black and grey of the typical gulls, and they are less graceful in form, though their speed and dexterity in flight are no less. They have acquired a kind of ill-fame as pirates, their practice being to attack and harry another gull until it either drops the fish it has caught or disgorges what it has swallowed, when the skua dives on and catches the falling object before it reaches the water. It is in these attacks that the skuas give the finest display of aerial skill; even the Greater black-backed gull and the gannet are often forced to give up their capture to the courage and dash of these robber gulls. The Great skua does not restrict itself to the spoil of which it robs its victim; it will raid the nest of the victim and devour its eggs and young.

Closely allied to the gulls are the beautiful terns, often called "sea-swallows," from their long, forked tails and slender wings; they are like refined and graceful versions of the gulls. They are light and buoyant in flight and feed mainly on small fish swimming near the surface.

The gannet, which breeds in great numbers on several rocky islands off the Scottish and Irish coasts (and on one Welsh island), is a large bird about 1 yd. long and with a wing-spread of about 5 ft. The colour of the adult is pure white except for the head, which is yellowish, and the wing-tips, which are black; but the young in their first year

WILD GEESE, EAST CANADA
Geese have to a large extent become land birds, although they still retain webbed feet and swim well. They are largely vegetarian, eating grass and other plants.

PIRATE OF THE SEA—THE GREAT SKUA

The Great skua is a powerful bird, about 2 ft. long, which breeds largely in the Shetland Isles. It obtains its food by attacking smaller gulls and forcing them to relinquish fish they have caught, but it will also eat the eggs and young of other birds.

are dusky grey profusely speckled with light grey, and do not acquire the adult plumage until their third or fourth year. Gannets are entirely marine birds, resting on the water when not flying, and rarely come to land except to breed.

Their method of fishing is to cruise over the sea until they observe a shoal of herring or other fish, when they will rise to a height of 80 or 100 ft. and shoot down in a lightning plunge into the water to secure their prey; the fish is generally swallowed under water unless it is large, when it may be brought to the surface and swallowed at greater leisure as the bird floats.

The wings are so long that the gannet cannot easily take the air and has to flap along the surface for some distance before it can rise, though the upward movement of a wave may help it. On land it can scarcely rise from level ground and prefers to take off from a cliff.

On the coasts of the southern oceans fly the Frigate birds—near relatives of the gannets, but differing from them in many important features. They are of long, slender build, with swallow-like, tapering wings, forked tails and beaks strongly hooked (not pointed like a gannet's). They have very little webbing on their feet, but excel in the air. Like the skuas, they live mainly by piracy, mobbing the birds that have had success in fishing and making them disgorge their catch. Even the large gannets are not immune from their attacks.

Another group of birds akin to the gannets are the cormorants, of which there are some forty species distributed over almost the whole world and of which may be taken as an example the Common or Black cormorant, which ranges over most of the northern hemisphere and is familiar round British coasts. The cormorant has a longish, slender body which, when it is ashore, it carries in a rather upright posture, and a somewhat snake-like neck and head, the beak being longish and ending in a strong hook. The cormorants have a very sombre colouring of blackish or dark brown, though their dark hue is somewhat relieved by a metallic lustre over the feathers.

The cormorant's hunting habits are very different from either the gannet's or the Frigate bird's. The cormorant is a true diver, and although when shoals are near the surface it will pick up fish without diving, it can and does pursue its prey under the water. The feet are strongly webbed and the bird swims under water by means of them, the wings being held more or less closely to the body. It may plunge into the water from a cliff ledge, but often enters without any splash, and under the surface its speed is sufficient to enable it to catch the fish by sheer pursuit.

The existing members of the auk family are relatively small, the largest being the guillemots and the razorbills. All have short legs placed far back on their bodies, with webbed feet, and when they are ashore they stand quite erect. All live on prey which they catch in the sea, their method of doing so being to travel under water, propelling themselves with their wings, the feet being held straight out behind, though perhaps used at times for steering. They fly quite well through the air and they

THE FRIGATE OR "MAN-OF-WAR" BIRD

The Frigate bird of the southern oceans has immensely long wings and as a flier is, perhaps, superior to all other birds. Like the Great skua, it robs other sea-birds of their catches, as well as devouring their eggs and their young.

CAPE GANNETS COURTING

The gannet, or Solan goose, is a large bird about 3 ft. long. It is almost entirely marine in its habits and rarely comes to land except to breed. It lives on fish, which it catches by diving into the sea from a considerable height.

fly equally well through the water. Their wings are shortish and rounded, as is to be expected in a dual-purpose wing, and they fly with rapid wing-beats.

Guillemots and razorbills breed in great colonies on cliffs and rock ledges; they make no nest and the single egg is laid on the bare rock. The egg is large for the size of the bird and is very pointed, so that if moved it will roll in a close ring and not travel and fall off the rock. These birds come ashore chiefly for breeding and at other seasons spend most of their time at sea.

THE QUAINT PUFFIN

The quaintest of the family is the puffin, smaller than a guillemot and remarkable in that the beak is decorated during the breeding season with a triangular growth striped with scarlet, blue and yellow. After the breeding season the beak ornament is shed. Puffins nest in burrows, either made by themselves or borrowed from a rabbit.

The Tubinares, so called because the nostrils open through two tubes (in some cases one) which lie on the top or sides of the bill, are in the fullest degree sea-birds. They include the albatrosses, shearwaters and petrels. They must visit the land to breed, for no bird can make a nest or incubate an egg at sea; but, nesting apart, they are almost entirely birds of the ocean, particularly of the southern ocean. The Tubinares range from the little Storm petrel, the smallest of sea-birds, scarcely larger than a skylark, to the great albatross, the largest of flying birds. The albatrosses and many other members of this order are very gull-like in general appearance and to some extent in habit.

With the exception of one small family, the members of this order do not dive much, though they may go beneath the surface in pursuit of prey, and the shearwaters apparently use their wings when under water and, like an auk or a penguin, fly through the water.

There are about thirteen species of albatross; the largest, the Wandering albatross, has an average wing-spread of about 11 to 12 ft. (nearly twice the wing-span of the Golden eagle).

The albatross alights on the water to feed and may rest on the water in calm, but the greater part of its life is spent in the air. When about to rise, it takes a run on the surface to gain impetus, then the great wings are spread and with a few powerful beats the bird soars upwards; catching the air current, it sails along with wings motionless, sometimes descending almost to the water, then rising high with a graceful sweep and with only occasional rapid movements of the wings. Albatrosses remain on the wing for incredibly long periods. Like the gulls, they persistently follow ships for scraps of food; but while the gull will give up the pursuit after, at most, a few hours, the albatross will follow with apparently untiring ease for days. A marked albatross has been noted following the same ship for six consecutive days. The food of the albatrosses seems to consist largely of young squids and cuttles, but they will devour any animal they can find, not excluding birds.

VULTURE OF THE SEA

The Giant petrel of southern seas rivals the smaller albatrosses in size, with a wing-spread of nearly 6 ft. Like them, it will devour anything it can find, not only cephalopods but also other birds (including young penguins) and even rabbits. It is inclined to specialize nowadays in the refuse of the whaling factories and has something of the habits of a vulture in its liking for carrion.

339

CORMORANT WITH ITS CATCH

The cormorants comprise some forty species of sea-birds, which are distributed over almost the whole of the world. They are all voracious eaters of fish, which they chase and catch under water, swimming by means of their strongly webbed feet.

The Fulmar petrel is one of the more common birds of northern seas. It is very gull-like in appearance, but can easily be distinguished from a gull by the tubes on top of its bill. Though it is so much smaller (no larger than the herring-gull), in its flight and its habit of following ships it resembles the albatross and is not averse to dining on whale scraps when available. It breeds now at many points of the northern Scottish islands and coast and in North-east England, but at one time its breeding-ground in Britain was restricted to the island of St. Kilda, where its body used to be used by the islanders as a kind of lamp. All the birds of this order secrete a stomach oil. The exact source of the oil is unknown, and its function is not as clear as it might be; it may serve as a feather dressing as well as

being a means of defence, for if one of these birds is approached by one whom it regards as an enemy it ejects through beak or nose-tubes a jet of this oil which has a disgusting and almost ever-lasting stench. In spite of that it was used by the Maoris of New Zealand for cooking food. The St. Kilda islanders took the body of a fulmar, passed a wick through its stomach and out through the beak, and applied a light to this very primitive "lamp" which burned until the oil in the stomach was exhausted!

The most attractive of this group is the Storm petrel. Scarcely larger than and looking very like a House martin, it flies as far across the ocean as the albatrosses and, like them, follows ships for long distances. Its place is taken in the oceans of the south by several closely allied species. The affectionate name which the sailors gave them was "Mother Cary's chickens."

Probably the most interesting of all sea-birds are the penguins—among the most remarkable and perhaps the most specialized of living birds. While they come ashore to moult and to breed, and at times to rest, the most active part of their lives is spent in the sea, and their adaptation to this mode of life has been carried further than that of any other living aquatic bird. Some zoologists believe that birds originated in the sea, and there are some who believe that the penguins are not descended from flying land-birds but are simply a very conservative group which never left the cradle of their class. Another opinion is that penguins are the descendants of land-birds which had lost the power of aerial flight before returning to the sea. A third, and perhaps the most acceptable, view is that they are descended from some primitive type of flying sea-bird, with wings well developed for flight in the air, with webbed feet for swimming, and with a firmly established habit of finding food in the sea by swimming and diving.

The penguins have never abandoned flight; but they have merely changed the medium in which they fly. It is no mere figure of speech, but a statement of plain fact, to say that the penguin flies through the water as the bird it is the custom to call a flying bird flies through the air. There are the same movements of the wings, in essentials the same form in the wings, the same speed and dexterity in darting and wheeling and

GREY-HEADED ALBATROSSES MAKE LOVE

There are fourteen species of albatross, and all of them spend the greater part of their lives on the wing. They feed mainly upon young squids and cuttles, although they will devour other birds, not excluding members of their own species.

turning; the only difference between the flight of a penguin and the flight of, say, a rook or a swallow is that the one is in water and the other in air. Considerable change, however, has taken place in the wings of the penguins. We have seen earlier in this section that birds such as the auks, which still fly in the air as well as in water, all have a dual-purpose wing which, like all compromises, is not of the fullest efficiency for either of the uses to which it is put. No such limitation was imposed upon the evolution of the penguins' wing and they were able to concentrate on adapting it for flight through the water. It is obvious that a wing best suited for flight in the air, with its long elastic primaries and secondaries, could not be the best for flying through water; thus the bones of the penguin's wing became more strong and massive, the long elastic primaries and secondaries disappeared and were replaced by a much greater number of short, stout feathers much more suitable for driving the bird at great speed through the more resistant water medium. All this took place very long ago, probably in early tertiary times, for by the end of the Miocene period the penguins were well established.

PENGUINS OF THE TROPICS

There is a widespread popular belief that penguins are entirely Antarctic birds—but though the majority of the existing species live in the far south, there is one in South Africa, well into the temperate region, and there are two living in the tropics on the western South American coast—one almost under the Equator. There are seventeen species of living penguins known and a much greater number of extinct species has been recognized. As the fossil remains of most of the extinct penguins have been recovered in the region to the south of South America, it is probable that the evolution of these birds began in that area.

The penguins, with their marvellous speed in the water and their freedom from enemies on land, were well able to hold their own until modern man came along and discovered their commercial possibilities. They had no means of defence or escape from so deadly an enemy and in the last century or less penguins of all kinds were slaughtered in countless millions.

SAVING THE KING PENGUIN

Until about seventy years ago King penguins were quite common on the Falkland Islands, but now only an occasional stray bird is ever seen there. Fortunately, before it was too late, protection, whole or partial, has been given to the species whose breeding-grounds are accessible, and not only has the remnant survived but many species are again increasing in numbers.

With the exception of two species, there is a considerable sameness in the forms and colouring of the various species of penguin; they all tend to be grey (in most cases a fairly dark grey) on the back, and white in front, and any distinguishing marks there are between species are shown chiefly on the head.

Of the more northerly species, the Black-footed or Cape penguin is the best known. It lives on the coast of South Africa and was at one time very numerous, but though, like most of the other species, it has undergone much persecution, it still breeds in great numbers on one or two islands off the coast. This penguin nests either in holes in rocks or in burrows which it makes in the ground. The Magellan penguin of southern Patagonia, Humboldt's penguin of western South America, and the Galapagos penguin of the islands of

WANDERING ALBATROSS ON THE WING
*The Wandering albatross, with a wing-span of about 12 ft. and a weight of 16 lb.,
is the largest of albatrosses. It can remain on the wing for incredibly long periods
and has been known to follow a ship for six days without alighting.*

that name are all very closely related to the Cape penguin.

There are several species which nest on the Australian and New Zealand coasts, but the remainder of the penguins now go farther south to breed and make their rookeries on islands such as South Georgia, Kerguelen, Macquarie, and other islands in the South Atlantic, South Pacific and South Indian Oceans. Most of these species are very similar in size, among them being the smallest of all penguins, the little Fairy, or Blue, penguin as it is called.

The Gentoo penguin (distinguished by a white mark across its grey head), the Ringed or Chin-strap penguin (so called from a narrow black ring round its white throat), the Rock-hopper and Macaroni penguins (who wear a bright spot of colour in the shape of two golden tufts above their eyes) all come ashore to breed and to moult. The habits of these species are sufficiently similar for one description to serve for all. Although they have fairly powerful beaks (especially the Rock-hopper), quite capable of holding a fish, their chief food seems to be a kind of prawn. They come ashore to breed in the Antarctic spring. They all make some kind of a nest, using such material as the sterile nature of their breeding-ground permits, usually a heap of stones, though the Gentoo penguin makes a rather softer nest of tussock grass or other litter which it may find. The male bird makes his first proposal to the lady of his choice by picking up a stone which, waddling forward, he lays at her feet. If she looks on him with favour she will pick up the stone and re-lay it in a somewhat different position; he will then hustle off to bring more stones, which he will put in a pile on which the lady will seat herself and, turning round and round, shape a small hollow in the top. In this hollow the two eggs are laid; both parents take turns in the incubation. The chicks hatch after six weeks' incubation and are fed on pre-digested fish pumped up from the parent's stomach and taken by the chick from the old bird's throat.

During the time occupied by the growth of the chick, the parent birds have to go from the nesting-ground to the sea to find food, not only for themselves but for the chicks, and return to the nest with it. The Gentoo penguin sometimes makes its rookery a considerable distance from the sea and has, therefore, to make a long march to and fro. By the time the chicks have grown up and the old birds have completed their annual moult the Antarctic autumn is advancing and they then take to the sea, travelling in most cases northwards and probably spending more than six months entirely at sea. It has been suggested, however, that in certain of their breeding areas these penguins do not become migratory.

Another species—a close relative of the Gentoo and the Ringed penguins—is the Adélie penguin, which has its range farther south and has chosen the Antarctic continent for its breeding-ground.

There remain two other species of penguin, differing in a great many

· CROWD STUDY, S. AFRICA
The Black-footed or Cape penguin, best known of the more northerly species, lives on the coast of South Africa, where it still breeds in large numbers. It makes its nest either in holes in rocks or in burrows in the ground and, like all penguins, is highly gregarious.

KING PENGUINS WITH CHICK

With the exception of the Emperor penguin, the King penguin is the largest of the species. It stands about 32 in. high, and breeds on numerous islands on the fringe of the Antarctic Circle. It makes no nest and lays a single egg, which it holds on its feet during the eight weeks of incubation, preventing it from being chilled.

respects from their relatives, and the largest and finest of all. They are the King and the Emperor penguins. The King penguin stands about 32 in. high. The colour of its back is a fine steel grey and, of course, the front is the usual penguin white. The head and face are black and on the sides of the head and on the throat are patches of bright orange. It breeds on South Georgia, Macquarie Island, Marian Island, Kerguelen Island, and other islands round the edge of the Antarctic Circle. This penguin lays only one egg and makes no nest, but holds the egg on its feet (which are covered by a flap of skin and feathers of the lower abdomen), during the incubation period, which lasts for almost eight weeks. Both sexes share in the work of incubation. The chicks are clothed at first in a nestling plumage of brown, the individual feathers of which, by the time it is full-grown, may reach a length of 3 in., so that the young bird appears as if wearing a thick fur coat. The chick at first is held on the feet of the parent bird, as the egg was, until it grows too large for this accommodation, a fact which enters its head only slowly, as a youngster quite half as large as its mother will make ludicrous efforts to hide itself on her feet.

THE EMPEROR

The Emperor penguin is larger still than the King, standing at least 40 in. high and weighing 80 to 90 lb. Its form and colouring are similar, but the yellow patches are not so richly coloured as those of the King penguin. The Emperor penguin lives on the Antarctic ice. It lays its single egg in the depth of the Antarctic winter, when the temperature may be as much as 80 degrees below zero, and rears the chick in that intense and bitter cold. The nestling coat of the young Emperor penguin is white, not brown, but when the King penguin chick is hatched it shows for the first day or two vestiges of a white nestling coat which quickly disappears and is replaced by the brown one. This suggests that the King penguin was originally an inhabitant of the polar ice but has moved northwards and acquired a secondary nestling coat which harmonizes more with the surrounding mud and scrub of the rookeries.

STERN PRECAUTION

It has been mentioned that the penguins have few enemies on land apart from skuas, gulls and albatrosses, but in the sea they have many, in particular the Leopard seal. In consequence, penguins are very careful before they first enter the water and gaze for a moment to make as sure as they can that no Leopard seals are about. The method of the Adélie penguin has been amusingly described, for they gather in numbers on the edge of the ice and while those in front are hesitating, those behind try to push them in; the idea seems to be that if the first to go into the sea escape, the coast is clear: while if a Leopard seal lying hidden under the edge of the ice should dash out and capture one it is just too bad for that one, but a helpful warning to the others standing near.

LYRE-BIRD DISPLAYING ITS SPLENDID PLUMES

The lyre-bird wears its remarkable tail-feathers throughout the Australian winter, from June till October, in which month they are shed. Only the male bird is adorned with this beautiful plumage. He has a habit of building hillocks, upon which he stands to show off his plumes. He is among the most accomplished of bird mimics.

Some odd birds

ENERALLY speaking, the birds of the world fall into fairly well defined groups so that there is little difficulty in assigning any particular species to one family or another, but here and there we come across odd types that are baffling in their relationship. They would appear to be either primitive forms that reached their limit of evolution millions of years ago, or forms that have evolved along different lines to those of the vast majority. Some of these seem to have no close relationship to any one family of existing birds but show points of affinity with many.

If we commence with the American continent, pride of place for unusual birds must certainly be given to the hoatzin (*Opisthocomus hoatzin*). This bird is a sort of living fossil, the young of which have wing-hooks, that recall in many ways the extinct toothed and lizard-tailed birds that existed 150 million years ago. Everything about the hoatzin is strange, even down to its feeding-habits and distribution. It is confined to a few widely separated, but restricted, riverside localities in British Guiana, North Brazil, Colombia, Ecuador, Peru and Bolivia.

Hoatzins live in colonies and can be seen every day in the same places eating their favourite leaves, and leading a mode of life that does not necessitate travel. They are striking birds with a prominent crest, and are somewhat pheasant-like in appearance and size, though in their arboreal habits they remind one more of an African family of birds, the turacos. The hoatzin gives off a peculiar musky odour which seems to be the main factor in its survival. It is obvious that such a sluggish bird would have been greatly persecuted by man were it not for its objectionable smell.

The most notable of the hoatzin's other peculiarities are its wing-hooks, which are situated on the small bones at the extremities of the wings known as the thumb and index finger. These are found only in young birds and are of value in enabling them to hang on to branches and thus clamber over the Pimpler thorn bushes, in which the nests are situated. The latter are always built over water, and one peculiarity of the young is that they are adept at diving and swimming and can regain the tree-tops by climbing with their feet and wing-hooks, whereas the adults lead an entirely arboreal existence. Moreover, the latter lose their wing-hooks, which atrophy in early life.

The hoatzin has no close relationship with any other existing bird, and so is placed in an order—Opisthocomiformes—entirely by itself.

Another queer South American bird with unusual habits is the oil-bird, or guacharo (*Steatornis caripensis*). Like the hoatzin, this bird is limited to a few widely separated but restricted localities in the tropical zone, such as Trinidad, Venezuela, British Guiana, Colombia, Ecuador and Peru. The oil-bird, however, is not restricted to one area or another so much by food as by suitable nesting and roosting places. It is strictly nocturnal, and by day sleeps in sleeping-dens. The action of disgorging appears to be effortless. Such a restricted diet is unusual in any bird, but it is even more remarkable to find a nocturnal bird that is solely a fruit-eater, and in this respect it appears to be unique.

The young are covered with masses of yellow fat, which accounts for the popular name—oil-bird. In this stage they are much sought after by the

ONE OF THE WORLD'S RAREST CREATURES

Until this Grey-necked picathartes was collected by Mr. C. S. Webb in the British Cameroons, tropical Africa, in 1948, only two Europeans had set eyes upon living specimens of this bird. Timorous, wary and excessively rare, it is much of a mystery even to the natives. Its nest is built against an overhanging rock-face.

caves or caverns, where it also nests. Highly gregarious, it congregates in large numbers in its sleeping-quarters, emerging in the late evening, like bats, to feed. Its food consists entirely of the fruit, or nuts, of certain palm-trees, which are swallowed whole. The fleshy covering of these fruits is digested, while the stone is disgorged, and it is usual to find large deposits of these regurgitated nuts on the floor of the natives, who enter the caves in the breeding season armed with long poles on which are fixed torches and hooks. The young are dislodged from the numerous ledges on which the nests are made, and are then melted down for their fat.

In spite of the wealth of bird-life in Africa, there are very few birds that can be truly said to be singularly unusual, but there is one—called picathartes—

that is quite as remarkable as the hoatzin of South America—at least in its external characters.

There are two species of this extraordinary bird—the Yellow-necked picathartes (*Picathartes gymnocephala*) and the Grey-necked picathartes (*P. oreas*). They are both rare and very little is known about them. The former was discovered on the Gold Coast, but has not been seen there for over eighty years. Recently, however, they have been seen in Sierra Leone, some seven hundred miles farther west. The Grey-necked species is apparently confined to the Cameroons, not far inland.

"BALD CROWS"

Both species are remarkably similar in plumage and both have completely bare heads and were formerly called Bald crows. The colouring on the bare skin of the head is unique, and differs remarkably in the two species. The Yellow-necked picathartes has the bare skin yellow, with a black patch on either side of the head, whereas the Grey-necked species has the fore half of the head blue, the hind part red and the sides black.

Picathartes is rather jay-like in size and form, but has a longer neck and longer legs. It was originally placed near the Corvidae on account of its rather crow-like legs and beak, but has since been found to be related to the starlings by its anatomy and feather tracts, and to have no affinities with the crows.

For so large a bird its nesting habits are remarkable, for it constructs a mud nest like a swallow's on an overhanging rock-face. The nest is made of mud interwoven with fibres, and reinforced with small sticks round the rim. Owing to its large size it collapses easily when wet, hence the necessity of an overhanging rock-face to keep off the rain.

Such places are distinctly rare, and it is doubtless this lack of suitable nesting-sites that accounts for the bird's rarity.

Another of the African starlings with an unusual head adornment, although conforming to type in other respects, is the Wattled starling (*Creatophora carunculatus*). In the past there has been some mystery concerning the development of wattles in the male bird. In museum collections it is not unusual to find an odd male with well-developed wattles on the throat, forehead and crown, and a completely bare head, out of a large number with rudimentary wattles and with the head only partly bare. It was assumed that only the very old males went through this transformation. The explanation is that in the dry, or non-breeding, season Wattled starlings congregate in large flocks and are very much in evidence on settlements, coming to farmyards to pick up surplus cattle- and poultry-food. At this season the males look very much like the females, and their black wattles are only just discernible, while their heads are fully feathered. Most museum specimens have been collected at this period, for the simple reason that this is the only time that they are easily obtained.

ODDLY DIFFERENT PARTNERS

An oddity of distinction, and one, strangely enough, that is also related to the starlings, is the Huia (*Heteralocha acutirostris*) of New Zealand. This bird has attracted much attention on account of the remarkable difference in the bills of the two sexes—a divergence that is so great that at first sight one might think the two belonged to totally different families. The male has the beak almost straight and sharply pointed, whereas the female has a long sickle-shaped bill.

Both are mainly insectivorous, eating

SOME ODD BIRDS

BOWER-BIRDS WITH THEIR "BOWER"

Outstanding for their oddity, even in a land of odd animals and birds, are the bower-birds of Australia. Their arched bower is built of twigs and often its vicinity is adorned with gay feathers, flowers and other brightly coloured objects. Some species show a marked preference for objects of a particular colour, which others carefully avoid.

the larvae of beetles found in rotting wood—but they have a different technique in gaining their livelihood. The male, with his very sharp compressed bill, might be called a hewer or chiseller, whereas the female, with her long slender curved bill, is more of a prober. The difference in the length of the bills is considerable—that of the male's being 2¾ in., and that of the female's 4 in. Some observers have stated that pairs of Huia birds assist each other in searching in rotten wood for beetle grubs—the male chipping off much of the outside wood, the better to enable the female to probe deeply for the hidden larvae.

New Zealand can boast of a number of other queer birds, of which the

kakapo or Owl parrot (*Strigops habroptilus*) certainly deserves mention. It is a true parrot that has a marked resemblance to an owl in appearance—especially in the head—and has nocturnal habits. It spends the day in slumber, hidden in holes under roots of trees or under rocks, and issues forth at night or in the late evening to feed. The kakapo is possessed of fairly large, strong wings, yet, strangely enough, is flightless. This has probably been brought about by lack of natural enemies and the fact that the bird is a vegetarian—feeding mainly on mosses and grasses. The kakapo is invariably extremely fat, a condition that may either have led to or been caused by its lack of flight.

In some districts dogs and cats have

352

become feral, and so the kakapo, having adapted itself to an existence free from predatory mammals, has small chance of survival.

The group of birds known as bower-birds is in some respects the most remarkable of the avian kingdom. The males of the various species construct bowers or playgrounds, and in so doing they display an artistry that would seem to indicate a sense of aestheticism. The surprising thing is that this bower-building, which is often elaborate, is not linked up with courtship—at least not to any marked degree, although the female may occasionally visit her mate at his bower. He may then be prompted to dance and show off, but as he is in attendance at his playground for the greater part of the year, it is evident that courtship is not the main inspiring motive. This behaviour is unique in birds and does not occur in the birds-of-paradise, the bower-birds' relatives.

The various species of bower-bird differ remarkably from one another in anatomy, colour of plumage, colour of eggs, powers of mimicry, as well as in construction of bowers. Some even show marked preferences for certain colours when gathering the flowers and shells with which they often decorate their bowers.

On the average the various species are about the size of the common jackdaw, although rather plumper, and whereas they nest in trees the bowers are made on the ground. They inhabit Australia (particularly Queensland) and New Guinea, and the best-known species is the Satin bower-bird, which is fairly common throughout East and South-east Australia. The adult male has shining purplish-blue plumage, in contrast to the female and immature male which are greenish in colour with

HARD AT WORK ON HIS FIVE-TON NEST

Australian Brush turkeys, like other mound-builders, are notable for the huge mounds of decaying vegetation which they heap up for the incubation of their eggs. This photograph shows less than one-half of the completed mound, which weighs between 4 and 5 tons and may be 10 ft. high. Building it often occupies weeks.

DISDAINFUL EMU OF AUSTRALIA

The emu is about 5 ft. in height and bulky in proportion. Like all ratite birds, which have lost the power of flight—if, indeed, they ever possessed it—it is admirably adapted for running. Its plumage is bushy and hair-like, and its voice is a loud boom. The emu defends itself with powerful backward blows of its strongly clawed feet.

speckled underparts. Both sexes have eyes of the most beautiful light-blue.

The male Satin bower-birds (like the male birds-of-paradise) take many years to assume the full adult plumage. The young greenish-coloured males start to show a few purple feathers in their plumage in the third or fourth year and these increase annually until the sixth or seventh year, when the full adult plumage is attained. From an early age they seem to love juggling with twigs and remind one of male weaver-birds who have a similar urge to juggle with dried grass and strips of leaves, with which they build nests that may never be used for normal nesting purposes. The bower consists of a platform of twigs from which two parallel walls of sticks rise to a height of a foot or more; an arch is usually built upon these walls so that a partly-covered run is formed, and a space is cleared around the bower, all unsightly and offending material being got rid of. The Satin bower-bird shows a definite preference for blue and decorates the space around the bower with blue feathers and blue flowers; in districts where there are human habitations it is not uncommon to find blue rags, blue paper and even pieces of blue glass included in the decorations. Apart from the Satin bower-bird's artistry at bower-building, it is an intelligent, sprightly bird, always smart and tightly feathered, and has the reputation of being a wonderful mimic.

THE DANCING CATBIRD

There are several species of Spotted bower-birds, and these, unlike the Satin bower-bird, shun blue objects when decorating their bowers but show a marked partiality for bleached bones.

The Golden bower-bird easily surpasses its rivals in the dimensions of its bower—a veritable skyscraper compared with the others. It is constructed between saplings which act as supports and may reach a height of 8 or 9 ft.! The walls are decorated profusely with moss and flowers. As a contrast to this, some of the catbirds, which are bower-birds that make cat-like, mewing noises, merely clear a stretch of ground and strew it with leaves which are placed upside down. Among these the catbird dances, tossing the leaves into the air.

A BIRD "ARTIST"

Undoubtedly the most artistic of the group are the Gardener bower-birds of the New Guinea jungles. The bower in this case is a shapely circular structure composed of orchid stems and twigs and covered with moss. On the open side of this "hut" a lawn of moss is made and decorated daily with fresh flowers which are replaced when withered. Fresh, colourful fruits are also used for decorative purposes, and all who have seen these colourful playgrounds agree that here is a bird that has risen above its fellow creatures—a bird to which beauty seems to have a strong appeal.

A strange group of gallinaceous, or game, birds is the one comprising the family Megapodiidae. All are inhabitants of the Australasian region and neighbouring islands and are collectively known as megapodes. Altogether seven genera exist which include the the True megapodes, the Mallee fowl, the Brush turkeys and the maleo.

Their eggs are not incubated in the normal way, but are either placed in a mound of decaying vegetation and incubated by the heat of the fermenting vegetable matter or placed in sand where they are incubated by the heat from the sun's rays.

The mound-builders have large, powerful feet, developed effectively for

KIWI OF SOUTH ISLAND, NEW ZEALAND
Kiwis seem doomed to extinction, for they are quite defenceless against dogs and other alien carnivores, which sniff them out in their slumber-holes. When probing for worms, the kiwi drives its long beak into the ground up to its root.

the purpose of scraping up quantities of leaves, sticks and leaf-mould. This material is collected at the centre of a large circular area over which the bird scratches—an operation which may take weeks on account of the enormous amount of material used. The mounds vary from a few feet in height to 10 ft. or more.

The eggs, which are comparatively large, are deposited at a considerable depth—the female scratching a hole for this purpose—and are placed vertically with the large ends uppermost. They are then covered over, the mound then taking on its normal convex shape. There is an interval of several days between the laying of each egg, and the hen bird appears to know their exact whereabouts in the mound.

The cock bird appears to assist in the delicate operation of keeping the eggs at an even temperature, for he may be seen at times adding fresh material to the mound and, at others, opening it up —apparently for purposes of aeration.

The chicks, which are hatched in an advanced state of development, are able to find their own way out of the mound and are at once quite independent of their parents.

The maleo, which differs from all the other megapodes in appearance, is even more reptilian in its nesting habits as it deposits its eggs in sand, and therefore relies entirely on sunshine for their incubation.

The maleo inhabits the island of Celebes and the Sanghi Islands. It is a striking bird of brown upper-parts, salmon pink under-parts and a bare head surmounted by a large black casque. The bare skin of the face is pale yellow. Its feet are smaller than those of the mound-builders and are therefore in keeping with its nesting habits, for the maleo merely makes a depression in the sand of the seashore in which to deposit its eggs. It is a forest-dwelling bird, but in the breeding season proceeds to the seashore to seek out isolated inlets where there is plenty of sand above the high-water level.

Although maleos operate in pairs, a considerable number may be seen at one time on a stretch of lonely beach, all busy scratching up sand, depositing their eggs and then covering them. When this has been completed the eggs are abandoned and the maleos return to their forest home. As with the mound-builders, the chicks are able to fend for themselves as soon as hatched and instinctively seek cover in the adjacent vegetation.

Australians are proud of the many strange forms of animal life peculiar to their country, and not least of these is the lyre-bird, which has become a national emblem. The male is famed for his beautiful lyre-shaped tail, the long plumes of which he spreads forwards over his head. Although he is otherwise of an inconspicuous brown coloration, the tail transforms him into an object of magnificent splendour. The hen lyre-bird (like the peahen) by comparison looks dull.

The lyre-bird's tail is not the only thing that has brought him into prominence. His powers of mimicry have thrilled all those who have been fortunate enough to hear him pouring out the call-notes of all the familiar forest-dwelling birds. In his repertoire may also be included the barking of a dog, the ring of a woodman's axe, the creaking of trees rubbing together, and the

MALE AND FEMALE OSTRICHES, EAST AFRICA
Largest of living birds, with a maximum height of 8 ft., the ostrich is still plentiful in Africa, owing largely to its fleetness. Of the pair above, the cock is on the right.

buzzing of a circular saw. He does not always indulge in mimicry when wanting to give vent to his feelings, for he has a wide range of liquid notes all his own.

There are two species of lyre-bird—the better known is *Menura novaehollandiae*, which extends from Victoria through New South Wales to south Queensland. Its favourite haunts are the fern-tree gulleys of the thickly wooded hilly districts. Although many people are familiar with its call-notes, comparatively few have seen it in the

the section on Water Birds. However, a few are worthy of mention here.

The ratites, or ostrich-like birds, differ from all the others in the shape of the breast-bone, which is flat and devoid of a keel. They are all flightless and have massive bones. Some of the extinct forms, such as the moa of New Zealand and the giant aepyornis of Madagascar, reached gigantic proportions. They were numerous in species and it seems strange that so many large types should have evolved in compara-

QUAINT KAGU OF THE SOUTH PACIFIC

The kagu does not fly, although its wings, unlike those of the typical flightless birds, are apparently of normal development. It often skips about playfully with outstretched wings, as it is seen doing above. It may even lie on its back, kicking its legs.

wild state. Dense vegetation and an acute sense of hearing enable the lyre-bird to conceal himself before he is spotted by the curious bird-watcher.

The other species—Prince Albert's lyre-bird (*Harriwhitea alberti*)—is more localized and is confined to north New South Wales and south Queensland.

A good many of the world's queerest birds are incapable of flight; some of them—the penguins—are dealt with in

tively small areas. They probably existed until a few hundred years ago. In the case of the moas, bones and shells, and even skin and feathers, have been found in the superficial deposits in New Zealand; and aepyornis bones, in a sub-fossil state, are plentiful near the surface in many parts of Madagascar.

In the dry southern districts of Madagascar fragments of aepyornis eggs are numerous, and occasionally an egg is found intact. When the author was there, one such egg was unearthed by an Antandroy native. It was unblemished and looked as if it had been laid only a few days before, but was probably several hundred years old. It weighed 18 lb.!

The existing members of the order are remarkably widespread though few in species. They include the rheas (South America), ostriches (Africa), emus (Australia), cassowaries (Australia, New Guinea, and neighbouring islands), kiwis (New Zealand). The largest of the group—the ostrich—is still plentiful in parts of Africa, and is quite capable of holding its own against its natural enemies, though it has been exterminated in many districts by human agency. It is keen-sighted and a swift runner and cannot be easily approached except in districts where it has been unmolested.

HAIR-LIKE FEATHERS

Cassowaries and emus differ from ostriches and rheas in the structure of their feathers. The two former have feathers which have the appearance of being double owing to the development of an after-shaft. The feathers of the cassowaries have a glossy sheen, but are coarse and hair-like, and the wing is reduced to a mere vestige. The various species all have bare heads surmounted by a helmet-like horny casque, and the bare skin of the neck is brilliantly coloured. Some stand as high as 5 ft. and are most impressive with their shiny plumage, massive legs, coloured necks and helmeted heads.

The kiwis (*Apteryx*), of which there are several species, are the smallest of the ratites, and range from the size of a fowl to that of a turkey. They have rudimentary wings and tails, but massive legs and hair-like plumage. The bill is very long and rather like that of a snipe, with the nostrils at the tip, and is evidently a sensitive organ, as it is used as a probe for locating worms and insects. Long hairs protrude from the face and forehead, which, added to the very long bill, rounded body and massive legs, give the bird a unique appearance—and a very comical one.

THE KAGU

Among the so-called wading-birds there are a number of aberrant forms which, although often grouped together by systematists, have no close relationship to one another or to any other group. Their classification is rendered difficult by the fact that they possess characteristics which form a connecting link between two or more families.

The kagu of New Caledonia is one of the strangest of this very odd group. It has some affinities with the cranes, herons, plovers, rails and sun-bitterns. Blue-grey in colour, about the size of a fowl, it stands very erect and has a long pendent crest projecting from the back of the head which it erects like a cockatoo. Although in possession of normal wings it does not fly, and like the kiwi of New Zealand it is mainly nocturnal and spends the day hidden among rocks or holes among roots of trees. Its food consists of invertebrate animals such as worms, slugs and snails.

One of the most interesting things about the kagu is its playful ways. It may be seen skipping and running with outstretched wings and erected crest, tossing up leaves or other debris and sometimes performing playful antics on its back, kicking its legs in the air as if in a fit.

Sun-bitterns (Eurypygidae), of South America, are perhaps the prettiest of the aberrant crane-like birds, although comparatively small in size. The

Their mottled plumage of brown, grey, black, white, yellow and red is most attractive and is shown to advantage when the wings are spread in display. A tame one that the writer had in British Guiana used to make a hissing noise, and perform snake-like movements with its neck whenever a dog came near it. This bluffing, aggressive and somewhat reptilian behaviour had the desired effect of frightening the life out of the dog, though the bird was comparatively defenceless.

One of the best known of South America's odd birds is the trumpeter (Psophiidae), of which there are several species. With the same habits as the forest-dwelling guinea-fowl (*Guttera*) of Africa, they roam the forests of South America—often in large troops numbering a hundred or more. They have very feeble flight, and normally do not take to the air except when disturbed or going to roost, which they do in trees.

VIGILANT TRUMPETERS

It is an impressive sight to see pet trumpeters wandering at large in the villages of the South American aboriginal Indians, where they often consort with fowls, but in spite of their tameness and confiding ways they are quite fearless and will attack almost anything in the way of an intruder. In this respect they make good watch-dogs and they will chase any hawk that swoops down after young chickens. It is amazing to see a trumpeter, otherwise quite friendly towards fowls, put an immediate stop to a cock-fight by attacking both combatants.

The head, which is black, is clothed with short velvety plumage almost like that of a chick, and the feathers of the lower neck have metallic reflections. Like several other South American crane-like birds, trumpeters are of doubtful affinity, having fowl-like heads and habits but showing some relationship to the cranes and bustards.

They get their name from their peculiar trumpeting cry, which is produced through a specially-modified windpipe.

The seriemas or cariamas (Cariamidae) are large, long-legged birds that frequent the more open parts of Brazil and the Argentine and are even more difficult to classify than the trumpeters, near which they are usually placed in the systematic list. They have some affinities with the rails, cranes and bustards. The general colour is greyish-brown, and a pronounced frontal crest, composed of bristly feathers, rises from the base of the beak.

THE SECRETARY BIRD

The Secretary bird (*Sagittarius*) of South and East Africa is unique, as it does not resemble any other bird of prey in external appearance. In the systematic list it is usually placed between the vultures and eagles, though one would hardly suspect this relationship without knowing something of the bird's anatomy. The long legs give it rather a crane-like appearance, though it cannot be confused with any other long-legged bird on account of its peculiar elongated central tail-feathers —nearly 2 ft. long—and its distinctive crest of long plumes directed horizontally from the back of the head. These latter have given rise to the bird's name—being suggestive of old-fashioned quill pens stuck behind the ear.

There is one more group of strange birds found in South America that merits a place in this chapter. These are the screamers (Palamedeidae), of which there are three species, and which are placed in a distinct order.

These rather large clumsily-built birds have certain affinities with the storks and cranes, though it is now considered that their nearest relatives are the ducks and flamingoes. However, they have certain anatomical peculiarities that distinguish them from all other birds. In habits they are very goose-like and graze like geese, though their beaks are fowl-like and their feet unwebbed.

When not grazing they often rise to great heights and soar in the skies like vultures and eagles, and are capable of performing the most astonishing aerial acrobatics. This hardly seems possible in view of the ungainly appearance of the bird, which is not in the least suggestive of elegance in the air, but is explained by the fact that a layer of air-cells exists between the skin and

A TERRESTRIAL BIRD OF PREY

Though slow and ponderous in rising from the ground, the Secretary bird is strong on the wing, though it hunts entirely on the ground. Its chief food is grasshoppers and locusts, as well as rodents, lizards and snakes, killed with blows of the feet.

muscles, giving the bird buoyancy.

Screamers pair for life, though they sometimes congregate in large flocks out of the breeding season. They swim well, and breed in reeds bordering lagoons and lakes, laying rather goose-like eggs.

One of the rarest birds in the world is the notornis of New Zealand. It is a curious flightless bird, very like a large moorhen, but is more heavily built, being almost goose-like in size. Its total length is 24 in. Its colours are striking, being mainly purplish blue except on the back and wings, which are green. Its under tail coverts are white as in the moorhen. The wings are feeble.

The story of the survival of this primitive bird is an exciting one. Prior to 1948 only four recent, as distinct from fossilized, specimens had been seen. The last, found in 1898, was a perfect specimen, and was the first well-preserved example to be mounted. As it was by then presumed to be extinct, the capture of this bird created great excitement throughout the world. Then in 1948 came the exciting news that notornis had been rediscovered by Dr. Orbell in the Fiordland National Park in South Island.

It speaks a lot for public interest that as a result of this discovery provision has been made to set aside nearly half a million acres as a natural sanctuary, into which no one can enter without a permit. Thus a serious effort is being made to save the remaining notornis from the same fate that has overtaken most other small flightless birds. The latest report is that from ten to twenty breeding pairs are known to exist, but it is doubtful if the population will recover rapidly owing to the fact that only one egg is laid in a season. This slow rate of reproduction is evidence that formerly notornis had few, or no, natural enemies to contend with.

TIGER BITTERN

Bitterns epitomize oddness among birds. When alarmed they stand "frozen," with neck and beak stretched upwards.

Backwater of
evolution

THE amphibians and reptiles inhabited the earth long before the
birds and mammals came into
existence. The amphibians were the first
arrivals. They in their turn gave rise to
the reptiles, from which later on came the
birds and mammals. In their anatomy,
their methods of reproduction, their
habits and their intelligence, the amphibians and reptiles are on a considerably
lower scale than the warm-blooded
vertebrates.

Some groups of the amphibians and
reptiles have remained unchanged since
they first appeared. The tuatara of New
Zealand, the most primitive reptile now
living, resembles its ancestors of
200,000,000 years ago. We do not know
the origin of the tortoise and turtles.
The earliest fossil specimens are similar
in form to the species that are living
today. The Crocodilians have not
changed; evolution has left them alone.
Other groups, however, both in the
amphibians and reptiles, have moved
forwards, developing along their own
lines. All the modern amphibians differ
radically in structure from the primitive
species. The Squamata, an order which
includes the lizards and the snakes, is of
comparatively recent origin. Moreover,
in the multiplicity of their forms—
new forms are continually being evolved
—these groups are still on the upgrade.

In their own particular way many of
their members are highly specialized
animals.

The intelligence of the amphibians
and reptiles, as measured by their
ability to learn, is undoubtedly inferior
to that of birds and mammals. The
actions performed by them, although
some appear to show considerable
intelligence, are instinctive. The ability
to perform is born in them and has not
to be learned by experience. Moreover,
an ability to learn implies a memory, a
faculty which the cold-blooded vertebrates possess only in a very limited
degree.

The tailed Amphibia (Caudata) have
a more primitive nervous system than
the toads and frogs (Salientia), and
their intelligence is on a lower scale. It
can be judged in many ways.

The migration of the Amphibia to
water in the spring for the purpose of
breeding is a well-known phenomenon,
but the ability of the Caudata to find
their way to water is much less highly
developed than it is in the Salientia.
Newts taken from a pond in which they
are breeding and set down in the vicinity
cannot find their way back to the water
unless released comparatively near to it.
Individuals set down forty or fifty yards
away often do not find it at all. Toads
and frogs, on the other hand, will travel

MIDWIFE TOAD

The male of the midwife toad attaches the eggs to his hind-quarters as soon as they are laid on land and in that way takes charge of them.

long distances to reach their breeding grounds, moving across the country with remarkable directness towards their objective.

A few years ago an experiment was made in the United States of America with the Carolina toad (*Bufo terrestris*) to discover its ability to locate its breeding site. From a large pond which served as a focal point for their breeding activities, 444 individuals were taken and liberated at varying distances away from it. Each individual was marked by removing a toe or toes. Sixty per cent of those liberated three hundred yards away found their way back to the pond in a short time, and 18 per cent of those released a mile away were caught ultimately at the pond, although some of them were not found until three months after liberation. The percentage

figures are probably on the low side, for it is not likely that every individual that returned was caught. Two individuals released three hundred and eight hundred and fifty yards away, respectively, were back at the breeding site in twenty-four hours.

The ability of the Amphibia to find their way to the water to breed must not be confused with the homing instinct, which is the habit of returning to a particular spot which has been chosen as a home. In the Caudata this is poorly developed. Their wanderings in search of food are haphazard in character and they seldom return to the same place on successive nights. On the other hand, many of the Salientia having chosen a retreat return to it regularly night after night for months at a time. It is recorded of the Common toad that one lived in a hole under the doorstep of a house for thirty-six years and was made a great pet of. Experiments with the American Pond frog (*Rana clamitans*) have shown that two out of three caught in a spring in which they had made their home, and released several hundred feet away on the other side of a stream, returned to their home although to do so they had to cross water where other Pond frogs lived.

Another way of testing intelligence—and also memory—is to train the animal to find its way out of a maze. Salamanders, toads, lizards and snakes have all been experimented with in this way and all in time learn to do it, some species much more quickly than others.

Learning in connexion with food and feeding-time is quickly acquired by individuals in captivity. Newts that are kept in a tank placed in such a way that when they are fed they are looked down upon, soon learn to associate the presence of a face above them with a meal, and if hungry will rise to the surface of the water and even poke their snouts out of it asking for something to eat. If, however, the tank is placed so that they are looked at through the glass, they do not respond in the same way. Toads kept in a cage quickly learn to come out of hiding at the sound of footsteps. A French naturalist once trained a number of Sand lizards to gather around him at the sound of a gong and take food from his hand. Many species of snakes learn to associate the opening of a cage door with food and will come forward to it at once if they are hungry.

Memory is not a strong point with the amphibians and reptiles. Toads and frogs that eat bees and get stung in the process will learn in a week or less to associate bees with the pain of stings and after that will avoid them. But if the training is left off for two or three weeks the experience is forgotten and the lesson has to be relearnt.

In all the Amphibia there is a strong association between food and movement. Their prey must be alive, and prey that does not move will not be touched. They can, however, be easily deceived, but in their ability to learn the Salientia show more intelligence than the Caudata. If a piece of paper is agitated in front of a toad it will snap it up, and then discovering its nature will reject it. This may be repeated two or three times, after which the toad will have nothing more to do with it. Newts, on the other hand, will go on snapping at a moving object until exhausted.

EUROPEAN TREE FROG

The European Tree frog, seen above, is brilliant green in colour and, like all Tree frogs, is able to change colour rapidly. Tree frogs are equipped with adhesive climbing-disks on the ends of their fingers, with which they attach themselves to leaves.

MOST PRIMITIVE REPTILE

The tuatara is of outstanding interest to zoologists, for it is the oldest living link between the primitive amphibians and reptiles of two hundred million years ago and the recent forms that have evolved from them. A diminishing species, it is now found only in a few small islands off New Zealand and is strictly protected by law.

In their sense of smell, however, the Caudata are more highly developed than the Salientia. It is by the sense of smell as well as by sight that newts find their food in the water. If a piece of chopped worm is concealed in a bag and dropped near them it is quickly discovered by smell, and this sense of smell is not lost when they are on land. The "juice" of a worm that has been smeared on the ground can be detected by smell. Food, in fact, that smells right will be eaten by newts even if it does not move. A piece of raw meat is readily eaten. Toads and frogs, although they have an olfactory organ, do not appear to have any sense of smell. Their tadpoles, on the other hand, have a quite well developed sense of smell.

Toads (Bufo) are more intelligent than frogs (Rana). They learn more quickly, they react more readily to many forms of stimulation, they show greater curiosity and they have better memories. The Common toad in captivity will quickly learn that glass is a barrier that cannot be passed, while the frog will dash himself against it to his own injury for days before he learns. This is partly due to fright, but in many other small ways the frog shows that it is not as quick at learning as the toad.

It is not usual to credit the amphibians and reptiles with parental feelings, and certainly none of them, as far as we know, take any interest in their families after they are born. Yet quite a number of species guard and even nurture their eggs while development is proceeding. All the Amphibia pass the first stage of their life as tadpoles. Most of them lay their eggs in the water and then abandon them. In a few species, however, the development of the tadpole takes place in the egg and away from water—it is called direct development—and in these a parental instinct has developed. The brooding habit is well established in many of the primitive salamanders (Plethodontidae). The eggs are laid on land and the mother coils herself about them until the embryos are hatched. *Desmognathus fuscus*, a North American salamander, wraps her eggs around her neck and carries them about with her during their development. With many species of toads and frogs the male looks after the eggs instead of the female. The male of the Midwife toad (*Alytes obstetricans*) attaches the eggs to his hind-quarters as soon as they are laid on land and in that way takes charge of them. Periodically he resorts to the water to moisten them and finally—after about six weeks—when the embryos are sufficiently developed to leave the eggs, he releases them in the water and they continue their lives as aquatic tadpoles in the usual way.

Not many of the lizards have any parental instinct. It has been observed

BOA-CONSTRICTOR WITH NEW-BORN YOUNG

Boa-constrictors are non-poisonous snakes found in South America. Like the Old World pythons, they kill their prey by crushing it in their coils. The species shown here is viviparous, the young being born alive instead of hatching from eggs.

in the Chinese and American skinks of the genus Eumeces, and is present, though less highly developed, in the snake-like lizards of the genus Ophisaurus. The brooding is done by the female in a cavity or "nest" made underground. The chief object of brooding is to protect the eggs from enemies, and some species of Eumeces will put up a spirited resistance when any attempt is made to take their eggs from them. They will defend them against mice that are put into their cage. If the eggs are removed they will hunt for them and, having found them, bring them back to the nest. The female has been observed to turn her eggs over regularly, much as a bird turns her eggs during incubation, using her tongue or her snout for this purpose. She has been seen to pick up the eggs in her mouth and place them carefully among the others in the nest. Considerable care is taken by the mother to keep her clutch together. The eggs of another individual of her own kind that have been placed in her nest will be accepted, but those of other species of lizards, although they resemble her own closely in appearance, will be refused. They are detected by smell, the tongue being employed to pick up scent in the way that snakes do.

BROODING OF EGGS

Incubation of the eggs of Eumeces takes from four to seven weeks, the time varying with the species. The female naturally cannot remain with them all the time; every day she leaves the nest for an hour or so to bask in the sun, to drink and to feed. It is possible that basking in the sun and so raising her own temperature assists her in the incubation of the eggs.

Many snakes also brood their eggs. Both pythons and boas do so and it is now definitely established that the female assists in the hatching of her eggs by raising her temperature at the time. For many years this point was disputed, it being thought impossible for a cold-blooded animal to raise its temperature above that of the surrounding air. It is now known to be effected by muscular action. Muscular output is always attended by heat production, and during the period of incubation, which lasts from sixty to eighty days, the female keeps up a constant twitching of the small muscles which lie beneath the skin. By this means her temperature can be raised as much as three or four degrees Centigrade.

HABITS OF THE COBRA

In their parental instinct, as well as in their social behaviour, the cobras are more advanced than other snakes. The Common Indian cobra, having selected a mate, remains with her, at any rate for the season. They live together, they make a "nest" together underground and, when the eggs are laid, both parents take it in turns to guard them. Most of the watching is done by the female, but once a day, to let her have a breath of air and perhaps a drink, the male takes her place on the eggs for a short period.

The King cobra, or hamadryad, also guards its eggs, but in a loosely constructed nest of sticks, leaves and grass made above ground. The nest is divided into two chambers. In the lower one the eggs are deposited, while the upper one is occupied by the snake. It is not known if both parents take part in the brooding.

The Amphibia were the first vertebrates to develop a larynx and with it came a voice. The acquisition of a means by which one individual could communicate with another has had a far-reaching effect upon their habits. The

VENOM-SPITTER OF SOUTH AFRICA

The Ringhals cobra, when annoyed, spits venom in the form of a fine spray over a distance of several yards. This photograph well illustrates the broad belly-shields by means of which the most advanced snakes can crawl, climb and even swim better and faster than can most lizards with their four well-developed legs.

369

DEADLY PUFF ADDER

The Puff adder is among the most highly poisonous of African snakes. Its general colour is brown, with white markings, and it has a peculiarly flattened head.

larynx of the Caudata is a more primitive organ than that of the Salientia. The salamanders can utter a faint squeak, which they often do when caught. It is a cry provoked by fear and is possibly involuntary. As far as we know, none of the Caudata uses the voice as a means of communication.

Beyond this primitive state of affairs the toads and frogs have advanced quite a long way. Most of them have a voice and that of the male can be very loud. Each species has its own distinctive breeding call which to the trained ear can be recognized as easily as can be the songs of birds by the ornithologist. Moreover, in the same way that the song of a bird can vary in "accent" in different parts of the country, so may the call of certain species of toad or frog vary in tone in parts of its habitat.

The purpose of the breeding call of the male is to attract the female to him, but many toads and frogs make other sounds, each one of which no doubt has its own meaning. The female of the Common frog has a special grunt which she utters when she has spawned, thereby informing the male that he is no longer required by her. Other cries are used as a means of sex recognition, for, strangely enough, the Salientia do not depend upon their sight for this purpose. The clasping impulse in the male toad and frog in the breeding season is very strongly developed. A male will clasp indiscriminately any other male or female that happens to be near him, but it is by voice, by touch, by certain movements made by the female, and not by sight, that he knows her sex.

Vision with the Amphibia is not a

highly developed sense, although they depend upon it to a large extent as a means of obtaining food and avoiding danger. A moving object attracts their attention at once, although their conception of what that object is may not be very clear. The sight of an intruder will silence at once a colony of breeding frogs and send them hiding beneath the water. By keeping perfectly still they will in time reappear, only to vanish again if any movement is made. On the other hand, one can talk quite loudly in their presence without alarming them.

The voice of toads and frogs is very definitely a means of communication between themselves. It is a language of its own. The majority of the species use it only in the breeding season, for except at that time they lead solitary lives.

Certain semi-aquatic frogs, however, such as the edible frog, whose habits confine them to one pond and thus bring them into frequent contact with their fellows, have developed more social habits. The males croak to one another all through the summer.

In contrast to the Salientia, the reptiles as a class are strangely silent. Many of the Chelonians hiss, but they have no voice. The Crocodilians can bark and bellow and they do so particularly in the breeding season. The very young of the true crocodiles, genus Crocodilus, have a high-pitched croak. In captivity they use it frequently when they are picked up, or when they hear footsteps approaching their cage. They will croak in reply to anyone who imitates them. It is evidently a means of

ALLIGATORS AT MEALTIME

Crocodiles have narrower snouts than alligators, and the large fourth tooth in the lower jaw fits into a notch in the upper. Otherwise the differences between the two reptiles are slight. The males of both species indulge in loud bellowings during the mating season.

371

communication of some sort, but it is used only by the very young. The Estuarine crocodile (*Crocodilus porosus*) builds a large nest of sticks, rushes and weeds in which she deposits her eggs. The Marsh crocodile (*C. palustris*) and the Nile crocodile (*C. niloticus*) bury their eggs in sand-banks at the river edge, and all three species guard their eggs by remaining in the vicinity until the young are hatched. Voeltzkow, a German naturalist, who spent many months in Madagascar in order to observe the habits of the Nile crocodile, has given us a good account of what takes place. The eggs are laid in a hole dug for them by the mother, which is then carefully covered up so that no trace of the spot can be seen. The mother, however, returns to sleep at the nest and in that way its position can be discovered. Voeltzkow believes that when the time for hatching arrives the mother uncovers the eggs and conducts the young to the water. The actual operation was never witnessed by him, but the examination of the nests in which the young had hatched showed that the sand and the shells had all been scratched out. The mother is informed of the time to do this by the croaking of the young while still in the egg. Voeltzkow kept a box full of eggs in one of the rooms in his house, and although the eggs were buried in sand to the depth of two feet the cry of the young could be heard quite distinctly. If he tapped the box they would reply by croaking.

Of the many species of lizards, only one family, namely the Geckos, has a voice, although many of them hiss as the snakes do. The hiss is a weapon of

SACRED CROCODILES
Hindus regard the Marsh crocodile as sacred, and they are sometimes kept in a state of semi-domestication.

373

FRILLED LIZARD AT BAY
When chased by its enemies, the Frilled lizard will turn suddenly with its mouth open and its frill fully stretched out.

defence. Its purpose is to intimidate enemies, and some lizards, in addition, open their mouths widely and at the same time inflate their bodies, thus increasing their size. It is largely bluff, but as such it succeeds. One of the most striking examples of this type of behaviour is given by the Frilled lizard (*Chlamydosaurus kingi*), an inhabitant of northern Australia. This large lizard, measuring nearly 3 ft. in length from the tip of its snout to the end of its tail, is provided with a large frill-shaped expansion of skin on each side of its neck. By means of prolongations of the hyoid bone, which extend into the frill like the ribs of an umbrella, it can be erected. When not in use the flaps of the frill lie flat upon the neck. When chased the lizard will turn suddenly at bay, standing in a semi-erect position, with the frill stretched out to its full extent and the mouth wide open. It can, indeed, look quite a formidable creature, and its appearance when at bay certainly intimidates many birds and mammals that might otherwise prey upon it.

Some snakes also have adopted this type of behaviour, opening the mouth widely and inflating the throat and fore part of the body. Snakes hiss continually when they are excited or alarmed. It may be of value as a warning, an indication by the snake of its presence to an enemy. But that its real foes are ever intimidated by this means is very doubtful. We are too apt to judge the behaviour of animals by their effect upon ourselves. Most people are born with a dread of snakes, and a hissing snake is something to be avoided. But no bird or mammal that normally preys upon snakes—and in nature they are their chief enemies—is put off by such means.

No snake has developed a voice, and it would be of no use to it if it had, for snakes appear to be deaf to sounds conveyed in the ordinary way. Having no external ear, they cannot receive vibrations borne upon the air. Experiments with snakes, by rattling tin-cans and blowing bugles above their heads, have proved this pretty conclusively. On the other hand, they are sensitive to vibrations conveyed through the ground. The snake with its head on the ground is thus in a position to receive sounds conveyed by that route. That snakes can hear there is no doubt; exactly how we do not yet know.

In other ways, also, the snakes have become highly specialized, perhaps the most spectacular change of all being the loss of limbs. The Caudata, which arose from the fishes, were the first vertebrates to develop limbs; legs were necessary to enable them to move about when they left the water and invaded the land. They were the earliest four-legged animals. Having acquired legs, with all the advantages that they give their owner, it would seem to be a step in the wrong direction to lose them.

Yet that is what happened to the snakes. We do not know the origin of the snakes, but we believe them to have been evolved from some four-legged, lizard-like ancestor. A similar step in evolution, with the production of a snake-like body, is taking place in several families of lizards living today, such as the Anguidae and Scincidae. In these families, the most advanced species (or as some prefer to call them, the most degenerate) are snake-like in body, but as regards the skull, the tongue, the ears and the eyes they are still typical lizards.

In the family Anguidae, to which the slow-worm belongs, it is possible to arrange a series showing species in every stage of reduction in the size of the limbs and number of digits, starting with a typical lizard-like form with four well-developed legs, and culminating in the slow-worm in which there are no external limbs at all.

The gradual reduction in the size of the limbs is invariably accompanied by elongation of the body, a change in structure required as a compensation for their diminishing size. Deprive a lizard of its legs and, as regards locomotion, it becomes helpless. But endow it with sufficient length of body to acquire the serpentine form of movement, and locomotion again becomes possible.

The snakes having once acquired this particular form of movement have then proceeded to specialize in it, partly by the development of a broad set of shields on the belly to make better contact with the ground, partly by changes in the vertebral column to give it increased flexibility and strength. As a result of these changes the most highly advanced snakes today can crawl, climb and swim better and faster than most lizards with four legs.

The increase in the length of the body has necessitated profound modifications in the shape and disposition of the internal organs, particularly of the lungs and the alimentary canal. It cannot be said, however, that the snake is in any way handicapped by these changes.

SNAKE-LIKE LIZARD

There are several families of lizards living today which are gradually losing their limbs and assuming a snake-like form. The slow-worm, seen above, has no external limbs at all, but is, nevertheless, still a typical lizard as regards skull, tongue, ears and eyes.

LARGEST OF THE MONITORS

The Komodo dragon is the largest and most powerful of the Monitor family of lizards.
It grows to a length of 12 ft., or even more, and is found only on the small island of
Komodo, in the Malay Archipelago. Its tongue flickers continually in and out of
its mouth like that of a snake—possibly the mechanism of smell in operation.

Snakes have not much sense of taste, but they have a very keen sense of smell. In addition to the usual channel of smell, namely the nose, they have a special structure called Jacobson's Organ, lying in the roof of the mouth and connected with the palate by two small openings. Many other groups of vertebrates, including man, have this organ, but it is only in the lizards and snakes, and particularly the latter, that it is highly developed and serves a definite purpose. It is an important sense organ, its function being to appreciate the nature of odorous particles that are picked up by the tongue and so conveyed to the palate and thence to Jacobson's Organ. It is for this purpose that the tongue of the snake is in constant motion. It is by the sense of smell, in which the tongue plays an important part, that snakes find one another in their haunts, and by which, when they hibernate in numbers together, they find their way to the dens, one snake picking up the trail of another that has preceded it. It is by smell that the poisonous snakes find their prey when it has disappeared from sight after having been struck. It may be of value in sex recognition. In their sense of smell the snakes appear to be ahead of all other vertebrates except the mammals.

Lizards have not the same keen sense of smell, except perhaps the monitors (Varanus). In these large lizards the tongue is long and snake-like in form and is continually played in and out of the mouth in the manner employed by snakes. By smell they can detect food such as a piece of meat or a dead animal or bird that has been concealed underground; having located it, they will dig it out and devour it. The majority of lizards, however, have a broad, flat, feebly forked tongue, and they do not make constant play with it. It is used in the selection of food, but the object to be tested must be first touched by the tongue. How much of this examination is taste and how much smell we do not know.

Courtship as a preliminary to mating is well known in snakes. The chief feature of the performance is the continual flicker of the tongue of the male up and down the back of the female.

The precise meaning of this action is not known. It may be some form of stimulation ; it may be a caress. It has been suggested that it is by the tongue as well as by special tactile organs in the chin that the male locates his position on the body of the female when union finally takes place. Lizards never use the tongue in courtship as the snakes do.

Mating and courtship in the Sauria is a fairly stereotyped performance. The same type of behaviour is seen in species and genera that are closely allied to one another. In the tropical Agamid and Iguanid lizards courtship has often been witnessed, the male facing the female and addressing her by repeated bowings and noddings of the head.

Many lizards, however, have no preliminaries of any kind and their mating

COMMON IGUANA

There are several varieties of Iguanid lizards, but the best known is the Common Iguana (I. tuberculata). This species is olive-green in colour, may weigh as much as 30 lb. and measure 4½ ft. in length. Most of its life is spent in the branches of trees.

AGAMID LIZARD IN A

In common with many other animals, some lizards are in the habit of assuming a
threatening attitude to intimidate enemies. Some of them, for example, hiss like snakes,

performance is a crude and primitive act, the male seizing the female in his mouth by some part of her body and holding her down. By doing so he also makes his own position more secure, for in the act of union his body has to be curled beneath hers in what would appear to be a very uncomfortable position. Snakes, as a rule, do not maintain any hold upon the female during the operation. The slow-worm, although it has acquired the snake-like body, has retained the Saurian type of behaviour when mating.

In all the Squamata the part played by the female in the act of mating is a passive one. If she is ready for the male she remains quiescent ; if not she moves away. The female lizard that does not wish to mate will sometimes turn and bite the male.

Sexual variation in colour is distinct in many lizards, the male in the breeding season being more brilliantly marked than the female. In snakes this is very rare. The development of a sexual difference in coloration has had a considerable influence on the evolution of mating behaviour. Rivalry and combat between male lizards in the breeding season is frequent, and it is strongest in those that have the most conspicuous colours. Some lizards appropriate definite territories for themselves, as many birds do, and attack all other males that invade it. Other species merely remain by or near the female, driving away rivals that approach too closely.

The brilliant hues that the male Agamid and Iguanid lizards display is not a fixed coloration, but is dependent upon a psycho-physiological stimulus, and in times of excitement will sweep like a flush over the whole body of the animal. The sight of a female or of another male, and the fear induced by the sight of a snake, are among the stimuli which will provoke a flush.

THREATENING ATTITUDE
at the same time opening their mouths widely and inflating their bodies, as the Agamid is seen doing here. Other lizards have frills and crests that can be erected at will.

The belief originally put forward by Darwin that the gaudy coloration of the male was evolved for the purpose of attracting the female is no longer held. There is no evidence to show that the female is in any way attracted by the display. On the contrary, she often appears to be frightened by it and runs away, only to be chased and caught. A view more generally held is that the male coloration can act as a form of intimidation to other males. In the Agamid and Iguanid lizards just referred to, in which the colours are partly under control, it has been observed that the greatest displays are directed against other males and not towards females. Coloration can also be a means of sex recognition. A rival male approaching is at once spotted and attacked.

Sexual dichromatism, as already mentioned, is extremely rare in snakes. It is best marked in the vipers, and it is in that family that the most conspicuous rivalry and display between the males is known to occur.

Another character in which the snakes show extreme specialization is connected with the eye. They have lost the eyelids and acquired in their place a transparent covering (the brille) beneath which the eye can move.

The Amphibia were the first vertebrates to develop eyelids. The toads and frogs have a well-developed upper and lower lid, but they are fixed structures and cannot be moved independently. No one has ever seen a toad or a frog asleep, if by that we mean resting with the eyes closed. The only way in which the eye can be shut is by withdrawing the eyeball into the head ; this action drags the upper lid with it. This is regularly done when swallowing food. It is actually employed as an aid to swallowing. The movable eyelid of frogs and toads is the nictitating membrane, or third eyelid, a more or less

POISONOUS GILA MONSTER

*The Gila monster and the Beaded lizards are the only two known poisonous lizards.
The former is a plump, brightly coloured reptile about a foot and a half long, and
equipped with grooved teeth for the transmission of its venom.*

transparent structure which when not in use lies folded behind the lower lid. It is drawn up to cover the eye when the animal is in the water.

With the exception of the snakes and some lizards, all reptiles have movable eyelids. The lower lid is the larger of the two and closure of the eye is effected almost entirely by the lower lid. Eyelids serve two purposes: they wipe the eyeball and keep it moist and clean, and by covering the eye and thereby shutting out external impressions conduce to better repose. The loss of the eyelids, therefore, once they have been acquired, would seem to be another step in the wrong direction, although the acquisition of a fixed covering by which the eye is protected from injury has its advantages, particularly in an animal like the snake that lives upon the ground.

The origin of the brille of the snake is not known. Certain lizards living today, however, such as Ablepharus in the skinks and Ophisops in the Lacertids, have acquired a brille, and the stages by which this has been evolved can be traced in the skinks in the same way that the loss of limbs can be followed in the Anguidae. It is probable that snakes acquired their brille in the same way. It has been accomplished first of all by a thinning of the scales of the central portion of the lower lid so that a transparent "window" is formed, then by the gradual enlargement of the "window" until it occupies the greater part of the lid, and finally by the union of the lower lid with the upper.

Snakes more than any other reptiles have become highly specialized in many ways. They have lost structures that to us appear invaluable, but have gained others in their place which seem adequate for their needs. For their own particular mode of life they are by no means decadent but are a highly progressive group of animals.

INDEX

Page numbers printed in *italic* type refer to illustrations.